WHAT'S TRUTH GOT TO DO WITH IT?

To Bunty

Best Wishes

David Crisma

Nov 2006

Published by

Librario Publishing Ltd

ISBN: 1-904440-79-7

Copies can be ordered via the Internet
www.librario.com

or from:

Brough House, Milton Brodie, Kinloss
Moray IV36 2UA
Tel /Fax No 00 44 (0)1343 850 617

Printed and bound by Digisource GB Ltd

WHAT'S TRUTH GOT TO DO WITH IT?

David Crigman

Librario

About the author

A practising QC specialising in criminal cases. Educated at King Edward's School, Birmingham, and University of Leeds. Of indeterminate age. Married with one son. Frequently escapes the Courtroom to travel to remote places. Sometimes not sure what to do when he gets there.

Author's Note

This novel is the first in a trilogy featuring the character Naomi Nicholas. The constituent books are entitled:

What's Truth Got To Do With It?
The Molecule Man
In Death We Trust

The time period covered within the whole trilogy runs from the mid-1990s to the current day. Thus, the events in "What's Truth Got To Do With It?" occur at the beginning of that time period and are deliberately set at a time prior to the enactment of The Criminal Justice Act 2003 which changed parts of the Law relevant to this story.

PROLOGUE

*T*here was something incongruous about the couple dressed in black as they emerged hurriedly from the doorway, turning sharp left into the dark alleyway beyond and heading towards Fleet Street. His hand upon her right arm appeared a touch too heavy, her head was turned almost defensively away from him and neither their step nor the contours of their bodies seemed in harmony. The bearded male was shorter than the female and significantly older with thread-veined cheeks, blotched complexion and drooped, puny shoulders. Yet she was so elegant and so strikingly beautiful. Beautiful, but acutely uncomfortable in his presence, as he talked at her incessantly, repeatedly thrusting his face towards her as they walked, their footsteps on the cobbled pathway echoing ominously off the high-walled buildings.

Displaying an agility and speed of foot that took her completely by surprise, he propelled her suddenly and violently into the narrower adjoining alleyway where there was no light at all. Whilst his timing was skilled, it was luck that decreed the absence of any passers-by as his wet mouth now urgently sought hers. His arms were wrapped tightly around the woman's waist as his full weight forced her back against the crumbling brickwork of the wall behind, grinding the sharp particles of red brick into the fabric of her black, tailored jacket.

Still talking at her, his left hand moved clumsily to her breast and clutched fiercely at the prize he had been coveting all evening whilst his right hand went directly up her skirt and into her pants, his nails catching the top of her stockings and scratching her inner thigh. Surprise, disgust and fear had effectively paralysed her and it was not until she felt his fingers actually seeking entry that she was able to react. His excitement was intense as he probed and squeezed, still leaning heavily against her, his rough beard against her soft cheek whilst his breathing came in quick gasps. As his tongue forced its way into her mouth, her mind gradually came under control. Despite this attack being in the middle of London, there were no people to help her. Fleet Street was over a hundred yards away. This alley was unused at night. She was alone. In the pitch black. And this man had power. Should she succumb or should she fight?

CHAPTER 1

Statement of: CHECKLEY, SARAH ANN (nee PARKES)
Age if under 18: OVER 18
Occupation: HOUSEWIFE

This statement, consisting of 14 pages, each signed by me, is true to the best of my knowledge and belief and I make it knowing that, if it is tendered in evidence, I shall be liable to prosecution if I have wilfully stated anything which I know to be false or do not believe to be true
Signed: S. A. CHECKLEY

I am the above named person and reside at Blossomfields, Alwoodley, Leeds, with my husband, Paul Michael Checkley and our three-year-old daughter, Emily. I am giving the information contained in this Statement to police officers from my bed in Ward 17 at St James's Hospital. The doctors have told me that I am still in shock but I have a very clear recollection of what happened.

Last Tuesday, at about 11 p.m., I was downstairs in the kitchen of our house making myself a drink before retiring to bed. My husband was out, attending a black tie boxing event at the Mountjoy Hotel in the City Centre and was not due back until after midnight. Our daughter had gone to bed at about 8 p.m. and I had been watching the television alone in the main sitting room since that time.

Whilst in the kitchen I thought that I heard the sound of breaking glass. It was a faint sound and I formed the impression that it came from the area of my husband's study on the first floor at the end of the house, furthest away from where I was in the kitchen.

Our property is gated and has sophisticated security lighting and alarms. The alarms were not yet switched on as my husband was still out but I would have been aware of the exterior security lighting coming on if an intruder had entered the grounds of our house. I am sure that these lights had not been activated.

I stood in the kitchen for a moment listening but could hear nothing. There is a telephone in the kitchen and I tried telephoning my husband on his mobile phone but it was switched off. I did not leave a message. I knew that I must check that my daughter was all right but was nervous about leaving the kitchen. Remaining unsure that I had actually heard the sound of glass breaking, I was reluctant to phone the police. Our property is remote and I knew it would likely take any police vehicle several minutes to arrive and, in reality, I was unconvinced that anybody could have got into our house.

There is a large broom cupboard in the kitchen close to the back door in which my husband keeps his golf clubs. I went to the cupboard and pulled out a club at random. It was a Number 5 iron. Armed with the golf club I walked across the kitchen towards the door leading into the hall. When I was a few feet from the door I saw that the door handle was moving downwards very slowly. I froze on the spot. I knew instinctively that it would not be Emily as she never wakes up in the night once she has gone to sleep. I realised that there must be an intruder in the house.

I quickly moved to a position behind the door. I was barefoot and made no noise. The handle was continuing to move downwards and the door was very gradually beginning to open inwards. I knew that I would only have seconds to decide what action to take because when the door came into contact with my body the intruder would be immediately aware of my presence.

I manoeuvred my body and arm into the best position to get a good swing with the golf club, but my movement was restricted by my proximity to the wall and so I slid my hand down the shaft of the club which, whilst reducing the force I would be able to apply, gave me more room to swing. These thoughts and actions were taking fractions of a second, but my mind was racing to the clear conclusion that I was prepared to use the club and must make sure that I did so with as much force as I could achieve in the circumstances so as to disable the intruder. I was so petrified that I felt as if I had left my body and was watching my own actions from a distance.

The door opened 2 or 3 feet and I saw the rear and right hand side of the upper body of a person begin to edge into the room. The head was craning forward, obviously enabling the man to look into the kitchen as he entered. I only had time to observe that the head was completely covered in some kind of material and that the upper body was wearing a close-fitting, dark coloured shell suit type of garment. By this time he was half a step into the kitchen and was still pushing the door open. Within less than a second he would either turn and see me or at least sense my presence. Despite all of my efforts at self control, I actually heard myself involuntarily whimper in terror, prompting the head to turn sharply towards me and then the body began to surge forward. I took one step out of the corner and swung the golf club with all my force at his head. He must have turned at the last moment because the contact was with the back of his head and the back of his neck. Whilst my movement had been restricted and the arc of the swing lessened by my low grip on the shaft, I knew that I had delivered a heavy blow and was not surprised to see him stagger as if he was going to the floor. My intention was to press the panic alarm button on the landing which would alert the police through a call centre, grab Emily and then run to the car and drive away.

I heard him struggling to breathe and gasping in pain and then he collapsed on to the floor. The way he fell suggested to me that whilst he was badly hurt, he was still conscious and I knew that I had to act and move with great speed. It did occur to me to strike him again but I thought if I swung the club at his head with a full, unimpeded swing now available to me, then I would probably kill him and so I did not strike for a second time.

I did not take in very much more about him except for the covered head, dark upper clothing and the shell suit bottoms but I did particularly notice his footwear. He was wearing very thin shoes, which looked to me like ballet shoes. I could see that he wore poor quality, black socks and that he was white. It was only the skin of his left lower leg above the sock becoming exposed as he went to the ground that enabled me to see that he was white. He wore beige, tight, rubber gloves, like surgeon's gloves, so that no other part of his skin was visible. I could now also see that the garment covering the whole of his head and neck was a navy blue, full-face ski mask, to which an additional section of material had been sewn at the bottom, so as to create an extra skirt which extended the coverage across his upper chest and back.

All of these observations and decisions took, literally, a split second, for as I looked I started to run out of the room. I had to jump over him as he went to the ground and I feared that he would reach out and grab my legs, but I made it through the door. I was wearing jeans and a woollen sweater but, being barefoot, I actually felt my foot brush against the material of his upper garment as I leapt through the door. I have a vivid memory of the sensation of my skin against the material and I remember that the material felt soft and smooth. The sensation of that physical contact with him made me actually vomit as I ran to the stairs. I tried to shout Emily's name but my throat felt constricted and my voice had no power.

We have three flights of stairs, with two quarter-landings where the staircase turns. The nearest panic button was on the second quarter-landing. I could only have been three or four steps from it when his hand caught my ankle. I had not heard him in pursuit, perhaps because my brain was just teeming with fear.

The grip of the rubber glove on the bare flesh of my ankle petrified me. I tried to scream but could only make feeble, animal-like whimpers as he dragged me backwards down the stairs into the hall. I was on my back and side and bumped down every step, dropping the golf club as I went. His grip was like a vice. I begged him to stop. He did not speak. At the bottom of the stairs I lay on my back and he stood above me. I could now see clearly that he was wearing ballet shoes. They were black.

I began telling him that he could take whatever he wanted, but before I could complete even a few words he lifted one of his legs and stamped with all of his weight and force on my stomach. I had never experienced such pain. I could not breathe in or out, nor could I shout. It felt as if his foot had smashed all of my internal organs against my spine. I did not believe that I had any chance of surviving. I thought he would also kill Emily if he had not already done so.

Through the pain I saw him lean down and reach out towards my chest. The area at the bottom of the stairs where I lay was lit only by the light coming from the kitchen and it was only as his hand passed close to my chest that I saw the knife. The blade was long and narrow, like a filleting knife. He held it with his thumb uppermost and sliced me in an upwards direction. It was done slowly and deliberately with the blade ripping open my jumper at waist level and the blade entering my body at just above my navel and being drawn up my body and running straight between my breasts.

I was still in such pain from the stamp that I could not feel myself being cut, but I could feel the wetness and stickiness of my own blood flowing from the long wound. The knife was so sharp that he was able to cut me open with seemingly very little effort. I have been told by the surgeon who operated on me later that the wound was fourteen inches long and between one and two inches deep. The surgeon's view was that he had not intended to kill me, but to terrify me and disfigure me. His mask had slits for the eyes but I could see nothing of them. He had still not spoken and the effects of my blow with the golf club appeared to have worn off. Now I had no doubt that I was going to be killed.

He bent down over me and squeezed my lower face in a pincer grip with the thumb and fingers of his right hand. I remember smelling the rubber of his gloves. I could not see the knife, but he must have transferred it to his left hand for I then felt it slice open my jeans and pants at crutch level and could feel the coldness of the point of the blade pressing right between my legs. I waited for him to cut inwards and upwards but instead he spoke. I can remember his exact words. They were spoken in a grating voice with his face only inches from mine and, as he spoke, he was beginning to penetrate my vagina with the knife at the same time as increasing the pressure on my face.

"I know there's a safe in the house. Take me to it or I finish opening you up, you privileged bitch."

Despite the voice being partially muffled by the mask and, despite my pain and terror, I was able to recognise the lilt in the voice and the hardness of the accent. This man had been brought up or had lived in the north-east of England.

There is a small safe fitted and hidden beneath the floor of our bedroom. I have no idea how he knew of its existence as my husband and I are extremely discreet and cautious about such matters. Access to the safe is gained by rolling back a rug and lifting a specially constructed trap door. The safe itself is a combination safe and I do know the combination. I also knew that inside the safe was most of my jewellery which is valued at approximately £250,000, some important documents including our wills and house deeds, about £200 in cash and in excess of £20,000 in American dollars which is something to do with a business arrangement made by my husband last week. Normally we only kept important documents and my jewellery in the safe, with a small amount of cash.

I immediately told him that the safe was in the bedroom and I would open it. As soon as I agreed he released his grip on my face and removed the knife from between my legs. He began to stand up and so did I. I was losing a lot of blood from my wound and pressed the damaged jumper to my chest in an attempt to stem the flow. I was already feeling light-headed from the loss of blood and trying to get to my feet made me feel as if I was going to pass out. Seeing that I was in such difficulty he grabbed me by the hair, yanked me on to my feet and dragged me towards the stairs. It was as I reached the first stair that the front door opened and my husband walked in.

13

This time I did manage to scream out a warning to my husband. Even in the poor light I could see the shock registering on his face as he tried to take in this terrifying scene. For a second there was no movement by anyone, just the sound of my scream. Then, my husband launched himself at the intruder, throwing himself forwards and trying to grab the man around the neck. I doubt that my husband ever saw the knife as it flashed with such deadly speed straight into his chest. It was not like the slicing movement with which he had slit open my body. It was a precise, forward thrust delivered with force and obvious expertise. Once the blade was embedded in my husband's chest, I actually saw the man turn the blade within the wound, before pulling it out. Paul grunted but said nothing as he fell sideways like a dead weight to the floor. The intruder leant over him and stabbed him in the side of the neck and I could see the blood gushing from the wound. I realised he must have hit an artery because the blood shot from his neck like a fountain with horrifying velocity.

The intruder had released me but I was quite useless. I ineffectually grabbed at him, trying to pull him off my husband by wrenching on his balaclava mask at the back, but he elbowed me violently in the stomach where I was already cut. He knocked my hand away and I felt material tear as I fell backwards. By now I was struggling to retain consciousness. As I collapsed to the floor I saw the intruder running, soundlessly, out of our front door. I remember thinking of those grotesque ballet shoes.

I crawled on my hands and knees to the telephone in the kitchen and dialled 999 and asked for the police and an ambulance. The white phone was covered in my blood as I replaced the hand piece and started to drag myself back into the hall to help my husband. It was only after putting the phone down that I realised that I had something in my other hand. It was a part of the piece of material that had been sewn on to the bottom of his mask which must have come away as I wrenched at his balaclava. I threw it on to the kitchen table before staggering back into the hall. My husband lay slumped in the same position in a pool of blood. He was not moving, nor making any sound. I struggled to turn him on to his side, put my ear to his mouth and did detect some signs of breathing. The gushing had stopped and the gash in his neck was now oozing rather than pumping blood. I did not try to remove his overcoat to see the chest wound but crawled back into the kitchen, grabbed some tea towels and pressed them with all my might against the sites of the two injuries. It was hopeless, as it was obvious that he was dying. I prayed that Emily was unhurt but I knew that I did not have the strength to get up the stairs.

Apparently, I was slumped over my husband, still holding the towels on his wounds, when the ambulance arrived and the paramedics eased me away from the body. The rest you know from the paramedics and police officers who arrived at the house. As I was carried out to the ambulance one of the paramedics informed me that Emily had not been hurt and was upstairs with a policewoman. I have undergone surgery on my abdomen and chest and have been told that the stamping to my abdomen may have caused serious injury to my liver. The long knife wound will leave my body badly disfigured but it did not penetrate any vital organ.

I have made this statement from my hospital bed over a period of two days and will add any further details that I may remember at a later stage.

Signed
Sarah Checkley

* * *

The adrenalin was coursing through his veins as he raced up the long drive and made for the lower section of the perimeter wall, which he had identified as the weak point in the property's defences when he'd first cased the joint, after learning about the safe from that loser in Wakefield Gaol who'd got nicked trying to pull a job there before. Whilst he was in a fury that he had failed to get into the safe, this was the kind of circumstance in which he was at his best. Acting on instinct, athleticism and guile, he entertained no doubt that he would evade arrest. Scaling the wall in one fluid movement, he made for the thick bushes on the far side of the road where he had hidden the stolen mountain bike, straddled it and headed for the parkland just over two miles away, where the stolen hatchback Escort on false plates was parked. It would take him only five minutes to cover the distance and, with the balaclava rolled up so as to appear like a simple woolly hat, he reached the car without incident. It was pouring with rain and the streets were deserted. Even if anyone had seen him, the Checkleys' blood on the front of his dark, wet clothing was indistinguishable from the effects of rain in the dark of the night.

The car was parked in a quiet, unlit road running alongside the park and the hatchback was opened, the bike stored within and the immediate escape completed within seconds. Driving at leisurely speed, with the balaclava now removed from his head and lying on the passenger seat, he kept on the minor roads all the way to Rotherham. It was only as he left Leeds well behind and adjusted to the prospect of a long night ahead that he became aware of the dull ache in the back of his head and neck where that bitch had landed the golf club. As he gingerly rubbed the large lump and contusion that had developed, he lamented that the husband had come home as early as he did, otherwise he would have made her pay even more dearly for that blow. En route he did not espy a single police vehicle. There was no hot pursuit. He had not been seen at any crucial time. The only flaw was the missing piece of material that he had sewn so tightly to the bottom of the balaclava. It had been designed to keep the neck well covered, even if somebody tried to pull the balaclava up. He strained to remember when it had come off, but remained confident that its loss could represent little threat to him, although he now noticed that there was blood on his hand from rubbing the back of his head and the bottom of the inside back of the balaclava also felt damp and sticky.

On the desolate outskirts of Rotherham he pulled into a dark recess of a public house car park and grabbed the red Manchester United holdall from the floor behind the driver's seat. He removed every item of clothing that he was wearing including the bloodstained rubber gloves, underpants and those special lightweight ballet shoes that helped him climb with such agility and made no sound. Awkwardly, in the tight confines of the car, he pulled on the spare set of clothing that he had brought in the holdall, which included the thick pair of leather gloves that he would need in a moment. The balaclava and all of the discarded, bloodstained clothing he thrust into the holdall. As he pushed in the special shoes a smile of satisfaction crossed his lips. The bastards would never outwit him.

The deadly knife had been down his sock, pressed against the flesh of his leg, so that he could feel it at all times, for he could not afford to drop it. Now he pulled it out, still bloodstained along the full length of its blade and slipped it into the bag amongst the clothing, followed by the black nylon socks. The weapon had done its work well, and serve the privileged bastard right.

Across the road a couple of youngsters, huddled against the rain, were slowly making their way towards the car park and he watched them intently in case they looked in the direction of the car, but they were simply cutting through to a walkway in the opposite corner and they passed harmlessly from sight. There was no one else around as he eased himself out of the car and, toting the holdall, walked briskly down the main road before turning right into the bleak area of the old, run-down foundry. The building containing the small furnace was only just inside the iron gates and, as his meticulous inspection last week had established, the gates were not locked at night and the bored security staff were slack. No surprise really, as there wasn't much worth stealing. Slipping silently through the gates he could see that the doors to the furnace area were open and unguarded and, protected by the thick leather gloves, he was able to pull open the lower furnace door without the need for any tool. The blast of the intense heat hit him full in the face as he bundled the holdall into the fierce redness and rapidly pushed the door closed. In seconds the evidence would be reduced to a handful of ashes.

South of Rotherham he took the motorway as far as the first Nottingham exit. The roads were quiet and, by the time he reached the narrow country lane he was seeking, it was after two o'clock in the morning, but he felt stimulated and alert. Double-checking that there was no person or vehicle in sight, he stopped just beyond the river bridge and dragged the bike out of the rear of the vehicle. The water was deep here and the noise of the splash as he hurled the bike into the river echoed through the night. For a moment the bike seemed to float downstream, but soon its weight sucked it beneath the blackness of the swirling waters and into oblivion, bringing a smile to the thin lips of the white-faced man. Exquisite moments such as these brought him an almost primeval sense of elation, as he travelled back to the times of his ancestors and felt the dangers of the naked hunter. The predator seeking its prey. The kill. Now the survival.

By 5 a.m. he was in the middle of a vast tract of derelict industrial wasteland. Where once the factories had belched their smoke and the iron wheels had turned twenty-four hours a day, there was now an empty silence. The lights of West Bromwich could be seen to the west and a few miles further to the south he could just make out the grim outline of the northern edge of Birmingham. As he emptied the red petrol container all over the cheap plastic upholstery of the Escort, he spat with venom in the direction of Birmingham. Over a year of one sentence had been spent in that cesspool they called Winson Green, when he had to be transferred out of Strangeways because of the troubles, and they had treated him like a dog. Caging him in a cell for twenty-three hours a day and feeding him pig swill. Still, he'd had the last laugh for they had never discovered who stuck the 'G' Landing officer in the back with a sharpened spoon.

Throwing the lit match inside the Escort caused immediate ignition and the blaze lit up the abandoned yard, revealing the full extent of the dereliction in all its squalor. Torching stolen vehicles in this area was as common as shoplifting, but that didn't mean that the police wouldn't send a car out if somebody did bother to report it and so he hurried away from the scene, head bowed, hands thrust deep into his pockets and made for the Bus Depot which was a couple of miles away.

From there, indistinguishable from the hundreds of other early morning workmen, he would take a bus to Wolverhampton Railway Station to catch the 6.40 to Manchester and then across to Sheffield. By mid-morning he would be back in his flat, showering away the evidence of the night's activities and watching the video of the previous night's documentary on the Amazon Basin, in case he should ever need an alibi. Once that was erased and the video machine and tapes had been smashed and abandoned at the landfill, he would grab a few hours' shuteye and think about the next job. After all, adrenalin rush apart, this venture had been a serious failure.

CHAPTER 2

Resources at the decaying Leeds North Central Police Station were down to an all-time low and, recently, the Policy Committee had actually issued a directive to stop prosecuting minor offences of dishonesty because the undermanned Force was already being suffocated by the existing paperwork, thereby giving the twopenny-halfpenny crooks a free hand to pinch and cheat at will. The very fabric of the bleak Victorian building exuded an aura of failure and inability to cope with the modern demands of an ever-increasing crime rate, whilst the disenchanted officers wandered hither and thither at a snail's pace, dragging the heavy, brown bags of Court exhibits up and down stone staircases, filling in endless forms amidst constant grumbling from their colleagues and abuse from the hapless prisoners penned in the steel-doored cells below.

Detective Chief Inspector Ernest Noble had retreated to his spartan office amidst the out-of-date calendars and obsolete charts that littered the walls and was presently seated at his battered desk in disconsolate mood, his face redder than ever, as a result of blood pressure so high that his doctor had advised early retirement, but Ernie Noble had no intentions of being put out to grass quite yet. Overweight he may be, and the faded blue British Home Stores suit may have appeared stretched at all vulnerable points, but he still knew how to work a case and put a rogue out of circulation. While statistics-driven bureaucrats may have sapped the morale of some, turning them into ineffectual pen-pushers, there remained a nucleus of hard-nosed, old-fashioned thief-catchers who could be relied upon to get the job done. The fleshy face sagged, particularly around the double chin, and the few remaining strands of hair lay flat and lifeless across the dome of the head, but the mind within still operated as keenly as ever. Deep furrows were etched into the brow as he sat, tapping the point of his chewed biro on the coffee mug-ringed blotter on his desk and pored yet again over the opening paragraphs of the police report on this wretched Alwoodley murder. The edges of the blotter had turned up with age and the doodles of a thousand empty minutes converged into a meaningless blue-black kaleidoscope.

Like he'd always said to the top brass, the only answer was zero tolerance. If you let the criminal classes get away with it at the bottom end, then you sent a message to the top end and, sure enough, in the last two weeks alone they'd had five robberies, two aggravated burglaries and now this Checkley murder in Alwoodley. It was a real shocker with "professional" written all over it and the enquiry had got precisely nowhere in several days of intense police activity, even with the unusual luxury of specially funded extra manpower. The fat index finger turned each page slowly as he reassessed the grim facts within the report.

YORKSHIRE (SOUTH) CONSTABULARY
DIVISION HEADQUARTERS

STRICTLY CONFIDENTIAL
POLICE REPORT (PRELIMINARY)
RE: MURDER OF
PAUL MICHAEL CHECKLEY

This preliminary report has been prepared by Detective Chief Inspector Ernest Noble. Copies are to be provided ONLY to Superintendent Clive Playford QPM and the 12 Officers specified within the Briefing Orders relating to Operation Lexington as Code Blue Authorised Officers

1 : Antecedent History of the Deceased : Paul Michael Checkley
Managing Director of Checkley Textiles PLC. Self-made millionaire businessman with numerous commercial interests. Owns two clothing factories in Leeds and three fabric manufacturing factories in Oldham. Until recently was a Member of Board of Directors of Premier League Football Club until boardroom dispute led to resignation. Qualified Private Pilot and flies company's Lear jet. In top 500 of Sunday Times List of "Britain's Wealthiest Men". Described by associate sources as "very tough negotiator in business but essentially straight".
Married twice.
Firstly to Penelope Heston (daughter of Lord Heston), divorced (wife's adultery) after 2 years. No children.
Secondly to Sarah Parkes (28) – ex senior British Airways air hostess Living together at family home (Crime Scene) at time of offences.
Has homes in Leeds, London, and Barbados. One daughter (Emily) aged 3.
Checkley was 5' 8" and about 11 stone. Whilst, on Mrs Checkley's

description, shorter and lighter than the intruder there is no doubt that he would not have hesitated to confront him on discovering him within the premises, as he kept himself extremely fit and had arrested and detained a man in a previous attempted burglary at the house.

2: The Pathology. Report by Dr Peter Mitchell. Home Office Pathologist.
    Name of Deceased : Paul Michael Checkley (aged 35)
    5' 8" tall and weighing 11 stone 4lb. Medium build.
    Had sustained 2 major injuries, each of them would have been fatal in its own right. The first was a penetrating incised wound to the left centre of the chest. It was just over 1 inch long and, on internal examination, was found to have passed inwards and slightly upwards tracking through the chest wall and severing the aorta. The minimum depth was 6 inches. The aorta had been severed right through the full thickness of the vessel. The amount of lacerating damage to the surrounding tissue was so extensive that whatever instrument had been used must have turned violently in situ, either by the movement of the deceased's body or, more likely, by the turning of the hand that held the instrument. The wound had caused massive haemorrhaging.
    The second injury was to the left side of the neck. This was a deep penetrating stab wound that had severed the carotid artery and sheared off the right hand edge of the jugular. The surface length of the injury was also 1 inch and the depth was such that, if it had penetrated one inch further, the blade would have exited on the other side of the neck. There was extensive injury to the windpipe and throat with haemorrhaging on a scale even more profuse than that caused by the first injury.
    Both injuries were consistent with having been caused by the same instrument which, in my opinion, was a single-edged, very sharp knife with a blade of at least 5 inches in length."

Noble's wise grey eyes under the heavy eyebrows wandered momentarily from the well-thumbed pages with their stark recital of the facts of death and came to rest on the tarnished silver photograph frame at the far corner of his cluttered desk. Years of being pressed up against the orange plaster of the wall by wire baskets, lever arch files and coffee mugs had cracked the glass but the rugged features of the grinning young man in his cricket whites clutching the red, seamed ball transported the Chief Inspector's mind back to another time. Beryl had always wanted a son but their marriage had seemed destined to remain childless until, on her thirty-fifth birthday, the doctor had given her the stunning news. They had called him Leonard in honour of the finest batsman that Yorkshire had ever reared and when, twenty years later, the boy had opened the bowling for his County, a dream had been fulfilled. What a day that had been. Lunch in the Pavilion at Headingley on the Chairman's table with Beryl at his side and then, to cap it all, the boy had taken three wickets for twenty-six in the afternoon session. Noble quickly forced his eyes away from the photograph as the pain of the two hammer blows flooded back. The specialist's verdict on Beryl had been coldly delivered in October of that same year and by December she was dead. Leonard's standard of cricket had declined and when, a couple of seasons later, the offer of a teaching and coaching job at a school in Queensland came his way, he had seized it with both hands and emigrated to Australia. Father and son had seen each other barely half a dozen times since.

Shifting his bulk in the hard chair he deployed the psychological device that bitter experience had taught him and let murder occupy his mind and allowed concentration on the anguish of others to ease his own pain. It had been his idea to give the press no indication at all of how the victims had been attacked. Suppression of that kind of crucial information was often invaluable when they came to interview a suspect who might blurt out an unreleased detail. The trouble this time was that they hadn't turned up any evidence pointing towards a single suspect. Even the narks were silent and seemed to know nothing. Jane Bewley at the Forensics Science Laboratory had promised him some news today and so, yet again, he meticulously picked his way through the clinical details of the preliminary forensic findings set out in the report.

3: The Forensic Evidence

Scenes of Crimes Officers made the following findings:

[a]   The filaments had been removed from the exterior heat-activated security lights.

[b]   Entry to the house had been effected by breaking a small window on the first floor. The intruder had climbed on to the roof of the conservatory to reach this window. Without a ladder or an accomplice this would require significant climbing ability. No evidence of fibres was found on the conservatory roof or wall beneath the window, indicating that he wore man-made outer garments which are less likely to have shed fibres than those made of natural materials.

[c]   The golf club which had been used to strike the intruder was a No 5 iron and has been submitted to the Forensic Science Laboratory to see if any fibres can be detected on the club face.

[d]   There was no evidence of any fingerprints at or near the point of entry. [In view of the surviving victim's account that she actually observed thin rubber gloves on the intruder's hands, attempts at fingerprint lifts were limited to the point of entry]

[e]   The piece of material torn from the bottom of the intruder's balaclava/ mask has been submitted to the Forensic Science Laboratory to see if it bore any blood/hair/skin capable of DNA analysis.

[f]   There is no sign of the murder weapon despite extensive searching in the grounds of the house and beyond. It can only be assumed that he took the weapon away with him for disposal elsewhere.

[g]   In view of the surviving victim's clear description of the intruder's footwear, attempts were made to identify footprints within the pools of blood at the scene and/or material that may have been shed from the bottom of this type of footwear. These attempts were unsuccessful. There was one footprint in blood which was capable of some tentative analysis. On balance it was likely to have been made by footwear of size 8– 10. It had left no sole tread pattern. This may be because the sole had no pattern, as in a ballet shoe, or because the print is too light and imperfect. It is recorded that the female victim's shoe size is 5 and the deceased was wearing size 8. The soles of the deceased's shoes had no pattern but had a manufacturer's logo visible to the naked eye stamped into the sole, but this was extremely worn and faint.

[h]   There were extensive areas of blood in the hallway at the bottom of the stairs. It was in pools on the floor and in heavy spots and runs on the wall opposite the bottom of the stairs in the hall. The distribution and pattern on this wall was consistent with an arterial spraying of blood from a fallen victim.

One large pool was in the immediate area where the body of the deceased had been found. The second was directly at the bottom of the stairs.

Various swabs were taken for comparison with samples taken from the deceased and the surviving victim.

[i]   There was no sign of blood in the area of the kitchen doorway where the intruder had been struck a heavy blow across the back and side of the head and neck. If this blow had caused bleeding it is likely that the blood had been absorbed into the balaclava/mask, although there is a possibility that some of the blood may have run onto the material torn from the mask, but none is visible to the naked eye..."

Suddenly the harsh ring of the telephone interrupted his reading and the Chief Inspector stretched out a weary arm to pick up the receiver.

"Noble," he grunted charmlessly.

"Morning, Chief Inspector. This is Jane Bewley at the Forensic Science Lab. I promised I'd ring you today. We've just completed running that crime sample from the Checkley murder. You know, checking the DNA Database against the partial profile raised from the trace of blood on the black material that was torn from the mask?"

"Yes," replied Noble anxiously, "I've just been taking another look at the Forensic Report. What've you come up with? Precious little, I suppose."

The younger voice on the other end of the telephone spent much of her time talking to disenchanted police officers, their appetite dulled by bureaucracy, resigned to just serving out their time until the pension kicked in, and she had learned not to let them bother her. Give them the information the tests had turned up and let them moan and groan to their heart's content was her policy, but she'd always had a soft spot for Ernie Noble and the old hands at the lab claimed that he was the pick of the bunch. Perhaps a little gruff at times but principled and decent.

"Actually, it may be of some use to you, Chief Inspector," she continued cheerfully. "Two profiles on the Database may be a match with the DNA recovered from the material torn from the attacker's mask. We only raised a partial profile from the piece of material and so you're only likely to get a fairly weak match on that kind of evidence. Anyway, the two names identified are Raymond Arthur Doyle and Gary Peter Trevors. No doubt you'll research them in the Criminal Records Files…"

"I don't need to research Trevors," interrupted Noble, his spirits immediately lifting as the first real lead emerged. "He's got a record as long as your arm. Vicious bastard. Loner. This is just his cup of tea. The other one, Doyle, rings no bells, I'll have him checked now. What kind of frequency of match are we talking about here?"

There was a short pause on the other end of the phone as she consulted her notes before the carefully worded answer was provided. "You certainly won't have a strong enough match to obtain a conviction against anyone on this DNA evidence alone. You'll need something else. The chances of a random match with this crime sample is about 1 in 600. In other words, in a city of 600,000 people, over a thousand would match."

"That'd do fine for me if Trevors was one of the thousand," came the cynical response.

"Yes, but you're a policeman, not a juror, aren't you," laughed the young girl.

"But juries like DNA evidence. Solid science. Doesn't lie," replied the Chief Inspector.

"In scientific terms the statistics aren't strong enough on their own in this case," the scientist insisted. "Like I said, you'll need something else."

"I'll find it, love. You've given us a start and I'm grateful for that," he answered as he pressed his finger on the receiver rest, cutting off the call and immediately dialling the internal number connecting him to Perry's office.

Ronald Perry. The hungry new Detective Sergeant who had been allocated to him last month and whose addition to the team had served only to contribute to Noble's low spirits and frustration. A reputation for sailing too close to the wind had preceded his secondment to North Central, but Noble had refused to prejudge the man. Coppers' gossip was notoriously unreliable. On the other hand, Noble's observations suggested that Sergeant Ron Perry was driven by a determination to nail the villains at any cost. The line between those who offended and those who apprehended could be fairly narrow at the best of times but "The Peril", as he was universally known, hailed from the same council estates where many of the most criminally active families resided and he shared much the same sense of morality. Going to school with them, sharing the same women with them and breaking the rules with them, albeit from different sides of the fence. The result was that he was equally despised by both villains and coppers alike. Much of his history remained unknown to Noble who had struggled to keep an open mind, but even Perry's physical appearance provoked an instinctive sense of mistrust. Tall, bird-like, sharp-featured and with the tiresome habit of always craning his head on its long neck right into your space when you were talking to him.

"Perry," he barked as soon as the phone was picked up at the other end.

"I want you to run two names on the CRO files right now. Raymond Arthur Doyle and Gary Peter Trevors. I want to know their present whereabouts and fast."

"Is this the Checkley enquiry, sir?" asked Perry.

"Of course it's the Checkley enquiry. That's why it's urgent."

"Then I can tell you that you can forget all about Doyle, sir. I locked him up last year for an armed robbery in Chesterfield. He got twelve years. So unless he did a Houdini out of HMP at Durham, he'd seem to have a pretty good alibi," came the smug reply.

"Well, check with Durham that he didn't fly the coop and then trace the whereabouts of Trevors. He's such an active criminal that there's a good chance he's inside as well."

"What's the evidence that it may be Trevors then, sir?" enquired Perry.

"DNA. But only 1 in 600. Pretty thin stuff, really."

"Then, we'll be needing some more won't we, Chief Inspector? We'll have to find a little bit extra to sweeten the pot. I've heard of Trevors. He was a target criminal on our Division only a couple of years ago. Big time. Violent. Operates solo. Do I remember rightly?"

"You do remember rightly. Go and do your homework and let me know where he is. But, as to little bits extra to sweeten any pots, be warned by an old soldier. We play enquiries of this importance by the book, do I make myself clear?"

"Crystal clear, sir. I was only meaning that once we've got a name it becomes easier to know where to go looking for evidence."

"So that's what you mean by sweetening the pot, is it?"

"Exactly."

"You find out Trevor's whereabouts. If he's in the nick we can forget about him. If he's out, I want to know where he lives, who he sees, who he's screwing, where his money's coming from, which boozers he's using, what snouts we may have on his territory. You got all of that?"

"Loud and clear," came the hollow reply.

"Don't you mess me around, Perry. You're still new here. Never forget you've got me breathing down your neck. We operate within the rules. No exceptions. Straight dealing. By the book. Then get back to me," demanded Noble urgently.

"I'll be back to you very shortly," the Sergeant replied, gently replacing the receiver. "Straight dealing? By the book?" What kind of way is that to catch today's shit, Perry thought to himself as he sat back in his chair, smiling. Leeds North Central needed bringing up to date. You get these bastards locked up any way you can. Then the smile broadened for he could smell a big result here. A really big one.

Back in his office on the third floor Noble swung his feet on to the grey metal desk, 1970s Home Office standard issue, and looked out of the unwashed panes of the old sash window at the industrial panorama beyond. The new buildings in the city centre that had given Leeds its contemporary, racy image of vibrancy and energy were not visible from this side of the building as his view was across the police station yard towards the railway lines, the empty factories and mills and the rows of terraced houses beyond. Somewhere out there, within the teeming masses, a killer was lurking and Ernie Noble intended to catch him fair and square. Picking up the report again he continued his reading, concentrating hard on every word in the light of Jane Bewley's encouraging findings.

4. First Report from the Forensic Science Laboratory

[a]   Blood samples have been obtained from the sample blood provided from the deceased (Paul Michael Checkley) and the surviving victim (Sarah Checkley). Full DNA profiles have been raised from both samples. The 2 victims have different DNA profiles.

[b]   With one exception (see Para [e] below), the blood found at the scene is made up of 2 separate DNA profiles. In some places the blood samples match the profile of the male victim, in other places they match the profile of the female victim. In some places the sample contains 2 profiles, a major   profile and a minor profile; where this has occurred the 2 constituent samples match the 2 victims' profiles respectively.

[c]   In each sample referred to in [b] above, the chances of a random match with either victim respectively is less than 1 in a billion. This represents extremely strong evidence that the blood at the scene is that of each of the victims. Where 2 profiles were raised from one sample this is very strong evidence that the blood of each victim has mingled after each has been wounded.

[d]   With the one exception referred to in [b] above no sample of blood recovered from the scene raised a DNA profile which differed from either victim.

[e]   The exception hitherto referred to relates to a trace of blood recovered from a piece of black material allegedly attached to the assailant's mask and ripped off during the struggle.

This trace of blood was at the top edge of material close to where strands of black cotton remained, presumably the means whereby the material was attached to the balaclava.

The trace of blood recovered was human blood and raised a partial DNA profile, differing from either profile attributable to the victims.

If the wearer of that material had been struck with a heavy instrument and injured, it is possible that the injury exuded blood of which this is a trace.

Running his yellow highlighter pen heavily over every word of Paragraph [e], Noble felt that sharp tingling down the back of his policeman's neck that always occurred when the first real clue in a case began to emerge, before pressing on with his reading.

[f] A partial DNA profile is likely to produce only limited evidence of a match with any profile obtained from a suspect or from the DNA Database. The trace of blood is so small that even enhanced DNA techniques will not improve upon the profile produced.

[g] As it is possible that this blood is the assailant's blood, comparisons are presently being made with profiles on the Police DNA Database to see if the profile provides any kind of match with any known criminal.

[h] Fibres were recovered from the head of the golf club with which the female victim states that she struck the assailant. These fibres do not match fibres recovered from the seized material. These fibres are wool, of a type and of a dye commonly used in the production of woollen headwear, handwear and footwear.

This finding supports the proposition that the recovered material bearing a trace of blood was attached to the article that shed the fibres on to the golf club rather than being a constituent part of it. Thus, blood from any injury may have seeped downwards on to the recovered material or any injury may have bled on to the material and on to the article that has left its fibres on the head of the golf club.

[i] The footprint in blood identified at the scene is imperfect. It is likely to be of size 8 – 10. Sizes do vary to a degree according to the manufacturer but, applying laboratory measuring techniques, the tentative scientific view is that it was probably made by a shoe towards the larger end of that bracket rather than the smaller.

[j] The footprint displayed no pattern or tread.

[k] The female victim was apparently barefoot and is size 5 and can therefore be safely eliminated as a source of the print.

[l] The footprint has been compared to the recovered shoe of the male victim. This was a size 8 with a smooth sole and heel although, originally, the manufacturer's logo was stamped upon the sole, it is so faded as to be unlikely to have left any imprint within the blood.

It is therefore possible that the male victim's shoe was the source of this print but this is unlikely because forensic opinion is that this print was more likely to have been made by a shoe size of about 9 ½ or 10.

Noble went back to Paragraph [g] and, highlighting it in yellow, entered the updated information in the margin. "Odds of a random match are 1 in 600." That was the key. Jane Bewley had done her tests and had indeed matched the partial profile on the inside of the material wrenched from the killer's mask with two known criminals. Tossing the report back on his desk the Chief Inspector eased himself slowly out of his chair. Jane was absolutely right in expressing a cautious approach because the statistics of the match were only fairly weak, but, unlike him, she'd never seen the Collator's Intelligence File on Trevors. This crime was right up that bastard's street.

CHAPTER 3

Doncaster, Rotherham, Barnsley, Sheffield and all the rest of those grim Northern towns. The very names had a bleakness to them, whilst the damp air had a smell and bitter taste that centuries of misery and hardship had exuded into the atmosphere, now mingling with the belching industrial smoke, acrid chemicals and stinking exhaust fumes of modern times. Three white, unmarked Rover saloon cars made their purposeful way along the deserted back streets, their headlights illuminating the endless rows of poor, terraced houses with curtains still drawn as the inhabitants lay in their beds awaiting another impending empty day, unaware of the convoy that sped past their doors.

Just before five o' clock, in the eerie orange light thrown across the car park from the nearby dual carriageway, the Rover vehicles disgorged their occupants. Nine men. Three per vehicle. Two of them were Special Services Marksmen armed with high velocity firearms which they clutched menacingly across their chests. The other seven carried canisters of MACE. All nine were wearing dark blue, heavy-knit sweaters underneath bulky, shape-distorting flak jackets and sporting baseball caps with "POLICE" etched across the front in bold, white lettering. The dreary grey tower block of council flats was in darkness save for the perspex-encased, low-wattage lights of the windows running up the central stairwell. Powerful binoculars were produced followed quickly by animated gesticulation towards the third floor window on the east side. One observer was left at the side of the cars with binoculars fixed on the window and sophisticated radio equipment immediately at his side. Another man was dispatched to the rear entrance while one remained in position at the entrance doors after his colleague had smashed the lock on the glass double doors with his heavy gauge metal puncher. Six through the doors and up the stairs. No use of the lift. Voices now crackling urgently over the radios fixed to the lapels. Swift, determined steps before turning inwards through the stairwell door leading on to the third floor landing. Overpowering smell of stale urine emanating from the area in front of lift doors. Red and green graffiti all over the walls.

Checking the number. Pushing and jostling as the metal puncher was positioned just beneath the Yale lock. Two other deadlocks on the brown door, one at the top and one at the bottom. Activate the hydraulic mechanism and, with a crash, a hole the size of a saucer appears. Reactivate. Down to the lower lock. Smash. Now the upper. Smash. Solid shoulders against the now demolished door and into the uncarpeted hallway. Running hard. Screaming "Police!"

First right. Kitchen. An open, half-consumed tin of baked beans sat on the grubby, yellow Formica-topped table. A plastic fork was sticking out of the tin and a can-opener with encrusted sauce on the blade lay abandoned on table. No plates. Eaten cold, straight from the tin. An almost empty bottle of milk without any top, stood alongside the beans.

Heavy police boots pounding along the hallway. Second right. Bathroom. Empty. Thin, damp, towel tossed carelessly on floor. Lavatory soiled. Toilet roll on cistern, a stream of paper unfurled and dangling down.

Next left. Bedroom. No curtains. Smell of old sweat. Bare electric light bulb hanging from ceiling. Clothes strewn across the green linoleum floor. A cheap, melamine single wardrobe in the corner of the room with its door hanging half-open. Double bed. No sheets or blankets. A man struggling desperately to get out of stained, lime green sleeping bag. Naked. Dark blue tattoo of a spider's web readily visible on left shoulder as his arms reached out for the window catch. Shouting. Swearing. One black leather gloved fist smashed into the white, mean face of the naked man as another impacted directly under the rib cage and hard into the kidneys. Pulled like vermin from deep within its nest, struggling, snarling, kicking, spitting. A grotesque scar on the side of his neck, reddening and pulsating with fury. A long tattoo on the lower stomach of a naked woman, her hand reaching down towards his matted pubic hair. More shouting. Gloved hand over mouth. Suffocating. Four pairs of hands forced the creature over on to his front on the bed. His arms were wrenched round behind his back as the handcuffs were snapped on. Captured. Now the job of permanent caging could begin in earnest.

STRICTLY CONFIDENTIAL
YORKSHIRE (SOUTH) CONSTABULARY
POLICE REPORT (NUMBER 2)
RE: MURDER OF PAUL MICHAEL CHECKLEY

1: Source Material

Senior Investigating Officer's Confidential Report including latest intelligence

Name – GARY PETER TREVORS.

Suspected alias PETER TRAVIS but no criminal convictions under this name.

2: Family Background

Born and brought up in Gateshead.

Now 31 and based in Sheffield but no permanent residence. Occasional relationships with women. Sometimes moves in with them but violence usually destroys relationship.

Mother (Jane Trevors) was a machinist in a local factory. Killed in an industrial accident when Trevors was 16.

Father (Martin Phelps) was a soldier (Lance Corporal – dishonourable discharge) – never married mother. Lived together for 2 years after birth of Trevors, but left her for another woman. Now living in Newcastle. No contact with son for 29 years.

One half-sister, Elaine McNeil (now 35), as a result of mother's relationship with unknown male. Married and living in Glasgow. Very intermittent contact with brother. Her husband is a postman who despises (and fears) Trevors as a result of a domestic incident in which Trevors repeatedly kicked him to the head, leading to partial deafness. No prosecution as victim refused to make formal complaint.

Trevors has one child (daughter named Amanda, aged 7) from a casual relationship with Tracey Mullins. Child resides with mother and mother's current partner (female) in Dewsbury. No contact with father. No support for child by father.

3: Education

Local primary and Comprehensive school education. Described as disruptive, bullying (particularly towards females), lazy but with agile mind, highly manipulative.

Excluded from two schools at 13 and 15. First exclusion for kicking female teacher in stomach in front of whole class (caused internal bleeding but school refused to instigate prosecution – suspected intimidation of victim and headmistress).

Second exclusion for throwing school desk through plate glass changing room window, causing £1750 damage.

4: Employment

Mainly casual short-term jobs in building trade. Longest employment was as skip-carrying lorry driver in North-East (18 months) – dismissed for dishonesty (stole wallet containing cash and credit cards of fellow employee). Employers describe him as confrontational, unreliable but very astute. Worked eight months in textile factory. Believed to have served twelve months in Merchant Navy on tankers, under alias Peter Travis. Currently self-employed lorry driver on casual basis.

5: Physical Description at time of last arrest

White Caucasian. 5' 11" tall and weighing 13 stone.

Hair (mid brown) thinning but worn very short.

Deep-set grey eyes in unusually white face. Thin lips. No facial hair.

Broad-shouldered and muscular

Tattoos –   Spider's web on left shoulder
              Naked reclining woman across lower abdomen
              Dagger and scabbard on outer right calf

Scars   Jagged and livid 4" scar on lower right neck (from blow with a broken bottle) – tends to wear high collars to conceal
              Irregular deep circular scar on inner right forearm (human bite removing substantial section of flesh)

6: Previous Convictions

2 x Possessing Offensive Weapons (both knives)

4 x Assault Police Officers

2 x Assault Occasioning Actual Bodily Harm

1 x Unlawful Wounding

1 x Causing Grievous Bodily Harm with Intent

22 x Burglary

7 x Minor offences of Dishonesty

6 x Public Order Offences

1 x Robbery

Has been sentenced to numerous Custodial Sentences as a Young Offender and as an adult.

In particular, 18 months imprisonment for Unlawful Wounding and 5 years for GBH with Intent (attacked female co-habitee with a claw hammer fracturing her jaw, 3 vertebrae in her upper back and her right arm)

Robbery conviction (7 years imprisonment) – sprayed CS gas in face of manageress of Supermarket in Sunderland.

7: Intelligence

[Source : Collator's files – all Northern Divisions]

Dangerous. Invariably armed, normally with knife, but known access to firearms. Relishes violence. Particularly enjoys hurting females. Normally operates alone but has known criminal associates in Manchester, Leeds, Sheffield and Newcastle. On fringes of organised crime with close connections to Babba Gang in Manchester (predominantly Yardies) but viewed as too unpredictable for major planned operations.

Suspected approach by splinter terrorist group in Northern Ireland, but no known actions. Informant believes group concluded that he was too volatile and too much of a loner for active service.

Has been Target Criminal in recent years but operational resources do not allow for this at present.

Last confirmed sighting prior to current arrest was in Sheffield where believed to be lorry driver (casual).

END OF POLICE REPORT (NUMBER 2)

* * *

YORKSHIRE POLICE
RECORD OF INTERVIEW
PLACE OF INTERVIEW: Leeds North Central
PERSON INTERVIEWED: Gary Peter TREVORS
INTERVIEWING OFFICERS: Detective Chief Inspector Ernest
Noble; Detective Sergeant Ronald Perry
OTHERS PRESENT: Roger Sylvester (Solicitor)
Tape Reference : EN/245/53/

SUSPECTED OFFENCES :
Aggravated Burglary of Blossomfields, Alwoodley, Leeds
Murder of Paul Michael Checkley (aged 35)
Wounding Sarah Checkley with intent to do her grievous bodily harm

Noble:

This interview is being tape-recorded. It may be tendered in evidence if your case is brought before a Court. You will be provided with a copy of the tape. We are in an Interview Room at Leeds North Central Police Station. I am Detective Chief Inspector Ernie Noble and this is Detective Sergeant Ron Perry. Would you please introduce yourself formally, Mr Sylvester.

Sylvester:

Certainly. I'm Roger Sylvester. Senior Partner of Sylvester and Stocks, Solicitors. My firm's instructed on behalf of Mr Trevors.

Perry:

Before this interview begins I must inform you that you've been arrested on suspicion of aggravated burglary, wounding with intent and murder. You do not have to say anything, but it may harm your defence if you do not mention when questioned, something which you later rely on in court. Anything you do say may be given in evidence. Do you understand that?

Trevors:

Yeah.

Perry:

We've disclosed to your solicitor the nature of the charges against you and I'm asking you to confirm that you have had an opportunity to discuss matters with him in private prior to the commencement of this interview.

Trevors:

I've spoken to him. It won't have been in private though, 'cos it's obvious ever since I was dragged out me bed at 5 in the morning you were looking to fit me up for this job, so you'll have bugged the conversation I had with Sylvester, for all the bloody good it'll do you.

Noble:

There's been no bugging. No listening in. No prying. What you say to your solicitor is your privilege. Full stop. If you want to break off during this interview to consult your solicitor again then we'll consider your request. I shall now ask the sergeant to start the interview formally.

Perry:

It's my duty to remind you of what you said when you were arrested by me and other officers at 5 this morning and to obtain your confirmation of its accuracy. Your flat in Sheffield was entered by armed police officers and myself with a properly obtained warrant. You tried to jump out the bedroom window, and had to be restrained physically, handcuffed and held down on the bed. You were informed that you were under arrest on suspicion of murder. Do you agree that this is what happened?

Trevors:

You've cleaned that up a bit, mate, ain't ya? As I saw it, six thugs with shooters bust into my drum in the middle of the night shouting "Murdering bastard!" I was smacked in the face, on me own bed, sat on and cuffed. I never tried to get out of no window – I just jumped out of bed when a bunch of gunmen burst into my bedroom. I was stark bollock naked.

Perry:

You then shouted at me that "No copper arrested me for nothing and there'd be a price to pay". You then said directly to me and very quietly, with your face close to mine, that "Sooner or later you can be expected to be sliced up as well".

Trevors:

That's a straightforward fucking lie. You bastards never change, do ya? Fit-ups. Verbals. Same old routine. I never said that nor nowt like it.

Perry:

I'm inviting you to sign my pocket book as an accurate record of what was said in your flat. I noted the conversation down, short as it was, within 20 minutes of the arrest. You know that's what you said.

Trevors:

Invite me to sign? I sign nothing. Mr Sylvester, this is seriously out of order. You know me well enough. I say nothing to the vermin. Nothing. Never.

Perry:

It was deliberate policy in this enquiry not to release any information to the press or to anyone about how the injuries to either victim were caused, yet you made immediate reference to "slicing up". How do you explain that, Mr Trevors?

Trevors:

You verballed me. You, Perry, are known round these parts as a bent bastard. Your name stinks. Stick that down in your fucking notebook and I'll sign it right enough.

Perry:

If that's what you wish to allege then fire away, but that's what you said on arrest, that's what I recorded and that's what any jury trying you will hear. You now have a final opportunity to explain why you said it".

Trevors:

There won't be no jury trying my case because you don't have no evidence to bring a case, so up your arse with your threats and your verbals.

Perry:

As Mr Sylvester can see, you have bruising to the face from where the officers were compelled to use violence to restrain you...

Trevors:

Bullshit. I was punched in the face, probably by you, Perry. That's why my face is injured. Some other bastard put one into me kidneys. Half-suffocated me. Trussed me up like a fucking chicken on me own bed. Police brutality. Mr Sylvester, I want photos taken of these injuries this morning, so there's some record of what these bastards have done to me.

Sylvester:

I do agree with that. Detective Chief Inspector, I'm formally requesting such photographs. Please make arrangements for that to be done today, before their appearance starts to fade.

Noble:

He's already been seen by a police surgeon after his arrest and he'll be photographed in the usual way at the end of this interview. My information is that he was extremely violent upon arrest and forcible restraint was absolutely justified.

Perry:

When the police surgeon examined you, apart from the injuries sustained on arrest, he found an old injury on the back of your neck. He was unable to be precise, but believes that you must have been struck in that area with some kind of object, so that a bump and a significant contusion were caused. What he saw was, and I quote from his report, "the healing aftermath of such a blow". Judging by the abraded appearance of the injury, the police surgeon also believes that it likely seeped blood. He ages this injury at not less than one week and not more than two. Can you account for this injury?

Trevors:

I'd have to think about that one. In my line of work you're always getting bumps and bruises.

Perry:

Well think about it now, because I'm suggesting that this injury was caused when Mrs Checkley struck you with a golf club after you broke into her house.

Trevors:

Again, bullshit. I broke into no bloody house. I've never set eyes on this Mrs Checkley, or whatever her name is. I ain't been hit by no bloody woman with no golf club. I do a rough job, mate. I get plenty of knocks. And you're right, a week or so back I took a whack. Happens all the time. Loading a skip on to the wagon. Some masonry fell off and caught me on the back of the neck – that's probably how that injury what your doctor found was caused.

Perry:

When was this?

Trevors:

Some time last week.

Perry:

Where?

Trevors:

Out at an industrial dump on the Wakefield Road.

Perry:

Did anybody see this?

Trevors:

I doubt it. I wasn't badly hurt. I don't go crying to mummy. I work for meself. I ain't got no employer providing me with insurance and a pension, like you lot on your cushy number.

Perry:

Did you seek medical help?

Trevors:

Of course I bloody didn't. If I went to the quack every time I took a bump, I'd need a season ticket. Next question.

Perry:

Why didn't you remember the incident when I first asked you?

Trevors :

'Cos there's nowt special about a knock at work.

Perry:

You sustained that injury whilst committing an aggravated burglary in Leeds, eight or nine days ago on the Tuesday night. The householder struck the intruder, with a golf club, in just the spot where you have evidence of a healing injury.

Trevors:

Don't you fucking listen? I explained that mark. Coincidence. Next question.

Perry:

I haven't finished asking about the injury yet.

Sylvester:

I would suggest that you have. You are merely repeating an unsupported allegation against my client, which he has now denied several times and given you his explanation for. You're just browbeating him by repeating the same question.

Perry:

Nobody could browbeat your client, Mr Sylvester. I'm making enquiries into a ruthless act of murder and will ask my questions in my own way. These offences were committed at around 11 p.m. on Tuesday night of last week in Alwoodley, Leeds. Where were you at that time?

Trevors:

How the hell do I know? It's over a week ago. I go all over the place. I could've been anywhere.

Perry:

I'm not asking where you could've been. I'm asking where you were.

Trevors:

No idea. I'm a busy fella. Too long ago for me to remember just like that. And, before you ask, I don't keep no fucking diary.

Perry:

You know exactly where you were. No doubt to the minute, with the

39

amount of planning you put into this job. You were in the Checkleys' house in Leeds trying to rob them.

Trevors:

Not guilty. Next question.

Perry:

Where were you at that time? 11 p.m.

Trevors:

This is the last time that I answer the same bloody question. Don't know. It's over a week ago. Not guilty. What you got that says I was there?

Perry:

As you know, because we've already informed Mr Sylvester, the intruder was masked, but he'd fixed a piece of material to the back of the mask, so that no part of his neck was visible to the victims. Mrs Checkley struck him a hard blow on the back of the neck and later pulled that material off him in the course of a struggle. The inside of that material had bloodstaining which, on DNA analysis, is a match for yours. That's the basis of this evidence that I'm putting to you.

Trevors:

I've already been told that by Mr Sylvester. What you haven't told him is what you mean by saying the blood matched. How many people's blood would it match, mate? You ain't said nowt about that. And you ain't bothered to tell us how much blood was found. You make fucking sure we ain't told the strength of what you call "this evidence".

Perry:

It's your blood isn't it?

Sylvester:

Why don't you answer my client's absolutely legitimate questions? What are the details of the extent of the match? And how much blood was there for your scientists to work with?

Perry:

Mr Sylvester, I'd be grateful if you'd allow me to conduct this interview in my own way. I'll deal with responses raised by your client in my own time. That blood on that material is yours, isn't it, Mr Trevors?

Trevors:

No. Now why don't you answer my fucking questions, Perry?

Perry:

Where do you buy your ballet shoes?

Trevors:

Ballet shoes? Is this some new interviewing technique? Give the punter a few jokes for light relief?

Perry:

The murderer wore ballet shoes.

Trevors:

Well, that should make your job easy. You're looking for a fucking fairy. There can't be too many of those knocking round Yorkshire on a cold winter's night, can there, Mr Sylvester? Oh, and by the way, I've been thinking, haven't I? I've remembered where I was on that Tuesday night.

Perry:

Where?

Trevors:

Wednesday night, I went down the match. United at home. You'll have been over me pad with a magnifying glass so you'll probably find the programme in there somewhere. Working back from that like, the Tuesday, I knows exactly where I was.

Perry:

So tell us.

Trevors:

In me place, mate. Never went out that night. Stayed in all night.

Perry:

Any witnesses?

Trevors:

I'm single.

Perry:

That doesn't stop you from having witnesses.

Trevors :

No witnesses. On me tod. In me flat. No doubts.

Perry:

What were you doing then at around 11 p.m.?

Trevors:

I'll tell yer what I was doing. Watching TV. I can remember it clear now. Been thinking. That's the night they had this special on, like. All about the Amazon. BBC2, I think. Don't 'spose you watch much BBC2 yerself, do you? You check what time that was on. When that was on, I was in me armchair, mate, tucked up in me own drum.

Noble:

I'll have it checked now. Pass me the phone, Sergeant.

(Sounds of use of telephone)

Bill, DCI Noble here.

A TV time check please. Immediately.

Last week. Documentary-type programme. The Amazon Basin. Probably BBC2. Call me back in the Interview Room.

Perry:

Interested in the Amazon, are you?

Trevors :

Made it a crime, have they then?

Perry:

While we wait, tell us about the programme.

Trevors:

Floods. Piece of skirt takes a boat up the Amazon from Maneus in Brazil, to some place in Peru, following the floodwaters. Showed wild life and trees was being wiped out. Grand stuff, right up your street. Meets a Peruvian kid whose family had moved into the town from the jungle and... (sound of phone ringing)

Noble:

Yes, Bill. Thanks. (sound of receiver being replaced). The Amazon Basin. Tuesday of last week. BBC2. Started at 10.50 p.m. Finished at midnight.

(Long silence)

Trevors:

You want some more about the Amazon then? Or have you bastards had enough of a Natural History lesson so I can go home?

Perry:

You're going nowhere. All you've proved is that you have a reliable video recorder and a good memory.

Trevors:

Video? No time for one of them. Too much fiddle. Never owned one. You got the keys to me flat. Go take a look. No video recorder. No video tapes. Just a TV. Send one of your SOCO crew along.

Perry :

Your flat has been thoroughly searched and will be again.

Trevors :

And trashed. You filth'll make sure you leave your mark. And ain't it about time you give us the answers about the blood 'n that, this DNA crap?

Noble:

I will answer that. You are entitled to know. There was a trace of blood and the odds of the DNA matching yours are 1 in 600. In other words, it will be matched by chance, once in every 600 people.

Trevors:

So it'd match half of bloody Yorkshire then, would it?

Perry:

That's a complete exaggeration. Mrs Checkley knows the murderer was male. So we are talking exclusively about males. It means there'd be a random match found in but a few hundred men out of a large city.

Trevors:

Have you got the other few hundred in for interview as well then, or just me?

Perry:

Just you. Because you're responsible. You've got an injury in the right location. An injury which would have bled. You knew the Checkleys had been attacked with a knife. Only the Police, the SOCOs, the experts and the murderer knew that. You've got the kind of convictions that make you a prime candidate.

Trevors:

My previous convictions've got bugger all to do with anything. They ain't evidence of guilt. You can't use them in charging me or in trying to get me done. That's so, ain't it, Mr Sylvester?

Sylvester:

In normal circumstances the police cannot use previous convictions in deciding whether to charge you. Whether a man's previous convictions ever go before a jury can depend upon a lot of different considerations. Now, Mr Perry, do you have any other evidence to put to my client, because if you don't, I shall ask you to bring this interview to an end as I doubt that you have sufficient evidence to justify charging him.

Perry:

What size shoes do you take, Mr Trevors?

Trevors:

Are we going back to fairy ballet dancers now, then?

Perry:

What size?

Trevors:

Nine or ten.

Perry:

A footprint in the blood of about that size was found at the scene.

It's yours, isn't it, from those special shoes you wear, that make sure no one hears you coming?

Trevors:

I take size 9 or 10 – the same as millions of men. Next question.

Noble:

There won't be a next question for the moment. I intend to terminate this interview at this stage. We'll inform you, Mr Sylvester, when we wish to interview your client again. He'll be kept in custody. A decision will be taken later as to what the next steps will be. Mr Trevors, you'll be returned to the cells.

INTERVIEW TERMINATED

* * *

A harsh yellow light from the adjacent main road now illuminated the crumbling orange plaster in Noble's office as he leant back in his chair reflecting ruefully on the inadequate scraps of evidence they had against Trevors. All of his efforts to exert any kind of control over the lawlessness and cruelty of this community had dominated his working life and yet, in truth, had not counted for very much. Was society any better off for his existence? Did anybody really care? Sipping tasteless, thin black coffee, from a polystyrene cup, that the dreadful machine down the corridor produced, he allowed himself a philosophical half-smile for he'd asked himself those same questions a thousand times and never come up with a satisfactory answer. No one had ever promised him that being a copper was going to be easy or even fulfilling. Dealing with the flotsam and jetsam of a dirty, soulless, industrial city was a tough business. You picked up the pieces of the victims' lives and tried to lock up the predators. That was exactly what Trevors was. A predator. A ruthless killer who would have no compunction about killing again. Judging by the expertise deployed in the Checkley attack, he had probably killed before. Yet, on this evidence, the police were virtually powerless to stop him.

Noble had come to believe that you could split the causes behind the violent criminal into three categories. Genetic, social and deviant. Trevors was made up of all three. A man wholly without conscience. Of course he had killed Checkley. You could actually feel it just from being in the same room with him. Put a decent man in his grave 40 years too early and walked away without a backward glance. Noble had looked into his eyes during that pathetic interview conducted by Perry and, whilst Trevors quite enjoyed making the police look like fools, the real message from the eyes was that they were dead. There was simply nothing there. No feeling. Nothing. Just a black, self-absorbed emptiness.

His black reverie was interrupted when Perry barged in without so much as a knock on the door. Exuding insolence, easing himself into the check padded chair in the corner of the room without so much as a by-your-leave, he stared defiantly into Noble's face, plainly anticipating the words that were likely to be coming his way from the Chief Inspector.

"You haven't got a bloody feather to fly with, Perry. The Custody Sergeant will tell you that there isn't enough to charge him," declared Noble emphatically, as he tossed the empty polystyrene cup into the green plastic waste basket at the side of his desk. "Let's face it – he spent that interview taking the piss out of you."

Perry was not in the mood to swallow insults easily from this ageing has-been. The torch had been passed to the new generation and these day-counting dinosaurs were clogging up the system. Anybody could see that his old-fashioned methods were obsolete. Playing these enquiries by the book got you nowhere slowly and the sooner he and his type could be dispatched to their potting sheds the better, although, predictably, Noble was displaying all the typical attitudes of the old order.

"Took the piss out of us, you mean. I might have had a better chance if I'd received some support from my Senior Officer, sir. You just gave your neck," he snapped insolently.

"I won't take that nonsense off you, Perry. You'd better learn to watch your mouth. What's more it sounded just like a verbal to me. I want Trevors just as badly as you do, but that kind of half-baked shit won't work."

"It was no verbal," Perry responded indignantly. "It was no bloody verbal. What I recorded that evil bastard as saying is exactly what he did say. Maybe half under his breath, but he said it all the same. He said it and by Christ he meant it. There's nothing he'd like better than to slice a copper in the guts."

"Well, we've sod all else. The DNA alone isn't enough," continued Noble despondently. We need more than the mark on his neck 'cos he's come up with an answer for that and we can't disprove it. I've taken another look at the Intelligence. Nothing. Not even the narks have turned anything up."

"Course they haven't. He copped for nothing at the Checkleys so there's nowt for him to flog in the boozers and he's a loner. No sidekick who might blab."

"Have you checked out all his neighbours in the flats? Anyone see him come or go?" Noble asked.

"They're all tossers. Thieves, few pushers. Flats on each side are derelict. Boarded up. Crud. Useless," came Perry's terse reply.

"I've had Traffic run all the CCTV cameras round that side of the city. Looked for nicked vehicles, false plates, pedestrians his size, anything. They've come up with bugger all. We're pissing in the wind here, if you ask me," sighed Noble.

"I guessed that's how you'd be thinking, sir, and so I've taken steps to deal with it," Perry suddenly declared with a note of triumph in his voice.

"It's your size twelve steps that worry me, Perry. What bloody nonsense have you come up with, now?"

"I've spoken with Mrs Checkley in hospital to see if she'd be prepared to attend an identification parade. She's agreed. She wasn't keen. But she's well enough to be brought here tomorrow morning. And I'll make sure she's up for it," announced Perry confidently.

"An ID parade?" spluttered Noble. "What kind of bugger's muddle are you trying to get us into? What possible point is there in holding an ID parade? The bastard wore a mask from start to finish. This Mrs Checkley has X-ray eyes does she?"

"There's every point. I don't mean a normal face identification. This bastard spoke. I want a voice ID. Each person on the parade, including Trevors, will repeat the exact words the killer said to her. If she picks him out then, bingo, we've got a case to take to Court. Once a jury sets eyes on that scum, he won't touch the sides."

"And what if he's skilled at disguising his voice?" came the Chief Inspector's response. "What then?"

"Mrs Checkley is no fool, sir. I've spoken to her. I was in the hospital for part of the time that she was making her Witness Statement. This is an intelligent woman. And she's tough as hell, I can tell you. For Christ's sake, sir, she's listening for the voice of the man that killed her husband. Knifed him twice right in front of her. Slit her straight open into the bargain. Left her scarred for life. She's been hearing those same words in her head, every night, alone in her bed. At least this gives us a chance. Are you prepared to let me put it to Trevors or not?" demanded Perry, now out of his chair and standing directly at the Chief Inspector's desk. "Someone in this shit heap needs to have some balls."

The older man stared intently at Perry. The sharp features of the sergeant gave him a bird-like appearance. One of those birds that screeches rather than warbles and with eyes that are too close together, so that he looks at you down the length of his nose, making it appear even more like a beak. The prematurely thinning hair was lank and out of shape. Noble could sense the calculating brain pulsating beneath the exterior, forever planning the next move. If Perry could be kept under control then he just might come up with enough to get Trevors into Court. What a choice. Hoping that Perry could be kept on the leash or simply letting a killer walk out. Still, Noble reflected with resignation, you can only play the hand that fate has dealt and there were no more cards coming his way. Not off the top of the deck anyway.

And ensuring that Perry played a straight hand was something that the Chief Inspector still believed that he could achieve.

"I don't doubt you've got the balls, Perry. It's your brains that bother me." There was a long pause before Noble continued. "There again, not much to lose is there? You might as well put it to Trevors and Sylvester," said Noble eventually, "but they may refuse."

"All depends on how it's put, sir. They aren't quite sure if we are going to charge him on what we've already got. If we do, he's banged up on remand for months. They may worry the case will build, what we might dig up," replied Perry eagerly.

"Well, we know the answer to that, don't we? We've not got enough and no sign of 'owt else coming our way," Noble answered.

"But they aren't sure of that, sir. If they think we'll probably charge him if he refuses the parade…" began Perry.

"But that if he agrees to a parade and she doesn't pick him out," Noble interrupted, "then he's definitely out. You think that may swing them into agreeing?"

"Exactly. Like I said. All depends on how it's put and you can leave that safely to me."

"It's leaving things to you that worries me. But you may have a point. He's a cocky bugger, all right. He may be just cocky enough to agree if he thinks that there's little chance of her being able to get it right and then he'll be out."

"And if he looks like refusing," Perry added enthusiastically, "I'll tell him that a jury will think that he was shit-scared because he was guilty. Anyway, I know his type. He'll believe that he can handle it easily enough. Like you say, he's a cocky bugger. Cocky enough to agree."

"It's a last throw of the dice. I warn you, no bloody monkey business," Noble ordered. "You got that? No bloody monkey business. Set it up for the morning. We've nothing to lose."

"Consider it done," nodded Perry, making his way to the door. "10.45 tomorrow morning."

"Remember. If she doesn't pick him, then he walks," snapped Noble as Perry marched purposefully out of the room.

"He'll be walking, all right. Straight into 30 fucking years without parole. That's where he'll be walking," grunted Perry under his breath, as he hurried away to make arrangements. He needed to have a quiet word with Inspector Raymond who ran the parades at that station and call in a favour owed. Everybody knew that was how it worked.

CHAPTER 4

Although Perry was early to collect Sarah Checkley from hospital, arriving just before ten o'clock, she was ready and waiting for him in the Ward Sister's office when he walked in. Her attractive face remained pale and gaunt, but there was a purpose in her manner as they set off along the echoing hospital corridors towards the side car park. Declining the offer of a wheelchair, she stared straight ahead as they walked, making no effort at small talk. Still immersed in her own personal nightmare, she needed all of her strength just to survive each day and the social niceties were the first casualty. Besides, desperate though she was to see the killer locked away behind bars for the rest of his life, she found herself unable to warm to this rather intense Detective Sergeant Perry, who seemed to have been put in charge of the day-to-day running of the case. During those long, ghastly hours when the smell of the anaesthetic was still strong in her nostrils, and that young woman police constable, Jill Bentley, was at her bedside painstakingly recording her Witness Statement in longhand, Sarah Checkley had recollections of this tall, bird-like detective hovering in the background, occasionally bullying the WPC to press her for more and more details, however exhausted she was after major surgery. His relish at the prospect of pursuit of the murderer was tangible, almost animalistic, and seemed to excite him, making it difficult for him to disguise his obvious irritation at her frequent need for breaks and rest.

Despite the time constraints on his plan, as taking too long over the journey might raise suspicions later, Perry deliberately set off slowly, thereby keeping his passenger calm and enabling him to pick the most opportune moment to embark upon the very delicate task he had in mind.

"Mrs Checkley," he began, staring intently at the road straight ahead.

"It may help if I explain the procedure on this kind of parade. There'll be about nine or ten men in a long room. All of 'em dressed the same in white paper overalls, wearing woollen balaclavas with eye slits and a hole for the mouth. You'll walk up and down the line. Judge their height and build. But, as I said on the phone, we're not after a visual identification…"

"How close am I to them?" she interrupted brusquely.

Other than a perfunctory "Good Morning" on his arrival, these were the first words she had spoken to him that day and, as in yesterday's telephone call and when he had listened to her dictating her Witness Statement from her hospital bed, he found himself captivated by the quality of her voice which, though feminine, had an obvious strength and resonance to it.

"As close or as far away as you choose," was the reply.

"I need to be close," she added urgently. "I must be close to have a chance. His face was inches from mine when he said those words. I need to hear him breathe, hear him exhale. I have to feel the words, as well as hear them. Every little detail is important or I may get it wrong."

"Of course, these situations can be a bit difficult. Nerves and stuff. Can force mistakes when otherwise you'd get it right. Sometimes it can help to have a bit of a…" his voice tailed away as he searched anxiously for the right word.

"Bit of a what, Sergeant?" she demanded.

"Maybe a bit of a …bit of an edge," he declared cautiously.

"Edge?" she queried, feeling slightly uneasy at his choice of word. Despite her instinctive dislike of this man, he had never struck her as stupid and, in dealing with her, his words seemed carefully chosen. "What exactly do you mean by 'edge'?"

Perry shifted uncomfortably in the driver's seat and bought himself a few seconds by seemingly concentrating on the roundabout that he was currently negotiating. It had not taken long for him to recognise that this woman was going to prove a handful. Until this murder she'd probably had things too bloody easy. Cosy upbringing. Decent education. Rich husband. Everything done on the straight and narrow. Now, glancing anxiously at his watch, he knew that he had only a few minutes to persuade her that operating in the gutter called for different rules. If the journey from the hospital to the police station took too long it might raise eyebrows somewhere along the line.

Turning his head sharply to his left, he looked her straight in the eye. "I can rely on your total discretion, can't I?" he enquired. "Your absolute discretion?"

"I don't know exactly what you mean," came the guarded reply.

"What I mean, is just how badly do you want to see this killer nailed?" he asked, quite unable to make the words sound respectable.

"What kind of question is that?" she breathed anxiously at him, recoiling at his words. "Who could have a greater desire than I have to see him 'nailed', as you put it? My husband's dead, my daughter's without a father and I have a scar on my body which is so hideous that I can't even look at myself in the mirror. All because of this man. Does that answer your question?"

Although the time factor was getting increasingly critical, Perry immediately pulled over to the side of the road and stopped the car. Switching off the ignition, he turned to his left and stared intently at her.

"Does that mean then that I can count on your absolute discretion?" he repeated.

Sarah Checkley was nobody's fool. Maybe her blonde hair and high cheek bones had been the first reasons why a successful businessman had wanted to take her out, but Paul Checkley had quickly come to appreciate that she had more than her fair share of brains. Perry also remembered her performance in her hospital bed when, still traumatized, she had managed to dictate in clear and precise language, the horrors of what had happened. He realised only too well, as her eyes remained fixed on his, that he was dealing with a sharp and formidable lady and that this could all go horribly wrong.

"Listen, Madam," he coaxed, "this is not your world. We're dealing with scum here. Cesspool scum. Sometimes the Queensberry Rules won't work."

"Why don't you just spit out what you're trying to say?" she demanded uneasily. "I'm not sure that I like some of what I'm hearing. But I may not be understanding you. "

"It's just a question, really, Mrs Checkley. A question of how much you're prepared to help us lock up your husband's killer. That's all. Sometimes that needs a bit of trust between us and you. I like to call it discretion."

Leaning towards her as he spoke forced his shirt collar slightly away from his neck, enabling her to see the grime within the top inside edges of the collar. There was dandruff that had fallen from the unwashed, thinning hair on to the shoulders of his creased suit and the car was filling with the rank odour of his sweat. "Cesspool scum," he had said and only now did it truly begin to dawn upon her that Perry himself may actually fall into that category as well.

"What on earth does my discretion have to do with it?" she exclaimed indignantly.

"Steady, Madam, steady," he interrupted immediately, now acutely aware that time was running out and seeking to calm her. "We're on the same side, you know."

"You haven't got enough evidence to convict him, have you? You're desperate," she spat out, now realising what probably lay behind his words.

"I wouldn't put it quite like that…" he began.

"How would you bloody put it, then?" she demanded aggressively.

"Our enquiries are continuing and we're hopeful that more evidence may emerge but, unless we have enough to charge him by 8 o'clock tonight, we'll have to release him on bail. I want a positive identification by you. This morning. Then we can charge him and he'll be kept in custody," Perry replied, as he watched the disturbing realisation of where this was leading finally register in her eyes.

"So I identify the voice or he's out. That's the long and short of it. That will give you enough to charge him and at least get him into the dock. It's all down to the victim," came her shocked response.

"You're very hard on us, Madam. We did find him after all. We know it's him and he's sitting in a cell at the moment. We haven't done so badly…" Perry hesitated before continuing. It was now or never. This had already taken far too long. "But you can make sure that we have enough to charge him," he added.

Now he had actually said it. However ambiguous he had tried to make it sound earlier, the proposition was now openly on the table. Either she went with it and they would have enough to charge him, or she refused and, unless she actually picked the voice out correctly without any help, then the bastard was out. The odds of an unaided correct identification were nine or ten to one against. A complete lottery, unless she was exceptionally good.

Sarah Checkley looked at him with undisguised horror. Any ideals she may have possessed, that a wicked murderer who had destroyed her family might be properly brought to justice by a competent and honourable system, lay dashed to pieces on the car floor. Not only was she the victim, but she was being invited to participate in perverting the course of justice – it was now blindingly obvious that he wanted her help in fixing the parade.

Yesterday, when Perry had phoned her at the hospital, she had been very apprehensive about taking part because she knew that the experience of being in the same room as that animal would terrify her. However, once she had agreed to participate, her spirits had lifted for she believed that the chances of her recognising that voice, when it spoke those chilling words again, were very good. Now, instead of encouraging her and supporting her, this unscrupulous officer had already hopelessly compromised her and was one step away from corrupting her. How she despised him, as he sat waiting expectantly for the fish to take the bait.

"You're offering to tip me off. Make sure that I pick him out and then keep my mouth shut. Have I really got this right? You're asking me to pervert the course of justice?"

"Not 'pervert', more like 'assist'," the Sergeant suggested disingenuously.

"I need an answer. And quickly, please. Sometimes one or two of the rules have to be massaged. The ends justifies the means."

Less than two weeks ago, Sarah Checkley had been making herself a bedtime drink in her own kitchen, her life had been orderly, sane and happy. Now she was widowed, disfigured and on the verge of being corrupted by a dishonest policeman. The grotesque reality being thrust upon her by this double-dealer was that either she cheated, or risked allowing her husband's murderer to escape scot-free.

"And what if you are wrong?" she exclaimed. "What if, despite all your self-assurance, the man you have in custody is innocent? You can't be sure, or else you wouldn't need to cheat."

"Cheat? It's not cheating. It's just an insurance policy, a chance to avenge your husband. To put his killer in prison for life. To stop him doing it again. We know this man did it. There's no bloody mistake here. This is a man who pinned his naked girlfriend on her back by putting his boot across her neck and then brought a claw hammer down on her jaw, fracturing it in three places and knocking out a dozen teeth. This is a man who squirted CS gas directly into the eyes of a woman so he could rob her."

Perry had now warmed to his task and, in making his pitch, his tone became more self-justifying as he pushed his head, on its long neck, closer to Sarah Checkley's face.

"This man left his DNA in your house," he continued even more urgently. "The scientists are so bloody frightened of losing credibility that they play down the statistics. Odds of 1 in 600, plus all the other little bits we have on him, make it a certainty that it's his DNA, but the scientists won't say that in Court. I'm telling you – this is the man who attacked you and then stabbed your husband to death."

After a long pause she heard her own voice. It was filled with self-disgust. "So how do you tip me the wink?" she breathed, beaten down by the force of his argument.

Perry relaxed. The sweat generated from the tension of the last few minutes was running down his sides from under his arms. It had taken too long and at one point it really had been touch and go, but he was confident now that the fish had been hooked.

"Once the parade starts, as one of the investigating officers, I'm not allowed to be there. The men will take up their positions. You'll be kept in a separate room. The suspect may switch his position up to the moment when you arrive in a small anteroom. Then, in the presence of the suspect's solicitor, an I.D. Parade Inspector will ask you to sign the Parade Form, confirming your identity and the time you're entering the Parade room. That form is kept on a clipboard which the Inspector will hold down on a desk and point out to you where to sign. As you sign, his hand or hands will remain on the board. The number of fingers that he's displaying will be the killer's position in the parade. One to ten. There'll be no more than ten men parading."

"So the rot spreads as high as Inspector level, does it?" she observed with unmasked contempt.

"Mrs Checkley, I want to see a murderer convicted. I'm the one taking the risks here. This Inspector has his reasons for playing ball. He can't afford ever to speak of this any more than I can. The topic need never be raised again, whether you say 'yes' or 'no'. But now is the time for you to give me your answer one way or the other."

"You know the answer is 'yes'," she responded with a sigh of hopelessness, "You've left me with no choice."

Sickened by her own words, she slumped back into the seat, as Perry turned triumphantly to the front, started the engine and hurriedly continued their journey to the police station.

Neither of them spoke until he turned left into the police station and was halted by the red and white mechanical arm that controlled access to the yard at the rear. Slipping his security card into the slot of the box through the driver's window, he turned to look directly at her while waiting for the arm to lift. Her head was back and her eyes were closed. At close quarters Perry could see that the suffering in her face was already beginning to take its toll on her looks and, he reflected, these were only the early days. But she had to be strong during this parade. He needed a good performance from her now. The next few minutes could bang that piece of shit up until he was ready for a bus pass.

"We're here now. Are you all right?" he enquired anxiously.

"All right?" she responded, opening her eyes and pulling herself upright in her seat. "All right? All right to conspire with you to cheat and lie? Is that what you mean?"

Perry simply smiled. Feisty. Tough. Angry. That was just how he wanted her to be.

"Don't forget," he remarked, "we stopped en route for me to ask if you were feeling well enough. Just to cover the time, you understand."

"I understand well enough," Sarah Checkley snapped back at him as the mechanical arm lifted slowly into the air and Perry eased the car forwards. "I understand that the victim is just to be used. The rules mean nothing."

Perry simply shrugged his shoulders and drove into the parking bay he had kept reserved by the rear door so that she did not have far to walk. In this dirty world he who played by the rules was always the loser and Detective Sergeant Ronald Perry did not like losing.

When they brought her into the small anteroom, she could hear the sounds of the restless men in the adjacent room, moving about as they took up their positions in anticipation of her entry. Perry had told her that they would all be wearing paper overalls and she was aware of the sinister rustling noises whilst Inspector Raymond explained the rules and procedures that would apply. A small, bald man with a feeble moustache had been introduced to her as Roger Sylvester, the suspect's solicitor, and he stared at her quite insensitively while the Inspector carefully detailed the routine.

"I have to tell you, Mrs Checkley, that the sight of ten men in paper overalls and, in particular in balaclavas, can be quite alarming. You have no reason to be frightened. You are completely safe. There are a number of uniformed officers on hand and there is nothing to fear," the Inspector explained in a rather flat and distant voice.

"The man who committed these offences at your house may, or may not, be here. Each of them will read out the words recorded in your statement as having been spoken by the offender. You'll stand in front of the individual as he reads. Then you'll move on to the next man. At the end you may ask any or all to repeat the words. The men will then be told to sit down and you should move to the doorway of the room. Then, in their presence, you'll be asked if you recognise the voice. Please answer loudly and clearly and then leave the room. Mr Sylvester and I will accompany you back into this anteroom, where I'll write down your answer on this form that I have, and you and Mr Sylvester will check and sign the form. Then the parade'll be concluded. Is all of that clear?"

She nodded, feeling those initial waves of nausea with which she had become so familiar over the last two weeks, flowing upwards from her stomach. Meanwhile, the Inspector had walked authoritatively through the side door into the unseen main room beyond, leaving her momentarily alone with the bald solicitor, who continued to stare at her intently, but said nothing. She could hear Inspector Raymond's voice, telling the men to put on their balaclavas and take up their final positions, and then he was back in the room, clipboard poised.

"Mr Sylvester. If you would kindly walk through and confirm your client's position and then return here," requested the Inspector. As soon as that was done the Inspector turned his attention again to Sarah Checkley.

"We're ready for you, Madam," he declared in his officious manner. "Just need you and Mr Sylvester to sign the form," he added, holding it out on the small table in the middle of the room.

"You first, Mrs Checkley, please. Just sign there would you, underneath where I have written 10.47 a.m."

He pointed to the spot with one finger, at the same time handing her his cheap Biro pen, which she took with a trembling hand. His left hand was at his side and, as she signed her name, just his right hand lingered on the form with all five fingers splayed wide across the page. The nails were bitten and unclean and she could see that his hand was also trembling before it was withdrawn to beckon over the solicitor to add his signature beneath hers. The message had been passed. She had seen. Now there really was no turning back.

None of the Inspector's words had quite prepared her for the chilling spectacle of ten white-clad figures standing menacingly in a long line, with their heads covered in those grotesque masks, and a card with a large number on it, dangling from a string around their necks. As the Inspector positioned her in front of Number 1, she realised that she was actually hyperventilating and the Inspector was watching her with obvious concern.

"Are you fit to continue, Mrs Checkley?" he enquired anxiously.

"I am," she replied emphatically.

"Are you ready for us to begin, Mr Sylvester?" asked the Inspector.

"Ready," the solicitor answered, in a quiet, thin voice.

"Man Number 1. Read the words from the card, please," came the order.

Clearing his throat Number 1 began to recite the lines.

"I know there's a safe in the house. Take me to it or I finish opening you up, you privileged bitch."

It was a young voice. Probably some student they had brought in off the street to make up the numbers. It lifted and fell. It was uncomfortable with the words. It had a softness the killer could never manufacture. It was one of the stooges and so were the next three.

As she stood in front of Number 5 her heart was pounding so hard in her chest that she thought that she might pass out. There was nothing about the frame or height of the man that particularly differentiated him from most of the others but, whether it was because of her dark secret or just instinct, there was an aura about him and before he'd even finished half the words she knew it was him. Speaking quietly, seeking to suppress the north-east ingrained in his consonants, pushing the voice a touch higher than where it naturally sat, she listened to her husband's killer. Her nervousness had evaporated to be replaced by intense, almost uncontrollable, anger, which was directed not only against this white and black apparition, but against Perry. She would have known this evil voice anywhere, under any conditions. The timbre, the pitch, the tone, the age, the inhalations of breath between syllables. There had never been any need to cheat. There had never been any need to compromise her and expose her to corruption. Now, to see justice done, she would have to carry this subterfuge with her to the grave.

She turned on her heel and walked towards the door where she stopped and looked back into the room.

"I don't need to hear any more!" she exclaimed.

"The man who attacked me and killed my husband is Number 5. I am quite certain of it. Now get me out of here."

* * *

<u>YORKSHIRE POLICE</u>
<u>RECORD OF INTERVIEW</u>
<u>PLACE OF INTERVIEW:</u> Leeds Central
<u>PERSON INTERVIEWED:</u> Gary Peter TREVORS
<u>INTERVIEWING OFFICERS:</u> Detective Chief Inspector Ernest
Noble; Detective Sergeant Ronald Perry
<u>OTHERS PRESENT:</u>
Roger Sylvester (Solicitor)
<u>Tape Reference:</u> EN/245/54

SUSPECTED OFFENCES

Aggravated Burglary of Blossomfields, Alwoodley, Leeds

Murder of Paul Michael Checkley (aged 35)

Wounding Sarah Checkley with intent to do her grievous bodily harm.

Perry:

This interview is being tape-recorded. It may be tendered in evidence if your case is brought before a Court. You'll be provided with a copy of the tape. As you know, I am Detective Sergeant Ronald Perry, this is Detective Chief Inspector Ernest Noble and your solicitor, Mr Sylvester is also present. You're still under caution. At just before 11 a.m. this morning, in the presence of your solicitor, a Voice Identification Parade was conducted by an Inspector at this police station. Do you agree?

Trevors:

Yeah.

Perry:

In the course of that parade, each of ten men including you, wore identical clothing and hoods. You stood at Number 5. Five of you spoke the words remembered by Mrs Checkley as having been spoken by the man who wounded her and killed her husband.

Trevors:

Yeah.

Perry:

Mrs Checkley picked your voice out as being the voice of the man in her house on that night. She recognised it as soon as you spoke and was so certain that she didn't require to hear the other five men speak. Do you accept that she picked you out?

Trevors:

Yeah.

Perry:

Very well. Now is your opportunity to respond to that identification. I put it to you that Mrs Checkley has correctly identified you as the man responsible.

Trevors:

And I put it to you that you're talking out of your arse. Of the four stooges she actually bothered to listen to, only one had an accent anything like mine and another of them couldn't even read the fucking words properly.

Perry:

Mrs Checkley recognised the voice, the accent, the pitch, the tone, its age and the lilt. She was very careful in her identification and very definite as soon as you spoke.

Trevors:

She was wrong. Most of the men had different accents. She only listened to five and, as soon as she heard the right dialect and the right age group, she jumped in.

Perry:

She listened to five separate male voices, all speaking the same words from under identical face masks. She heard again the voice of the killer and it was your voice and she recognised it immediately.

Trevors:

A decent brief will rip this crap to shreds and that Inspector at the same time. I wouldn't trust him any more than I trust you, Perry. What's more, she broke the fucking rules by not listening to all ten. There again, I 'spose you set the whole thing up anyway.

Perry:

Is that the best that you can do?

Trevors:

Is this the best that you can do?

Perry:

You hadn't counted on a terrified woman having the ability to remember so clearly, had you? We'll be charging you with murder later today. You'll be remanded in custody until your trial.

Trevors:

Bollocks. She's wrong and you're wrong. You haven't got a case because you've got the wrong man. Not guilty. Nothing more to say. Sylvester, you prat, I want words with you. In private. Now. You should never have agreed to this fucking circus.

INTERVIEW TERMINATED

CHAPTER 5

Roger Denstone shrewdly measured what use this particular favour might buy for him one day in the future. In his world of intrigue, like in the world of commerce, everything had its price, its value and its true cost. Sipping slowly from the glass of 1963 Taylor's port that had been a birthday gift from the Foreign Secretary, he carefully observed his old friend across the dining table. How Denstone loved moving the pieces around, pulling the strings, creating the networks and then manipulating them to his own advantage. But, best of all he relished storing away the favours owed and then calling them in with the exquisite timing that had always come so naturally to him. Tonight was an occasion for handing out the favour and he watched the ugly man opposite, puffing on his fat hand-rolled cigar, waiting expectantly, hanging on every word, every nuance, every gesture. There was almost a sexual gratification in the teasing, the silences, the eye contact and Denstone was a master at making his quarry wait.

As Hathington was skilfully held on the edge of suspense, Denstone reflected on the years since they had met. A lot of water had flowed under the bridge since those heady days at Brasenose College, Oxford where they had both read Law. Branded by their college contemporaries as an odious pair of self-opinionated egotists, they had ended up sharing a London flat for two years after graduation and, in the process, had learned a great deal about each other.

Remarkably, for two people who were so similar in character, they seemed to rub along together without mishap, despite the fact that both of them were selfish, arrogant and ruthlessly ambitious. Whilst they trampled roughshod over anyone else who stood in their upward and mobile path, they each seemed to recognise that, in the other, it was wiser to retain a friend than make an enemy.

Roger Denstone had realised that his friend possessed the keener intellect and, at the end of Hathington's pupillage, despite his universal unpopularity, it had not surprised Denstone when Hathington was offered a tenancy in one of the best sets of barristers' chambers in London. Intellectual arrogance, pomposity and an acid tongue were prerequisites of admission and he possessed all of those characteristics in abundance. It went without saying that he was a new-look Socialist, in constant and headlong pursuit of all the wealth and trappings of the class he purported to despise.

Within a year of accepting the place in Grosvenor Chambers, Michael Hathington had begun to command such substantial fees that he could afford to embark upon the purchase of his own flat, which had meant that he could then entertain the opposite sex without Denstone learning every detail about the woman he was currently bedding.

Denstone had witnessed Hathington's prodigious sexual appetite, forever wondering why, for such an extremely unattractive man, he had met with such surprising success. Many of his conquests had powerful and influential husbands tucked away at business meetings, whilst Hathington would slip surreptitiously away from chambers mid-afternoon to sample their wives' carnal offerings.

However, there were some matters of which Denstone, in his dining table musings, remained blissfully unaware. In particular, their seemingly mutual decision to seek flats of their own had owed much to Hathington's discomfort on learning that Denstone was then openly in pursuit of Julia Laine, for Hathington had previously taken her to Glyndebourne, pleasured her all night and then unceremoniously dumped her the following weekend. Denstone knew absolutely nothing about this and Hathington had never breathed a word of it, nor did he believe that Julia would have ever broadcast the details of her undignified rejection.

Reaching across the table to pour himself another glass of the vintage port, Hathington listened attentively to the small talk from his host. Julia and Laura had withdrawn to the sitting room so that the men could talk freely and Hathington well realised that the announcement he was so keenly awaiting would only come when Denstone was absolutely ready. The longer the delay, the more emphasised was the size of any favour bestowed. Yet, Hathington reflected with some satisfaction, the true irony was Denstone's ignorance of the fact that his wife of many years, now in the next room, had been deflowered by Hathington all that time ago.

Like Julia, many of Hathington's conquests had been extremely plain, for he had quickly learned the effect of overbearing flattery upon a plain woman. These women had rarely, if ever, been pursued by a man who so patently and ardently lusted after them. Their initial distaste at his ugly, ginger exterior gradually softened as he unleashed his intellectual weaponry in their direction. Coupled with the intensity of his obvious sexual desire for their bodies, he began to exert a control over them which led them, with occasional exceptions, to his bed for mid-afternoon activities of a fervour and variety which had hitherto only lurked in the darkest corners of their minds. Control meant everything to him and once they were completely under his power, thereby exposed, vulnerable and vanquished, he disdainfully tossed them aside.

Denstone was the more subtle, recognising early that he needed to establish a sphere of influence in which he could excel and build a base from which to launch himself to the top. At Oxford he'd feigned an interest in traditional jazz so as to ingratiate himself with Lord Elspeth's son who was Secretary of the College Jazz Society, thereby earning occasional weekend invitations to the Elspeth Estate where he would direct his energies into impressing the Lord, who was to become one of New Labour's most generous benefactors. He found stealth was an effective tool and sought to develop his skills of networking and social manipulation, equipping himself for his planned ascent.

Accepting a position with one of the new generation of City solicitors, Denstone had set himself the seemingly unattainable goal of an equity partnership in less than three years. Such a meteoric climb would demand a novel approach and, prophetically, he had identified the means before he had even left Oxford. Europe.

Despite all of the political camouflage, the axis created by France and Germany would soon run Europe. Indeed, it had been happening for years. Whilst the United States had stood by Great Britain for the best part of a century, proving itself to be the staunchest of allies in desperate times, America came to be viewed, in the smart, up-and-coming political circles, as internationally passé. France, historically hostile to Britain and congenitally incapable of ever forgiving the British people for their 20th-century resilience and courage, was to be pandered to and encouraged. Germany was to be hailed as the economic saviour and the industrial and financial role model.

Denstone had intuitively recognised all of this and realised that, if he established a thriving European department within the firm, then he would be in control of a critical piece of the jigsaw. Europe was so bogged down by regulations, so enmeshed by red tape, so submerged in paper and meaningless legislation that, if he mastered the intricacies and learned how British commercial organisations could operate successfully within that system, then he would hold the keys to real power.

When Denstone had been courting Julia Laine, her father was Managing Director of an extremely successful plastics factory in Watford. Charles Laine had prided himself on being one of the first industrialists to appreciate that, if you were astute enough at playing the game by the

European rules, then subsidies, grants and commercial opportunities across the breadth of the Community would be there for the taking. Laine's business empire had started to flourish and he was Chairman of three of the most influential sub-committees in Brussels. Absorbing into the family an ambitious new son-in-law, who was driving one of the most powerful firms of City solicitors right into the heart of Europe, had been a prospect he relished.

In the event, Denstone had exceeded even his own daunting timetable and, within two years, had been made an equity partner, as the European department of the firm then generated over sixty per cent of the partnership's net profits. Any commercial, environmental or industrial organisation which instructed Denstone to represent their interests in the European minefield, could be guaranteed to squeeze the best deal, the last centime in subsidy and the largest grant out of any commission, committee or tribunal between Strasbourg and the Hague.

Whilst the right hand had been moving the legal and commercial chess pieces around the European board, the left had been reaching deep into London's political enclaves and, when he learned that a safe Labour seat in one of the capital's frothiest constituencies was becoming available, a couple of telephone calls to his old College pal's titled father, Lord Elspeth, had ensured that the Party offered him the prize.

By the time their eldest son was ten years old, Roger and Julia Denstone had become one of the most potent political couples in London. The new post of Minister for Europe had passed to him almost as of right and his place at the right hand side of the Prime Minister in Cabinet was as safe as the Bank of England. There was only one more upwards movement left and he was quite content to bide his time, waiting for exactly the correct moment to strike.

Hathington had never failed to maintain contact with the Denstones. Best man at their wedding, provider of his house in the South of France for their spring holidays and godfather to their first child. Julia's social and political ascent seemed to have brought with it a hypocritical acceptance that past frivolities between the sheets were simply to be put down to experience and her rejection by Hathington was lost in history.

In the early days, Denstone had managed to direct some heavily marked commercial briefs in his direction, although Hathington was already winning the big prizes without any helping hands. By the time that Denstone was first elected to Parliament, Hathington was a QC and one of the five biggest earners at the London Bar. Cosmetically married to Laura Van Bilke, a rich and ugly Belgian socialite who turned a blind eye to his countless affairs, he had arrived at the exact destination he had chosen for himself those many years ago, when he and Denstone had sat alone in their modest Islington flat and sipped supermarket Chardonnay.

But Denstone had much more influence than Hathington. Denstone had moved adroitly from control via wealth, to control via power and Hathington envied him the authority and the fear that he generated in those answerable to him and under him. Wealth alone meant little without that added dimension.

To the Belgian, Laura, appearances were everything and where her husband desired power, influence and control, she craved social position and, in London society, the biggest prize was a title. "Lady Hathington" would suit her just fine. Putting up with a lecher for a husband for all these years, she felt that she deserved some higher reward and she had dropped several crude hints in Roger's lap since his Ministerial appointment, but to no avail. Hathington himself, had come to recognise that the easiest available route to the kind of power he coveted was the High Court Bench, but appointments to the Commercial Division were now rare because the previous administration had elevated several young silks to that Division and those present incumbents would not approach retirement for many years.

Recently sharing a box with the Denstones at the Cheltenham Gold Cup, he had deftly steered the conversation in the appropriate direction and Roger had intimated that he would put a few feelers out in the Lord Chancellor's Department, just as soon as a suitable opportunity arose.

Within a few months Julia had invited the Hathingtons to tonight's dinner party. Black tie, but just the four of them. These were clear, political signals that Denstone had some news to impart. Protocol had demanded that nothing was said in mixed company and now that the ladies had withdrawn to the sitting room, the two men eyed each other warily across the smoke-filled room. The cat and the mouse.

At last the moment came and the titillation approached its exquisite climax. "No go on the Commercial Bench, I'm afraid, Michael," Roger Denstone sighed. "Lord Chancellor says that they are at full strength and already have a reserve in the pipeline. You could be waiting three, four, maybe five years."

Remaining silent, Hathington took a long, considered draw on his Havana and leant back slowly in the hand-carved Sheraton carver, his eyes wandering up to the over-ornate crystal chandelier that typified Julia's inherently poor taste. Rigidly controlling himself so as not to let the disappointment show, he slowly exhaled a plume of blue-grey smoke into the heavy air, smiling, eyes narrowed, still waiting. Surely there had to be more to come or else Denstone would not have invited them to a formal dinner? A straight "No" would undoubtedly have been delivered on the phone.

"That isn't to say that the Lord Chancellor is wholly unsympathetic," added Denstone eventually, after he had allowed the full impact of the first refusal to sink in.

"There's a possibility that you could be found a slot in the Queen's Bench Division, trying some civil but mostly crime."

"Crime," exclaimed Hathington. "Crime. Bit beneath my station. I've never done a Criminal trial in my life. Don't know anything about the Criminal Law and I don't much want to. Don't know the Criminal Rules of Evidence. Don't know the tricks that are played, the stunts that are pulled by the Criminal silks. I could find myself badly exposed."

"You have the intellect to cope with that, Michael. The appointment wouldn't be for another few months yet. Intensive courses on new disciplines are available to the Judiciary. By the time you were let loose on the public you'd have mastered what matters and, thereafter, you'd learn to handle the problems one case at a time."

"Bit of a disappointment this one, I have to tell you," responded Hathington. "Crime is not my cup of tea at all. It's the infra dig end of the market. Not where I belong. Legal Aid and the also-rans. My mind was rather set on the mink coat litigation, libel actions, bank deals that went wrong, the record company contracts."

"Well, you can sit it out as plain old Michael Hathington for another three or four years and see if anyone dies, or take the bird in the hand now and feel the sword on the shoulder at the Palace. You get the knighthood whichever Division you enter. And, after all, if a place became available in the Commercial Division sooner than expected, then you'd be in a strong position to make the sideways move. It's your call."

Pushing his chair back from the table, Denstone started to get up, as the business of the evening was now concluded, for they both knew that Michael would not be able to resist the ermine trappings and, even if he could, Laura would make sure that he didn't. Sir Michael Hathington. Sir Michael and Lady Hathington. Denstone carefully watched his friend openly preening himself as he tasted the sound of the title on his lips en route to the sitting room and the ladies. Here was another massive favour done and, somewhere along the line, a debt to be called in. Everybody knew that was how it worked.

CHAPTER 6

The atmosphere in the cramped conference room in the cell area was tense and rank. They had not let him have a shower since his arrest and he still wore the same unwashed clothes that he had eventually been allowed to drag on as they pulled him, protesting, from his bed. The white face was even paler than usual, drawn and screwed up in a fury and the mean, thin lips were bloodless as he vented his anger on Sylvester.

"Some fucking advice, that was, Sylvester. A jury could draw inferences if I refused to go on a parade, and she weren't likely to pick me out in them circumstances anyway," fumed Trevors sarcastically. "Them was your fucking words of wisdom."

"Because you told me there wasn't a cat in hell's chance of her recognising your voice," came the terse reply. "I make judgements on the basis of information you give me. 'No chance,' you said. 'No chance.' So don't blame me, although I did feel that there was something very odd about that parade. The way she went for you without even listening to the other five. I didn't like that one little bit."

"And I don't like the way you're handling this case one little bit, either. If I'd refused the bloody parade they might not even have charged me."

"That's something we'll never know, so there's no point in worrying about it. My firm's represented you before and you know exactly how we operate. We're experienced and highly competent criminal practitioners. Our advice is sound. We know how to deal with the police. We know what to go along with and what not to go along with. And we know the right barristers to instruct. We know the right horses for the right courses. We know just how flexible the rules are and we know which barristers can flex them the most. So let's just get on with deciding who is to be the appropriate QC this time."

"I don't want that pompous prat you got me last time. The one who landed me with seven years for a robbery I never done," grunted Trevors.

"But you've never done the one they charge you with, have you Gary? Just stop pacing around. Sit down and let's talk this through sensibly. I actually have a name in mind already."

Kicking the chair into the middle of the room, Trevors slammed himself down into it. Sylvester noticed that whenever Trevors worked himself up into a state of high excitement that ugly, jagged scar on the right hand side of his neck seemed to become inflamed and angry.

"Give me the fucking name, then," he spat out without looking in Sylvester's direction.

"Ronan Cadogan. One of the new breed. London silk. Early 40s. Ruthless. Disliked by the other barristers. Makes life hell for the instructing solicitor and for the Judge. But gets the results. If he sees a way out, any way out, he goes for it and to hell with the consequences. Was nearly disbarred last year for allegedly pulling a flanker in Court but somehow he survived. Just up your street. A complete bastard. As soon as I get the papers off the Crown Prosecution Service I'll do my best to book him and fix up a conference."

"He'd better be as good as you say, Sylvester," whined Trevors, "because they've got the wrong man this time. I didn't do this one."

"Of course not, Gary. You're innocent. I understand that," agreed Sylvester unconvincingly, as he got to his feet. "Be in touch when we're ready for a conference with Counsel. Meanwhile, you keep telling everybody that you didn't do it."

* * *

Standing 6 feet 5 inches in his stocking feet and weighing in at 18 stone, Ronan Cadogan took up a lot of courtroom space. A massive presence with a booming voice tinged with a Southern Irish lilt, he dominated any forum in which he appeared and he used his bulk and noise to maximum effect.

At school he had been a formidable second row forward and at Trinity College, Dublin he had represented the University in the heavyweight wrestling division for three of his four years as a student. Twenty years on, his frame had lost much of its shape but had retained and added to its bulk. Those who had known him as a boy, and later in adult life, would have all agreed that he had also retained one overriding characteristic. He was a monumental bully. Physically, verbally and emotionally, he threw his weight around until he got what he wanted.

On the wrestling mat, when he had his opponent pinned so that he could not move and was freely submitting, he would press the hold harder and longer, inflicting the maximum pain until the referee pulled him off. Those extra seconds of hurt when the man was already well beaten were, for Cadogan, the most satisfying of all. It was a very successful policy because that opponent would never trouble him again. At the end of his University career he had competed in sixty-eight contests and had never been beaten.

When he married the daughter of the Chairman of a small pharmaceutical company he set about wearing her down and making her answerable to him for everything that she did. Their move to London, when he qualified at the English Bar, took her away from the immediate support of her family and he dominated and subjugated her, so that her own once-sparkling personality was suffocated beneath his mass. The arrival of their son made matters even worse and, as soon as the boy was old enough to play sports and showed himself to be quite useless at all of them, the father demeaned, belittled and humiliated him until all confidence was shattered.

Behind closed doors he was free with his fists and, by the time he became a QC, his wife despised him and his son felt only fear of him, but there were times when the bully in him temporarily abated and he would charm and flatter and the house acquired a calmer atmosphere, although his mood could turn with the wind and the hectoring and tormenting would then begin anew.

In court, the witnesses, other barristers and even Judges would often wilt beneath the verbal assault, intimidated by the sheer size and volume of the man. Of course, not all would give way and his appearances were littered with savage and bitter exchanges, which were incapable of repair in the pub at the end of the day, where normally barristers, however fierce their forensic battles, could look each other in the eye and smile. Victory was everything for Cadogan and the vanquished foe was to be left licking his wounds on the Courtroom floor, not sharing a convivial bottle of Pinot Noir at the nearest hostelry.

Last year he had tangled with Mr Justice Bessant. Roland Bessant was a slight man, bespectacled, short, in his seventies and soon to retire. A High Court Judge who had been trying Criminal cases for as long as anyone could remember. In 1945, still only a teenager, he had won the Military Cross when, alone, he had killed four German soldiers with his bayonet in total blackness in a French sewer. After that experience, any encounter with a belligerent barrister held little fear.

Cadogan was defending a rapist and had called a female schoolteacher to say that she had known the Defendant over many years and what a complete gentleman he was. In cross-examination, it transpired that she had been dismissed from teaching for stealing and had other convictions for deception. Bessant was firmly convinced that Cadogan must have known about this and yet had presented her to the jury as a respectable, and still-practising, schoolteacher.

At the end of the case, which Cadogan won, the Judge demanded to know the extent of what he knew and exactly what information was contained in his brief. Cadogan steadfastly refused to answer and, when the Judge ordered him to hand up his brief, he stormed out of Court taking the brief with him, at which the Judge immediately reported him to the Disciplinary Committee of the Bar Council. Six weeks later Bessant suddenly dropped dead of a heart attack in the library of the Royal Courts of Justice and the whole complaint had died with him.

The morning after successfully winning the freedom of an IRA terrorist in the Court of Appeal, Cadogan walked into his chambers in The Temple to meet with his clerk and discuss the next few months' engagements. Arthur Helliwell dreaded these occasions, for, whatever case he suggested his Master should accept was always wrong and he had therefore learned to measure his words with great care. Now he was under pressure from some firm in Leeds, who wanted to instruct the QC in a murder, and Arthur knew that a trip north would hold little attraction for the most offensive barrister he had ever clerked, unless the money was right or the case was very high profile or, preferably, both.

"My room, Arthur, if you please. Immediately," had been the brusque command as he swept through the chambers' door and past the clerks' office.

When Arthur scurried into the room, Cadogan was standing by the window looking out over the greyness of the Thames and, without so much as turning to glance at the elderly and cowed figure, he barked in his direction.

"Did you get my cheque in for the rape that I did in front of Bessant last year?"

"Not yet, sir," was the meek reply. "I did phone, but they said they were still waiting for some information from your Junior."

"I require the money, Arthur, and I want paying for that case in particular. It brought me a lot of aggravation and, to add insult to injury, the bastards have kept me waiting for the money for nearly a year. They've always got some excuse for delaying the payment. Different story no doubt if it's paying for one of their politically correct European Human Rights cases – they'll dole out endless supplies of money in that particular direction."

"I'll get on to it immediately and see what I can do," Arthur agreed. "May I just mention, sir, that a firm of solicitors from Leeds, Sylvester and

Stocks, have been on the phone every five minutes, wanting to know if you can do a murder for them. Very high profile up there. The chance of some good publicity."

"Where's the case to be tried?" enquired Cadogan.

"Probably Leeds, sir. Although there's talk of it being transferred off circuit, because of the extensive news coverage it has received, and the solicitors fear that local prejudice may be running very high."

"I don't want to go and do a case in Leeds. It's the back of beyond and, unless it offers some national publicity, I'm not interested. You know the places I'm prepared to appear and Leeds certainly isn't one of them, unless there's something very special on offer," stated Cadogan, as he moved from the window and walked over to stand alongside the unfortunate clerk, towering over him and dominating the surrounding airspace.

Arthur Helliwell had been a Barristers' clerk for forty-six years in the same set of chambers, commuting every day from his hometown of Northampton, and had seen enormous changes in the profession. In his early days Arthur clearly remembered carrying the Law Reports to Aylesbury for a QC who was defending one of the Great Train Robbers and actually being allowed to stay in Court at the end of the trial when Mr Justice Edmund Davies had sent the robber down for thirty years. The old Judge had even doled out twenty years to the only member of the gang who had pleaded guilty and had returned his eighty thousand pounds share of the loot. The Governor, a real gent, had bought him lunch on their way back to chambers after the sentence. Nowadays, most of the QCs behaved like self-centred prima donnas, demanding the best paid cases, playing the high and mighty and, without doubt, this bully Cadogan was the worst of the lot.

Arthur looked up at the imposing figure and gave him the hard information that he knew would be wanted.

"It's a bad one, sir. Professional criminal. Very difficult to handle. Likes to call all the shots and they want a barrister who can handle him. The evidence against him is a bit iffy. They want a tough guy, sir. That's why they want you. Legal Aid, I'm afraid, but the biggest murder up there for quite a while. Some gruesome stuff, I'm told. Knife in her privates and all that and just enough of a whiff of police skulduggery to whet the appetite."

Cadogan peered down imperiously at the unfortunate clerk, pursing his lips in distaste as he shook his great head in refusal.

"Legal Aid. Leeds. Just a whiff of skulduggery. Really, Arthur, I would have expected you to realise that this is just wasting my time. You may tell them that I am otherwise committed. What else is there on offer?"

Arthur watched the arrogant giant, as he ambled towards the high-backed, ornate chair at his desk and manoeuvred his eighteen stone into it, looking back quizzically at the clerk as he awaited an answer. There would be two big bonuses for Arthur if he managed to persuade Cadogan to accept the Leeds brief. Firstly, for all the protests about Legal Aid, a case of this magnitude would command a high fee, and 5% of what Arthur thought he could negotiate, would be a very acceptable little earner. Secondly, and almost as attractive, it would keep this overbearing hulk out of London for a while and that was indeed something greatly to be desired. With all of this in mind, Arthur had kept back one crucial snippet of information that he judged might prove to be irresistible.

"There's a chance of a drugs case at the Bailey, sir. I'll go and chase it up right now," replied Arthur as he headed for the door. "And I'll phone the solicitors in Leeds and tell them you're unavailable. Shame that sir, Mr Haskitt is prosecuting and we owe him one, don't we?"

Cadogan was out of his chair like a jack-in-the-box, stopping Arthur dead in his tracks as the clerk was actually opening the door.

"Haskitt, did you say?" he bellowed, pulling at the man's shoulder. "Why the hell didn't you tell me that in the first place, Arthur? You know the score as well as I do. Playing the trump card were you? Fancied your 5% and saw those as the best tactics? Now get yourself back in here and give me the full story."

Arthur pushed the door closed, allowing himself the flicker of a triumphant smile when his back was turned to the giant. It was tactics alright, red rag to a bull personified.

"The Leeds CPS wanted to instruct a local silk to prosecute but apparently the police were uneasy. They said they wanted one of the very best for this murder and it may prove necessary to go to London. Sylvester, who is the Defence Solicitor, from whom I get all this tittle tattle, suspects that the police didn't want anyone who might know a thing or two about how one of the detectives in this enquiry operated. They thought it was better to have someone from out of town, who'd got no preconceived local ideas or prejudices, and wouldn't be too bothered about complying with all of the niceties. Apparently, they're desperate for a conviction, as they consider this Defendant to be highly dangerous. So, they went after Haskitt. His clerk demanded a massive brief fee by all accounts, to which they instantly agreed and got their man. Of course, he'd no idea that you were about to be offered the Defence brief."

Listening attentively to every word, Cadogan wandered back to his position by the window and stood looking out of the window in silence for several minutes. The chance to take on Gordon Bertrand Haskitt QC was something that he could never turn down. Their paths had not crossed since the infamous incident and, despite many attempts to engineer a confrontation, Haskitt had somehow always managed to avoid him at the last minute.

It was nearly five years ago since it had happened, but time had not diluted the intensity of the anger. Haskitt had been defending the father and Cadogan was defending the mother. The baby had sustained a terrible injury, having been allegedly picked up by the heels, swung with full force, so that its skull crashed against the wall and then it had been laid out on the sofa and left to die.

Both parents had run the defence that it was all a terrible accident occurring in the course of some silly horseplay. Their baby had banged its head on the wall, suffered the injury and they had then panicked on realising that the infant was dying.

After discussions, both Defending Counsel had run their defences in tandem, co-operating with each other throughout, and cross-examining the pathologist along the lines that this death might have been accidental. The mother, represented by Cadogan, had been number one on the indictment and had therefore gone into the witness box first, where she had given evidence in accordance with their joint defence of accident.

Then, on the last day of the evidence, Haskitt had called the father, who immediately broke down in tears in the witness box, claiming that he could lie no longer. There had been no accident. The mother had lost her temper with the child's incessant crying, had picked him up by the heels and dashed his head against the wall, killing him and thereafter begging her husband to lend himself to the cover-up. Having reluctantly done so, out of panic and loyalty to her, his conscience could stand it no longer and now, in the witness box, he had to tell the truth.

Cadogan, taken completely by surprise, was uncontrollable and had ranted and raged at the father in cross-examination that this was a last, desperate attempt to save his own skin at any price, but the damage was done and was irreversible. At the end of the cross-examination he had asked the Judge for some time so as to take further instructions from the mother, in the light of this unheralded attack upon her by the father.

The Judge had agreed, and in the grim cells beneath Winchester Crown Court, a gripping drama had been played out, when the sobbing mother explained that the father had been a tyrant, dominating her and bullying the baby boy. True it was that the mite had met his death by being swung head first into the living room wall, but that had been the handiwork of her husband, not her. Afterwards, he threatened her that, if ever she spoke the truth, he would kill her and she knew that he had meant it. No one listening in that cell doubted one word of what she had said. On returning to Court, Cadogan had asked the Judge to discharge the jury and start again in front of a fresh jury, so that the mother could give this revised account from the witness box. He insisted that Haskitt must have had some idea that the father may blame the mother and a new jury should hear both versions, or justice would be defeated.

Haskitt strenuously resisted the application, asserting that this change of story by his client had come about unannounced when he went into the witness box. Up until that time, his client's defence had been that it was an accident, and that was why Haskitt had conducted the case in the way that he had.

Now, Haskitt claimed, he had been taken by surprise like everyone else when the father had changed his story, to what the jury may consider to be the truth. This jury knew that he had changed his story at the last minute and could hold that against him if they wished. On the other hand, they may believe that, at the eleventh hour, his client had let his conscience dictate his actions and had spoken the unvarnished truth. If the Judge allowed a retrial, the spontaneity of what had happened was forever lost and he could never re-create it. Nor should the Judge allow the wife to revisit the witness box, for her chance to speak the truth had come and gone. Haskitt argued that justice demanded that the case proceed in front of the present jury.

Agonising over the dilemma for several hours, the Judge eventually acceded to Haskitt's submission and the trial proceeded. After a retirement of four days, the jury acquitted Haskitt's client and found the mother guilty of murder, whereupon the Judge was obliged to sentence her to mandatory life imprisonment. In the robing room afterwards, Cadogan cornered Haskitt, and so terrified him with his threats, that Haskitt ran out into the street, still in his wig and gown, refusing to return until Cadogan had been ignominiously ushered away by his Junior and his Solicitor.

When they met again in the Court of Appeal, Cadogan told the three Appeal Judges the whole story, arguing that there should be a retrial of the mother, implying that Haskitt must have known that his client was about to double-cross his wife and had deliberately let it happen in the dramatic way that it had, so as to give the father the best chance of acquittal.

Pointing out in his judgement that any retrial could never include the father as he had been acquitted, the Lord Justice of Appeal rejected

Cadogan's argument, observing that it was indeed unfortunate to hear such an unwarranted attack launched upon the integrity of Mr Haskitt, an experienced and well-respected member of the Bar. Since that fateful day, the two men had never met again but now, at last, Cadogan was being offered the chance of revenge. Nothing would ever convince him that Haskitt had not foreseen exactly what was going to happen and had not merely let it develop, but had positively encouraged it do so, thereby inflicting a bitter, deeply resented defeat upon Cadogan, as well as securing the acquittal of a murderer and the conviction of an innocent woman.

Eventually, almost in a whisper and without turning away from the window, he announced his decision to the waiting Arthur.

"I want the brief by the end of the week. I want a full day's conference on Friday of the following week. I want the best Criminal Junior at the Leeds Bar. I want a suite of rooms in a 5 Star Hotel for the duration of the trial. And, most important of all, the fact that I have accepted the Defence Brief is to be kept a complete secret until after the case comes up for the formal Plea and Directions hearing. By then it will be quite impossible for Haskitt to withdraw, short of falling off his bloody horse. Go and make the arrangements, Arthur. Now."

CHAPTER 7

A mean, thin wind flicked across the surface of the Humber, picking up speed as it funnelled its way up the hill towards the bleak perimeter walls of the daunting prison. Even on the warmest summer day, the chill never left the walkways and passages of the grim penal institution that caged some of England's most violent criminals. All that Home Office propaganda about rehabilitation and regeneration was exposed for the bunkum that it was, once you stepped inside this hell on earth. Only one objective existed and that was survival. There was no compassion, no brotherhood in adversity, no mending of the soul, no salvation; just hard, pinched faces with darting eyes and sly mouths that had learned to speak while seeming still.

Whenever control was threatened, the straitjackets would be pulled lovingly from the cupboards and the offenders stripped naked by brute force, as they were laced with relish into the rough grey canvas garments of the insane. Once encased, the prisoner became more vulnerable than ever to the daily rounds of buggery and steel toe-capped boots delivered short and sweet to the kidneys. After all, these men were killers, rapists, robbers and child molesters, and pain was their common currency. You give it. You take it. That is all there is to life.

A battered white Datsun taxi, smelling of last night's vomit, driven by a downtrodden and silent Pakistani, delivered Ronan Cadogan to the formidable wooden gates. Passing through the Security Screening machines, emptying his pockets and opening his case full of papers was only the beginning. Separated from his belongings he was led, protesting and complaining, to a small side room, by two surly prison officers, who spent a good part of their working day checking inside the stinking socks and grubby underclothes of inmates and their visitors. These officers knew every trick and every orifice and were determined that nothing would get through. It was a matter of professional pride and, the more humiliation that could be meted out in the process, the more rewarding the task.

The solicitor Mr Sylvester, and Junior Counsel, had arrived separately and were undergoing similar treatment nearby. Forty-five minutes had elapsed before all three lawyers were summarily ushered into a disused cell, which was to serve as the Conference room. Introductions were briskly made as the trio organised their papers on the rickety, defaced table and shuffled their chairs within the inadequate space, awaiting the arrival of the man they had travelled to see.

Cadogan was deliberately making little attempt to hide his disdain at discovering that Junior Counsel was female when, handcuffed between two officers, the prisoner was brought to the door and a key was eventually produced to free his hands. As the small key turned in the lock releasing the manacles, the blue denim shirt material rode up the prisoner's arms, and Cadogan stared with undisguised distaste, at the deep round scar on the inner aspect of the right forearm, rightly speculating that it was just about the size and shape of a human mouth. The man would not have observed that he was being so closely inspected, for his eyes were held permanently down, gaze averted from captors and lawyers alike. His time to look up and make his judgements would be soon, but not until he was ready and not before he was unchained from these ghouls and standing free with at least a modicum of dignity restored.

"This is Leading Counsel, Mr Ronan Cadogan QC," began Mr Sylvester, as the prisoner positioned himself uncomfortably on the hard, wooden chair.

"And may I introduce Junior Counsel, Miss Naomi Nicholas," he continued, as perfunctory handshakes were conducted, with Trevors still steadfastly averting his eyes from any of them, keeping his head angled downwards.

"I propose that we get straight down to business, Mr Trevors. I want to start by identifying all that you can remember about that Tuesday night. What you did. Were you alone? Did anybody call at your flat? Did anybody phone? Every detail about the programme you watched about the Amazon," announced Cadogan.

This staccato burst of questions was met with a long, empty silence, during which Naomi Nicholas took the opportunity of carefully surveying the faces of both Trevors and Cadogan. Whilst, at only thirty-four years of age, she was probably one of the most able junior barristers in the provinces, she was far from the stereotype of old. Her thick, blonde hair was pulled back in formal style, emphasising her clear skin and prominent cheekbones, and her green eyes sparkled with both intelligence and fun. At 5'10", and with a figure kept in trim by daily visits to the gym at six in the morning, she looked quite stunning, and it was never a disappointment to her if the jury in any of her cases was top heavy with men. But she had taken an instant dislike to the two males whose faces she was now studying.

Obviously, it was hardly to be expected that she would warm to Trevors, and her personal feelings about a client were an irrelevance. Nevertheless, the overwhelming sense of disgust that she felt for him had taken her aback. It was not just the unnatural whiteness of the face, now exaggerated by the months inside this hellhole, but the thin lips were cruel and tight and he exuded a tangible sense of menace. That hideous scar on the side of the neck, no doubt from a broken bottle in some dark Northern alley, was worn in prison like a medal. She could actually smell the guilt upon him and feel it in the air around him.

Her assessment of Cadogan was prejudiced and, realising that, she had tried to make allowances. In all of her years in practice, she had never been involved in a case where the identity of the silk was being kept such a tightly guarded secret and she had been specifically warned by the solicitor and her clerk that if she breached the confidence before the case came to Court for the Plea and Directions hearing, then Cadogan would withdraw and she would have her brief taken away from her.

None of this had prevented her from making discreet enquiries about this high flier from London and, in every quarter that she had looked, she had found the same information. Arrogant, aggressive and ruthless. Clever, but full of himself. Rude to absolutely everyone, but with a track record of outstanding success. The QC who would do anything to win. Now, trying to make the allowances, she saw that he was even worse than described. Already he had treated Mr Sylvester and her as if they did not exist and had made it crystal clear that they would have precisely nothing to do with the running of the case. Sitting this close to him, in these confined conditions, enabled her to see the sour characteristics that had become etched into the face. The corners of the mouth had been turned down for so long that the lines ran into the heavy flesh around the jowls and the eyes had become small, as they had been held narrowed in contempt so many times.

Her observations were interrupted by the sound of Trevors' voice steeped in that hard north-eastern accent that Mrs Checkley had never forgotten.

"You'd better understand, Mr QC, that before I even think about answering any of your bloody questions I've got some of my own. Top of the list, how do I know that you're good enough to handle this case? I'd never even heard of you before Roger Sylvester mentioned your name at the police station."

As he spoke these words he lifted his eyes for the first time and pushed his face closer towards Cadogan, staring at him in defiance.

"You don't know how good I am, Trevors, but you have a very simple choice. Act on the advice of your solicitor, whose job it is to know the best and go with the man he has chosen, or act on the kind of tittle-tattle advice you pick up from the barrack-room lawyers in the prisons and go with a local boy. Either way, make your mind up right now, because I don't waste my time with whingers. Take it or leave it."

Throughout this reply Trevors' intense, close quarters gaze had not wavered and Cadogan had returned the stare unflinchingly. After several uncomfortable seconds the silence was broken by a mirthless, empty chuckle from deep within Trevors' throat.

"You found me a macho man, Sylvester. Let's hope he's as tough with the opposition and with the Judge. I suppose he'll do but I ain't having no woman in my team."

"Nothing personal, miss," he declared, turning to look towards Miss Nicholas, "but I operate in a man's world. No skirts give me advice or tell me what to do. You'll have to replace her, Sylvester."

Cadogan's reply was immediate and conclusive.

"She won't be replaced. I asked for the best Criminal Junior at the Leeds Bar and that's what we've got. Besides, a woman on your team is a positive asset. Any juror is going to be appalled at what was done to Mrs Checkley, let alone her husband. It helps to soften the impact if the man accused of doing that to a woman is represented by a team that includes a woman. Still, it's your choice, but if Miss Nicholas goes then so do I. Your call."

Naomi Nicholas knew full well that Cadogan was lying, for she'd observed his look of disdain earlier, when he saw that a female Junior had been briefed, but this had now become an exercise in laying down the ground rules, locking horns and establishing exactly who was in charge. None of it made for a very edifying spectacle.

Realising that he was cornered, Trevors looked for a means of retreat that did not steal his pride and found it, as was his usual way, in obscenity and aggression.

"OK. I s'pose there's a bit of logic in that but, if she stays, she keeps her dainty mouth firmly shut unless she's asked for an opinion and she does none of the fucking questioning of the witnesses in court. Is that agreed?"

"Agreed," nodded Cadogan, allowing his client to retain a modicum of self-respect. Victory in the early skirmishes was vital and both men knew unequivocally who had won the first battle of wills.

Undeterred, Trevors voiced his next demand.

"I want a courtroom where the jury's on my left. I don't want them staring at this scar on my neck throughout the trial. It's obvious it's from a broken bottle and they'll think I'm violent," he insisted, pointing to the livid and jagged scar which had grown its own red, fleshy welt over the years.

"Which courtroom we get is pure chance. I've no control at all over matters like that and I'm certainly not intending to ask any Judge to move a courtroom for that reason. You've got a fifty-fifty chance of the jury being on the left," responded Cadogan firmly.

"If you lose the bet, then you'll have to wear a high collar. Ask Miss Nicholas about that. I'm sure she's an outstanding fashion adviser," he added condescendingly.

"Right. Then let's go straight to the bottom line. You've read all of the papers, Mr Cadogan. So give me an honest answer. No bullshit. I want to know how you rate my chances," Trevors asked, urgently leaning forward across the table.

"I don't even begin to answer that type of question until I've taken all the instructions I need off you and heard some of the witnesses in court. I don't take a guess at this early stage. I work rather more scientifically than that," was the abrupt reply.

"You're defending an innocent man here, mate. There's no room for mistakes. You get it wrong and I get life without the option, so you'd better make sure that until this case is over you live it, breathe it and fucking win it."

"You don't tell me how to run the case, Trevors. Whether you're guilty or not guilty of these charges makes no difference to me, or to how I do the case. If in truth you're innocent, or if in truth you're guilty, doesn't matter to me. What matters, is what you tell me are your instructions. Once you say you're pleading not guilty then, frankly, I don't care whether you're guilty or not. I act in pursuit of your acquittal by all means at my disposal."

"But it's important that you know that I didn't commit these offences. You need to understand the truth," insisted Trevors.

"No. I don't need to understand the truth at all. Indeed, in certain circumstances, the truth can be an encumbrance. I just need to know your instructions. If, when it is all over, you are found guilty, when in truth you were not guilty then, in one sense, I don't care. Likewise, if you are found not guilty, when in truth you were guilty, then, equally, I don't care. This is because I will have done the case in exactly the same way, at the highest possible standard, with meticulous preparation, seeking only acquittal, whatever the truth of whether you're guilty or not. I act on my instructions. You say you're not guilty. That is what I shall be fighting for."

"So you're telling me that whether I'm innocent or guilty don't matter to you?" queried Trevors.

"I'm telling you that, once you give me the instructions that you're not guilty, then that is what I act on. I have no interest in the truth. Once I have those instructions, then there is no such concept as true guilt or true innocence. The only test of guilt or innocence is which side has the better barrister and they don't come any better than me. Now, let's get back to the Amazon Basin."

Thereafter, for over two intense hours Cadogan took him through every last detail of his movements and of the evidence against him, whilst the solicitor and Junior barrister scribbled furiously in their notebooks to keep a full and accurate record of all the replies. Answers that Trevors must have been rehearsing for weeks tumbled from his lips as he met the barrage of questions that Cadogan fired at him. On some topics, like the size of his shoes and the DNA, he responded with authority and apparent conviction, whilst on others, like the mark on the back of his neck and the Voice Identification, he was brittle and unconvincing. Throughout the entire session he seemed intent on proving his innocence to the lawyers, as if persuading them they were representing an innocent man would lend weight to their performance in court, putting them under extra pressure to secure an acquittal. This was the real barrack-room lawyer philosophy, thought Naomi Nicholas, as she continued writing as fast as his words flowed. If the lawyers believe you, then that belief is communicated to the jury.

When they reached the evidence to be given by Detective Sergeant Perry, the atmosphere in that miserable cell became electric. As soon as the topic had been raised, Trevors' face had become contorted in fury, and he had started banging his fist on the table, actually bringing a prison officer running in, only to be assured that all was under control.

"That bastard's made that up. Verballed me, because he knew they were struggling. It's a stitch-up, simple as that. You ask Mr Sylvester, in any of the cases they've done for me, if I've ever said something which done me damage. I know the way they play the game. When I'm arrested I say nothing. You can vouch for that can't you, Mr Sylvester?" he posed, looking over towards the solicitor.

For almost the entirety of this conference Mr Sylvester had remained studiously quiet, leaving it to Counsel to handle this verminous and dangerous man but, now pressed, he provided the required answer.

"It is true, yes. On every occasion we've represented Mr Trevors there's never been any question of him saying anything incriminating on arrest," was the measured response.

"That ain't good enough, Sylvester," snapped Trevors angrily. "The whole point is I say nowt on arrest. I never speak. I know what they do if you speak. They twist it and distort it and then shaft you with it. Let me tell you something, Mr Cadogan. Last year I was arrested for robbery. A big job. Shooters. A Building Society raid. Sheffield Crown Court. Trial lasted two weeks. Jury found me not guilty. When the coppers came to arrest me I was naked in bed with a tart at her place. Second floor flat, twenty-five feet off the ground. I jumped straight out of that bloody window. Straight out the fucking window on to the grass, ran into the road, threw myself on to the bonnet of a passing car, which slammed its anchors on and the driver leapt out. I was naked, remember. I shouted to that geezer, my name is Gary Peter Trevors. I'm about to be arrested by the police and I've got your registration number, and I'm calling you as a witness, to say that I told you I wasn't going to speak to the police at all, except on a tape recorder. They couldn't verbal me then, could they? That's how paranoid I am about not being verballed. I say fuck all until the tape's rolling and my brief's sitting there. I'm telling you straight, that bastard Perry has verballed me."

He leant back in his chair breathless after this outburst, but looking keenly at the three faces to see if he had satisfied them.

"Excellent answer," nodded Cadogan, "but of precisely no use to us at all in the trial. It isn't likely to impress a jury, trying you for murder and aggravated burglary, to learn that twelve months ago you were being tried for armed robbery. Hardly likely to do much for your image is it?"

"It was another fit-up, that's what it was and I'll tell them that," came the defiant response.

"Two trials for very serious crimes in the space of one year. Both fit ups. They'll think you must be a very unlucky fellow. I don't want the jury knowing anything about your past if we can possibly avoid it, which brings me on to the last point for today, and a tricky one it is too. Those ballet shoes."

"I ain't got no stinking ballet shoes. The coppers never found any at my place. They found nothing to link me with this murder. What's so tricky about them fucking fairy shoes?" he demanded indignantly.

"Well, I'll tell you what's tricky. As you rightly observe, Mr Sylvester has represented you many times in the past, and his firm religiously keeps all of the old briefs. I've been supplied with those and I've read them all, every last word. Ten years ago, you were prosecuted for a house burglary in Cambridge, breaking in while the householder was in bed asleep, but she awoke and disturbed you. It was well off your usual patch, but you were apparently staying with some woman who had rented a flat in Ely. When the police arrested you, they found a balaclava and pair of ballet shoes under the bed, and the householder who was burgled said she had noticed that, when the burglar ran off, his feet had made no noise, and his shoes looked soft and flat. Very unusually for you, you pleaded guilty and, for some reason, got off very lightly with eighteen months. Like I said, this could prove to be very tricky," declared Cadogan, watching the sly face keenly as it absorbed this deadly information.

"They weren't my fucking shoes," he shouted. "They belonged to the cow I was shacked up with. And lots of burglars wear balaclavas. Anyway, the Prosecution can't use any of that. It's ten years ago, and would mean telling the jury that I'd got previous, they aren't allowed to do that, ain't that the Law?"

"Not necessarily. They may argue that it's so unusual and striking a similarity to the facts here, that they should be allowed to call evidence about it. However, I'm pretty confident that they haven't realised that this evidence exists. With old convictions, where the sentence is not a very long one, they often only retain the barest outline of the facts. The details aren't contained in the summary from the Criminal Records Office, which is all the police will have obtained at the moment and I suspect that is all the records now disclose. Also, as it was a Cambridge offence, there's unlikely to be any local knowledge brought to bear on a case in Leeds, and the relatively low sentence means they're less likely to have kept full records. The only reason that I know is because Mr Sylvester's firm actually keep the old briefs, which is very unusual. You'd better hope that the Cambridge CPS don't keep them that long, or, if they do, that no one bothers to check. And you'd better hope that Prosecuting Counsel also misses it and doesn't instruct the police to check all the details of your previous. But I did check and so should the Prosecutor. Let's face it, if that evidence gets into this trial, it's seriously bad news."

Naomi Nicholas watched Trevors, as the white face drained even whiter and the thin upper lip twitched in nervous discomfort. Trevors had never seen that one coming, she reflected to herself, and, nor had she. Cadogan must have trawled through every minute detail of every page of all the old briefs, as well as mastering the present brief. It had never occurred to her that she should carry out that exercise.

"You're the fucking QC. You're paid to find the way to keep that stuff out of the trial. I'm here to be tried on the evidence in this case, not some crap from ten years ago. Those shoes belonged to the old cow. Sheila was her name. Sheila Noakes. The bastards made me try those shoes on in the cop shop, like bleeding Cinderella. Anyway, this lot up here don't know about it and we certainly ain't telling them."

"Sheila Noakes? Must have had big feet for a woman. Size 9 was she? A big girl?" asked Cadogan gently.

"Did the papers say that those shoes in Cambridge were 9, then?" Trevors enquired urgently.

"No. Not in specific terms. Simply stated that a pair of men's size ballet shoes were recovered from under the bed. No actual size. But my observations are to alert you to the futility of trying to find this Sheila Noakes to call her to say the shoes were hers, unless of course she had large feet for a woman. Did she, Mr Trevors?"

There was a long pause.

"No comment, no fucking comment," replied the prisoner.

"Was she a big woman? How tall was she?" Cadogan probed.

"I told you, mate. No comment, no fucking comment," Trevors repeated aggressively.

"What happened when they made you try them on? Did they fit?"

"Last time I'm saying this. No fucking comment."

"Well, fingers crossed that the Prosecution never dig it up. If they do, any Judge worth his salt will admit it as similar fact evidence and I suspect that your goose will be well and truly cooked. You'd better hope that the details are lost in the system," concluded Cadogan with a shrug of the shoulders. "We'll call it a day, now. I've got all the information I require at present. We'll have another conference at court on the day that the trial begins. Before that there'll be a short, formal Plea and Directions hearing. Until that formal hearing, please ensure that you don't tell anyone the name of your Leading Counsel. I have my reasons and it presents no problem for you to respect my wishes. After Plea and Directions, you can tell whoever you want. Mr Sylvester, do we know yet which Judge will be trying this case?"

Roger Sylvester shuffled through his bulging file until he located the appropriate piece of paper. "Yes, the Court faxed it through last week. A relatively new appointment, apparently. Mr Justice Hathington. Do you know him, Mr Cadogan?"

"Vaguely. Commercial bod. Very clever. Extremely unpleasant. Good news though, because he knows damn all about Crime," answered the silk.

Meanwhile, Naomi Nicholas had gone as white as a sheet and her hands were shaking uncontrollably. Fortunately, no one else seemed to have noticed and she somehow managed to pull herself together.

"Before you go, I want some idea, just some idea, of how you rate my chances, Mr Cadogan," insisted Trevors. You'll have picked up a lot of info during this morning and I'm bloody sure that you could give me a rough idea if you wanted."

Cadogan slowly got up from his chair, stretching himself to his full 6'5" as he carefully packed all of the papers away into his leather pilot's case, before looking down at the weasel face, anxiously awaiting his response which, when it eventually came, was short and to the point.

"No comment, Mr Trevors. No fucking comment. I'll bid you good day."

At that, he swept imperiously out of the room and along the narrow corridor, followed a moment later by the other two lawyers, scurrying to keep up with the giant's stride, as he headed for the next train back to civilisation.

CHAPTER 8

Most nights, at exactly the same time, he would wake up in a cold sweat, with the surgeon's fateful words echoing around his head. Eight minutes past three would always be showing on the red LED display of his bedside clock radio, and he would feel the nausea rising in his stomach and the panic attack beginning. Then, the realisation that he was at home in his own bed would intervene, and the recognition would dawn that, what he was hearing in his brain was now over two years old, and belonged to another time.

"I'm afraid, it's the a.c.l.s again, Jack." Those were the dreadful words that he still heard and that time could never erase. The anterior cruciate ligaments, torn, twisted and wrenched apart, but this time in the other knee. The old coach had told him that the odds of a repeat injury of that kind on the opposite limb would be long, and he would be extremely unlucky if it happened again.

That kind of optimistic assurance had not taken into account the awkward, lumbering stopper of York City Football Club clattering you from behind with fourteen stone of hard, black muscle, at the very second when the studs of your boot had anchored themselves in the cloying mud of Bootham Crescent and just when you were turning, ball at feet, ready to unleash a piledriver at the goal. The studs stayed glued to the spot, but the leg still continued to turn, only to have its whole torque reshaped by the fourteen stone of body mass that hit it. Something had to give, and it was the mechanical innards of the knee that were wrenched asunder, in a moment of agony that could never be described.

When it had happened for the first time he had been just twenty-one years old, playing for Port Vale Reserves. Two operations to correct the damage were followed by two weeks on his back, during which time he had to remain completely immobile. Within six months, assisted by the recuperative powers of youth, he was completely recovered and playing better than ever, reassured that the chances of repetition of the same kind of injury were extremely low.

The repeat performance at Bootham Crescent had occurred when he was thirty-four and the recuperative powers were slower and less effective. Such were the complications, and so extensive was the damage this time, that the task for the surgeon was not to save a career, for that was now obviously doomed, but to keep him walking without the gait of a cripple for the rest of his life and fend off for an extra year or two the inevitable onset of arthritis within the joint.

Eight minutes past three on that Saturday afternoon was when it had happened and his mind tormented him at the equivalent time in the night. When the panic attack began to subside, he would begin the frustrating task of trying to capture an hour or two's sleep, before it was time to get up and start the day. Somehow, it seemed that sleep only returned but a moment or two before the alarm went off at seven fifteen and then he would have paid a handsome price just to turn over and be allowed to drift back into that precious sleep, which had eluded him for the balance of the night. Yet, on Sundays, when that opportunity was available and the alarm clock would not have been set, seven fifteen would come and he would be wide awake and restless.

All of the old images would return. Within the excruciating agony of the knee he could feel the wet of the turf, seeping through his shorts as he lay motionless in the mud, surrounded by the physio, the coach and several of his own team. Players knew instinctively when there was a really bad injury. There was a sound associated with this kind of injury that seemed to pierce the air, followed by a silence on the pitch as one of their number lay so still. All of the diving and feigned injury prevalent in the modern game was accompanied by writhing and contorting on the ground; whereas real injury was signified by its stillness and silence, punctuated only by the player's battle to keep his breathing calm and deep, which his training had taught him was the first step required to take control of the pain.

Sometimes, he could still smell the plastic of the stretcher and flashes of the face of the opponent who had destroyed his career appeared in the dark of the night. Not a word of apology had been forthcoming; he had been far away, ostensibly struggling with a bootlace, looking in another direction, as the carnage he had caused was removed from the scene. Out of sight and out of mind. Away on the coach after the game without a backward glance and, by the time that the two clubs met again, this would be ancient history for him.

One disaster was so often but the prelude for another. With his career in ruins, there would only be small compensation for his injury and thirty years' working life stretching ahead with few skills. Football had been everything for him and it had been harder fighting his way into the professional game from his middle class upbringing than it would have been from a council estate in Liverpool. The reverse prejudice was far more poisonous. He spoke well, was articulate and had obtained a degree in English from Bristol University whilst still pursuing a place in the professional game. There were many who resented him for this and relished bringing the class barrier crashing down to block his path. Yet he had worked his way through a semi-professional Northern League Club into the full game, and, whilst Port Vale, Northampton Town and Rotherham were not at the giddy heights of Manchester United, he had carved himself a place and won himself some modest silverware en route.

Over four hundred games knocking about in the lower divisions was a fair record and, whilst he was never going any higher, his endeavour and enthusiasm had brought their own reward.

Trying to use his degree and his experience in the game, he had gone out looking for a job as soon as he regained some mobility and could drive again. Trekking up and down the country for interviews here and appointments there, he had sought a new life and was getting nowhere fast. His wife, Christine, recognising the harsh realities almost as soon as the surgeon had put down his scalpel, had applied, with immediate success, to the cosmetics company for whom she had been working when they had met three years earlier, to see if they might take her back.

So it was, that only four months after that fateful Saturday afternoon, they were both out of the house when the louts broke in. In the middle of the day a brick through the kitchen window whilst the neighbours on each side were at work. Their filthy boots on the windowsill and all over the carpets. They had jumped on the bed like a trampoline until it broke, thrown wine and whisky all over the sofa and walls and ransacked every room. Their thieving hands had rifled through the private corners of her life and her underwear lay torn and violated upon the bedroom floor. The video, TV, CDs and cash had gone, as had his few precious football cups and medals and there lay the deepest loss of all.

Six further months of looking for work, whilst Christine's income paid the mortgage and filled the fridge, came gloriously and unexpectedly to an end when the break came through a most unlikely source. A new local evening paper was to be launched and the Sports Editor was looking for a writer with a fresh style to become the football correspondent. One of the directors at Rotherham put in a word and an interview was arranged. With his experience, his English degree and his honest approach, he was given the chance and life had changed overnight.

His articles gave a fresh insight into the work, effort, practice and time that had gone into that final pass that led to the winning goal. From the ex-player, whose wage packet had never bulged, the ordinary man could get a better taste of what life was really like as you turned out in the wet and the cold, day in day out, took the knocks and got up for more and ran the risk of fielding the blow from which you never got up. Just like he had. In his match reports the reader felt the elbow in the face and the studs across the instep. Most importantly, the reader tasted the glory and the ecstasy when it all went right and the machine purred. Not a ghosted essay by a journalist merely utilising a player's name. Poetry and pain, written by a man who had been there, and who possessed the words and skill to take his reader with him into the battle.

Observing the major impact he was making with these articles, the producer at the local Television Station invited him into the studio to offer his comments on their next live broadcast. Of course, he was sensational, for he had the rare ability to speak as he wrote. The poetry of the game that he described in black and white was now brought straight into the living room, enhanced by his handsome, square-jawed face and honest, open delivery. Signing him up for the rest of the season meant he was, at last, really back on the way up.

Christine had watched with pride as the spring returned to his step, his head was held high and each day offered promise and purpose, instead of emptiness and despair. And then the final nightmare began.

Working that day in Manchester, she had set off early with a quick cup of tea and a peck on the cheek. Their lives were busy now. The last retailer she had to visit was late for their appointment and it was nearly ten o'clock at night before she was heading eastwards on the M62. Rain was lashing down, the car was being buffeted by the heavy crosswinds and she felt so tired. None of this however, had anything to do with what happened, as she maintained a steady 65 miles an hour in the middle lane.

From out of nowhere his headlights came racing up in the rear view mirror, as he tore along in a mountain of spray in his top of the line, metallic blue BMW. Firmly fixed in the outside lane, he was on the point of flashing past her, when he must have seen that he was about to miss his exit, which was immediately upon him. Without any warning, he swung the BMW right across her path, smashing into her driver's side and sending her car hurtling across the inside lane, where it struck a slow-moving delivery van.

The delivery van turned straight over, killing the driver instantly, whilst she ploughed straight on, into the parapet wall of the overhead bridge, where the life was crushed from her body. The BMW, damaged but undaunted, drove straight on, swerved through the traffic, off the motorway and disappeared at eighty miles an hour up the exit road and out of sight.

Receiving the call from the police at the newspaper's offices, Jack Farnham drove straight to the hospital, but it was to the morgue, not to a ward that he was directed. Careers destroyed by injury paled into insignificance in comparison to the inconsolable desolation that now descended upon him.

Meanwhile, a tanker driver in the inside lane behind the delivery van, had seen the whole catastrophe and had the presence of mind and keenness of vision to get the registration number of the BMW. Reaching for his mobile phone and dialling 999, that registration number was reverberating through the police computer system within one minute of the incident and the net was already closing in on William Dugdale of "Windmill House, Featherstone Lane, Rochdale."

By the time that the police car arrived at the six-bedroomed house, Mr Dugdale was seated in an armchair in his lounge, drinking a large whisky from a heavy, cut glass tumbler. A flustered Mary Dugdale answered the doorbell and was obliged to admit the uniformed officers, who wasted no time in confronting the man with their suspicions.

The immediate denial of having been on the M62 was short lived, as the young police constable left outside, found his way into a barn at the back of the house where, under a green tarpaulin, stood the metallic blue BMW 7 Series with its front nearside wing caved in and the engine still warm.

Protesting vehemently as the Sergeant breathalysed him, the driver insisted that it had all been the fault of the car on his inside and, foolishly, he had panicked, hurried home and only then had a drink. At the time he had not consumed any alcohol and had thought it was just a minor scrape and he had no idea that anyone was hurt.

Charged with two counts of causing death by dangerous driving, he came to trial at the Crown Court four months later, represented by Derek Longdon QC, instructed at great expense, together with a Junior. The Prosecution had instructed only a Junior Counsel, but Naomi Nicholas had earned an outstanding reputation on the circuit and was quite unfazed at the prospect of a contest against Leading Counsel.

Jack Farnham had gone straight back to work after the death of his wife. Only by exhausting himself at work could he struggle through the long days and desperate nights and make some attempt to carry on with life. He saw attendance at the trial as an absolute obligation, to be viewed in the same way as attendance at the funeral. The sensible lady at Court who worked for Witness Support sought him out and sat him on a bench in the well of the Courtroom, not in the public gallery and alongside Mrs Jennifer Derry, the widow of the delivery van driver.

Despite the emotional trauma of the trial, Jack Farnham found himself transfixed by the proceedings. Initially, he had viewed attendance as a solemn duty, to be alongside his wife almost as an act of fidelity. Listening to the dreadful injuries that had killed her assumed the duty of a religious penance, to suffer with her and, perhaps, thereby come to terms with the overriding sense of guilt that he was alive and she was not. However, as the trial proceeded, clinical and hard, everything came down to words. Hideous death, callousness, selfishness, ruptured aortas, tangled metal. Words. Everything was words.

Up until now William Dugdale had just been a name given to Jack Farnham by the police. Now he was a face and a body, showing all the telltale signs of the many business lunches and the after-work drinking sessions. Red faced, stretched shirt front, thinning hair and the darting eyes of a successful man, who was now in a situation which he could not control and, if convicted, would send him to prison and ruin.

Dugdale was the Managing Director of a large software company which was soon to have gone public. Thirty-nine years old, married with two young daughters. Jack Farnham saw him leave the Court with his wife during the first lunch adjournment, for the Judge had indicated that he was prepared to continue his bail throughout the trial. A plump and plain lady, defiantly standing by her husband who, as she had been persuaded, had done no more than panic, after a motorist on his inside had created the hazard which led to the accident.

The QC for the Defence was extremely effective and, before long, was selecting a word here from the testimony and another word there, which made it sound as if Mrs Farnham had swerved into Dugdale's path and not the other way round. Other motorists were called, including the tanker driver, who put Dugdale's speed at over ninety miles an hour. Yet, after Longdon QC had finished with them, their estimates seemed wild and exaggerated.

However, Naomi Nicholas, for the Crown, let nothing pass her by. Any damage done by Longdon, she neatly and calmly remedied in re-examining the witnesses. Her style was economical, stripped of irrelevance and flannel. She called a scientist who could make allowances for the whisky Dugdale had drunk in his lounge, and backtrack to the time of the accident, to produce a measurement of what his alcohol level must have been when he was on the M62. It worked out at nearly three times the legal limit for driving, but Longdon then produced a flood of statistics and expert evidence to suggest that this kind of retrospective calculation was suspect and unreliable. By the end of the Prosecution case the verdict seemed to be a very close call and, it was quite apparent to Jack Farnham that the outcome would depend on Dugdale's own performance in the witness box.

When giving his evidence-in-chief Dugdale was assertive, clear and impressive. Carefully coached and kept on a tight leash by Longdon, so as to disguise his sense of self-importance, he explained how the motorist in the middle lane had accelerated to stop him from moving in, even though he had his left-hand indicator flashing. When she actually moved out of the middle lane and cut straight into him, he had taken avoiding action, but had been clipped on his front left wing. Emphasising that he had no idea that it was a serious impact and that he thought she had driven straight on, he described leaving the motorway, unaware that the van had been involved at all, and making his way home. He had drunk no alcohol at all, until imbibing a very large whisky at home, immediately prior to the arrival of the police. His covering of the car in the barn and his initial denial, he put down to panic.

Against the background of this slick and polished performance, Naomi Nicholas rose to her feet to cross-examine this self-assured, successful businessman. Courteously and with complete restraint, she proceeded to destroy William Dugdale, leaving his case in shreds. To Jack Farnham it was like watching a physical dissection, in which she picked flesh from Dugdale's bones with a pair of tweezers, relentlessly ripping off small strips, one at a time, until he stood emaciated and bleeding from a thousand wounds.

The Judge had been masterly. Completely impartial. Keeping out of the fray. Allowing Counsel to get on with their respective jobs. He spoke to the witnesses in exactly the same tone, whichever side they were on and controlled the trial and the personnel with charm, courtesy and total fairness. The summing up was a model of correctness. The jury were out for two hours and forty minutes, before returning to Court with their unanimous decision. In the seconds prior to the foreman announcing their verdict, Jack Farnham felt nauseous with anxiety, but he need not have worried.

Now the Judge's turn really came and, in the light of the jury's verdict, he was able to express the anger of decent society at this unnecessary waste of life.

"You have been convicted of causing the death of two entirely innocent people by your dangerous driving. At thirty-nine years of age, you are a successful businessman, married and with two young children. You have never been convicted of a criminal offence before.

However, on this night, with judgement distorted by alcohol, which put you at nearly three times the legal limit, you drove at grossly excessive speed and, by appalling driving, took two lives and devastated the lives of others, some of whom sit in this Courtroom now.

You have shown little, if any, remorse. Your every subsequent action has been designed to avoid taking the responsibility, which is exclusively yours. You did not stop, you tried to disguise the extent of your drinking, you have tried to blame the incident upon Mrs Farnham so that, if you had succeeded, you would have left her bereaved husband thinking that his wife had been at fault and had caused the death of Mr Derry.

Your actions and your lies have added to the already unquantifiable distress of the bereaved. You are a callous and selfish man. On each of these Counts you will go to prison for seven years concurrently and you will be disqualified from driving for ten years. Take him down."

As Dugdale, in a state of shock, was bustled down the steps to the cells, amidst the cries of anguish from his wife in the Public Gallery, Jack Farnham felt no sense of elation, just a void. How many innocent lives had been ruined by this act of stupidity? As the Judge rose, Farnham had looked for Miss Nicholas, so that he might at least shake her hand and thank her, but, in a second, she had made her exit out of a side door and towards the labyrinth of corridors to which the public had no access. Jack was left to accept that Christine was gone. This was the end. All that was left was to try to utilise the anger and bitterness to make himself work harder and carve out some kind of life alone.

For the next twelve months he threw himself into his writing and broadcasting, driving himself harder and harder, so that in work he might find some relief from his despair. Whilst his professional success grew, so did his sense of loneliness. Established in a rigorous routine, he sought to insulate himself from any personal emotion and allowed himself to think only in terms of deadlines, interviews and broadcasts.

One evening he was due to attend a Charity Dinner at the Leeds Marriott Hotel and make a short speech on behalf of the newspaper, thanking a number of the sponsors. The food, like most of these events, was very ordinary, but the audience was enthusiastic when the comedian told his jokes and enthralled when the celebrity sports star treated them to some of his reminiscences. Jack Farnham however, paid scant attention to any of the jokes or anecdotes, because he found himself transfixed by a face on the outer perimeter of the dining tables. It was an exquisite face that, hitherto, he had only seen under a horsehair wig and from an awkward angle. Tonight he could look at the face full on and appreciate its extraordinary beauty.

Taking advantage of a short break in the proceedings, he nervously made his way across the room, summoned up his courage and spoke.

"Hello. I'm right, aren't I? You are Naomi Nicholas the barrister?"

"Yes, Mr Farnham. Of course, you're right. I recognised you, too. How are you?" she smiled, gesturing to the empty seat alongside her, by way of invitation to sit down.

"Getting by, getting by," he replied as he accepted the invitation. "I'm so pleased to have the chance to thank you personally for what you did in Court last year. I didn't feel it was right to speak to you during the trial and, at the end, you slipped away before I could reach you. So, now perhaps I can put the record straight."

"It's a job. It's just a job," she sighed. "Pretty dire at times as well. Cases like the one concerning your wife are some of the most depressing of all. But I have to defend them as well as prosecute them, you know. I'm only the piper who plays the tune."

"That's as may be, but you prosecuted the only one I ever had an interest in and you were my standard bearer. I can never explain to you how much I appreciate what you did," he insisted.

"It's very gracious of you to say so. Thank you."

Looking at her lovely face, relaxed and smiling, he heard his voice speaking on, revealing intimacies he had not intended to disclose.

"You know, Miss Nicholas, when I went to Court, I saw it as a duty. The last duty I owed Christine. To listen to the clinical descriptions of her final suffering. Of course, I hated Dugdale. I hated him as a name, before I ever saw him. Then, when I actually set eyes on him, saw his wife, heard he had young daughters and how he'd built up his business, the hate began to diminish…I'm sorry, you don't want to hear all of this," he said hesitatingly.

"You just say what you want to say. Sometimes it helps," she replied patiently.

"…if he'd admitted it was all his fault. Pleaded guilty. Accepted he'd made a terrible mistake and had the courage to face up to it, then, whilst I could never have forgiven him, the sense of hatred might have gone away and made accepting the loss just a little easier to bear. But when he started lying, blaming Christine, denying he'd been drinking, hiring the most expensive QC in town, if then he'd been acquitted and walked away, the sense of outrage would have added to my suffering."

"Human nature," she responded. "Selfishness. Survival. Call it what you will. Anything to avoid going to prison."

"Yes, but you stopped him. With your brains and skill. And, in doing so, you eased my suffering so that only one year down the road I'm mending. That's why I wanted to thank you. Long speech. Sorry. I wanted to tell you that at Court, but couldn't. When I saw you tonight, I knew that I must at least say thank you, although I hadn't intended to say quite so much."

"I'm touched that you did and I do understand exactly what you're saying. I'd have been deeply disappointed if he'd been acquitted but, I'd have had to shrug my shoulders, go back to chambers, collect tomorrow's brief and get stuck into that immediately. That's why I said it's just a job. I try not to allow it to be any more than that. Some people do wrong and get away with it. Some learn a lesson from it, while some just go on and do it again," she explained, before impulsively leaning over, taking his hand and then continuing.

"…but, hearing from you, directly, that it really did help make such a difference, is its own reward. It can't have been easy for you to say it. Thank you."

As she had touched his hand with her long slender fingers he had, for the first time since Christine's death, felt that pounding in his heart, which only the touch of a beautiful woman could ever produce. This was not what he had intended or expected at all and he felt his face colour and his embarrassment show. Of course, alert and astute as she was, this did not go unnoticed but, withdrawing her hand discreetly, she smiled openly at him, seeking to put him at his ease.

"I read your column, you know," she said lightening the moment. "I don't know the first thing about the finer points of football, but your words take me straight in to the stadium. I can hear the cheers and the boos."

"Praise indeed," he chuckled, "from a Master of words. I try to write not only about football, but about human nature. Football sometimes gives you a fairly accurate insight into human nature, the good sides and the bad…" His voice tailed away as he became entranced by her beauty, the clarity of her skin, the richness of her blonde hair and the shape of her cheekbones. In court, he had only seen her at that acute angle, constrained in formal dress and from a distance. Now she was free, in bright colours, close and immediate.

Jack Farnham had never been a vain man, but he knew instinctively that the beautiful woman next to him was not disinterested and there was a long and poignant pause as they looked at each other in silence, wondering just where this might lead. He knew nothing of her personal circumstances and, he reminded himself, he had no right to let his mind roam in this direction.

Fortuitously, the moment was interrupted as the Master of Ceremonies called his name, for it was now his turn to make his speech and encourage more donations.

"It seems that you're wanted elsewhere," she laughed, as the spell broke. "Goodbye, Mr Farnham. Thank you for what you said."

As he got up to approach the top table he leant over towards her. "If you take a day off from preparing your cases and want to sit in the press box and watch a match, then call me at the sports desk of the local paper. They'll put you through to me. It would be my pleasure to take you," he offered.

"But I told you I know nothing about football," she countered.

"Then I could teach you," he replied, "if you give me the chance. Goodbye, Miss Nicholas, and thank you again."

As he picked his way through the tables, the audience observed his approach and, with increasing enthusiasm, cheered and applauded the popular old player, who responded with customary warmth, honesty and wit in his speech. Naomi Nicholas listened to every word, studied every gesture, admired the broad shoulders and the handsome, open face. Perhaps she really ought to go to a football match, she thought to herself. Why not?

CHAPTER 9

Her overriding memory of him was his black pit boots. Whenever she thought about him, the first image that came into her mind was never his face, but those gruesome, steel-capped boots that he wore each day, as he set off to cycle to the colliery. Symbols of the hard, grinding job that he did at the coalface, yet their true significance to her was the sickening pain that they caused when he laid into her. With the benefit of hindsight, she supposed that the beatings must have begun shortly after Thomas's death, but her mental defences had so clouded her memory, that she could never be precise. Thomas had been fifteen when the doctors declared that his body could no longer withstand the onslaught of the disease and that all of the available drugs had now been tried and had failed. Being the younger child by almost three years, she had not fully understood that this declaration meant that her brother was actually going to die and, when it happened, she was completely unprepared for the despair that had enveloped her.

Family life had always been difficult, for her mother was a weak and ineffectual woman, who exerted little influence within the home, whereas her father was a dour and remote man, who never showed affection, viewing his wife and children as burdens he must carry until their turn came to care for him in later life. There was no denying that he worked hard in an industry which was doomed and where morale was at rock bottom, but the rigours of the job could never excuse the distance that he kept from his own family and the coldness of the regime that he created in their tired, terraced, backstreet house.

On the night of the death he had walked out of the hospital side ward, leaving his wife and daughter alone with the dead, still-warm boy, while he walked the black, empty streets, raging at the God that had wrought this disaster upon him. Bitterness and guilt consumed him, for he knew that he had seldom shown the boy any love in life and now, in death, he desperately sought someone else to blame. Naomi later rationalised that this must have been the moment when he turned his guilt upon her, almost resenting her survival, as she represented an enduring reminder of the wrong he had done the boy by his coldness and distance. Seeking relief in drink, the violence had begun, always directed at her and never at her mother who stood by, pathetically and ineffectually pleading with him to leave the girl alone.

During the week of her sixteenth birthday two events coincided which changed her world completely. The first was the announcement that the pit was to close at the end of the month and all the jobs would perish with the mine. Redundancy, retraining, rehousing were all on offer, but her father paid them scant attention, preferring to sit in his worn armchair with his head in his hands, wallowing in the self-pity that this latest turn of fate had brought down upon him. Quite predictably, he had lashed out at her with his boot as she had tried to pick up the newspaper that had fallen to the floor from his lap when he fell asleep in the chair and her movement had disturbed him. The steel of the toe cap had landed right on the back of her knee, making her feel sick with pain, but she scurried out of the room without a murmur, seeking refuge in her bedroom until she heard the heavy slam of the front door, indicating that he had set off for the pub.

At school the next day the second significant event occurred. She realised that there was little that she could do to hide the ugly bruising that had developed across her leg overnight, but she was determined not to miss school that day, for the results of the GCSE mock examinations were to be announced. Since Thomas's death and the ensuing violence from her father, she had found escape in her work, applying herself to her studies with determination and energy. Even before the declaration that the mine was to be closed, it had been made crystal clear to her by her parents that she had to leave school at the end of the summer term after her sixteenth birthday and get a job, so that her wages could go straight back into the running of the house. That proposed timetable at least allowed her to take her GCSEs and leave school with some academic success but, now that her father's future was blighted, she feared that he would force her to leave at the end of the Easter term, not even permitting her to sit the exams.

When the sealed envelopes containing the mock results were handed out at the beginning of the first period that day, her heart was pounding so hard that she thought she might pass out. As her eyes scanned down the column where the grades were set out alongside the particular subject she was filled with a sense of total disbelief. Out of the ten exams she had taken, she had scored nine As and one B. They were the best results in the whole school and were the clearest indication that, if she was allowed to continue with her education, she would undoubtedly be offered a place at university.

At lunchtime the headmistress, Miss Wickham had sent for her and Naomi faced the formidable old lady alone in her study. They came no tougher than this canny, old-fashioned headmistress who belonged to another time, for her job as a teacher was a true vocation and had dominated her life. Nothing mattered to her more than the welfare of her girls and boys and, such was her dedication, that she had denied herself a husband and a family of her own, so that all of her energies and time went into teaching. However, she ruled with a rod of iron and, even at this large Comprehensive school in a poor community, where discipline in the home was minimal and academic ambition a rarity, the children learned that they crossed Miss Wickham at their peril.

Perched nervously on the edge of the hard, wooden chair Naomi stared apprehensively across the battered desk to where Miss Wickham sat, surveying her with those piercing eyes, which glinted through the thick lenses of her out-of-date spectacles. Whilst the face was stern and the voice was sharp, Naomi recognised that, unlike her own parents, here was a woman who truly cared that every child should have a chance.

"Your mock results were quite outstanding, Naomi," she began. "They're the best results in the school and there's every reason to believe that you can repeat them in the June exams. I'd like to talk to you about the possibilities for the future. Have you thought about what you'd like to do?"

"I'm to get a job, Miss. I was to leave in July, but yesterday's news about the pit means I'll be told to leave at Easter," she replied sadly.

"That's what I feared when the news broke," nodded the old lady knowingly. "There'll be many children in the same boat. I intend to speak to them all over the next few days, but your results, and the way you've worked over the past three years, put you at the top of the list. I'd like you to tell me, if you had a free choice, what career you'd choose."

There was a long, uncomfortable silence as Naomi tried to gauge exactly how much she could say to this shrewd and demanding lady. What would happen if she disclosed her secrets and her dreams? Besides, whatever she might reveal to Miss Wickham, the hard reality was that, as soon as she got home, her father would be ordering her to leave school at the end of this term and find work to bring some money in. Her mother's few pounds from her cleaning job would hardly keep them.

As Naomi struggled to respond to the question, the headmistress was watching her intently. Not only was this girl capable of great academic success, but she was also on the verge of womanhood. The once gangly limbs had now become the shapely, elegant legs of a young woman and the face, with those high cheekbones, accentuated by the swept back blonde hair, was maturing into classic beauty. Miss Wickham felt a deep sadness as she observed the inner conflict raging in the girl's mind, for it had been obvious for several terms that Naomi wanted to continue her studies, win a place at university and live a life where she used her brain in a challenging arena, and not her hands on the controls of some soul-destroying factory machine.

"Come on girl," urged the teacher, breaking the silence. "What would you really like to do?"

"All right Miss, I'll tell you. I want to be a barrister," Naomi finally answered. "To speak for others who can't speak for themselves. To defend an innocent man. See him walk free. Stop the powerful from bullying the weak. That's what I want, but I know that I can never have it." Naomi leant back, breathless after the outburst that Miss Wickham had provoked from her, and embarrassed that she had said too much.

Behind the glasses of the old lady the eyes had moistened, as she listened intently. Forty years in teaching meant that little escaped her notice about her charges and she recognised all the signs in this girl of a domineering and selfish father, who sought to stifle all ambition in his children. Miss Wickham had seen the bruises on the child many times before and today's marks had not been missed.

"If you stayed at school until the summer, took your GCSEs and repeated your mock results, then I'd be prepared to put your name forward for a scholarship at the independent High School in the town, where you could transfer and do your A levels," the teacher declared in measured tones. "The scholarship'd pay your tuition fees and give you a subsistence grant as well, which you could give to your parents. It wouldn't produce the same income as a job, but it might be sufficient to appease them."

"Dad wouldn't stand for that," sighed Naomi sadly. "He's not got much time for education, sees it as fancy stuff for the upper classes. My place is to start bringing money into the house. As soon as possible, 'specially since the news about the mine."

"Would you be prepared to let me talk to your parents?" Miss Wickham enquired anxiously. "Perhaps I might be able to explain matters to them in a way that they haven't appreciated before. Surely it's worth my trying?"

The prospect of her disinterested father and this determined lady, sitting in a room together discussing her future, terrified Naomi, for the likely consequence would be shouting, anger and yet more violence at home. On the other hand, that kind of behaviour was likely to come her way in any event, without the need for any reason. Of course it was worth Miss Wickham trying and, as Naomi left the study, she had given her consent. The odds against Miss Wickham persuading her father to let her apply for the scholarship might be slim but, for the first time since Thomas had died, Naomi felt that she had found an ally.

It had taken two letters and the threat of a home visit from the Schools' Inspectorate to coerce Naomi's father into attending the school, dragging his timid wife behind him, to discuss their daughter's education with the headmistress. Bristling with aggression at the interference of this old busybody, he listened with increasing anger to the absurd proposition that she put to them, his fists instinctively clenching, as he struggled to control his temper. As she neared the end of her proposals, he could stand it no longer.

"You must think we're bloody barmy," he snapped. "Don't you realise that the mine is closing? Have you any idea how hard it is for people like us at the bottom of the pile? I left school when I was fourteen and Naomi's had nearly two more years than that. We'd given her 'til July but this news means she leaves now. The way you're talking, she'd be in her bloody twenties 'fore she ever brought in a penny. She leaves school at the end of this term and starts earning. That's the top and bottom of it."

"Mr Nicholas, do you realise just how bright Naomi is? If you let her finish her education, she'll be qualified to earn in a month what would take her a year in the kind of job she'd get now."

"Oh yes, join the ranks of the middle classes. Lose her accent, buy instead of rent, cars, holidays abroad. All the trappings of the posh. Don't you understand those are the values we reject and don't want for our daughter?" he retorted.

"Have you considered what she may want? Have you ever asked her what she'd like to do with her life, given the chance? Has she spoken to you of her ambitions or her dreams?"

"We don't talk about dreams in our house. We talk about having enough money to pay the bloody rent and buy the dinner. Our dream would have been that our son was still alive, not some fancy notion about mixing with the middle classes. This conversation is pointless. Naomi leaves at the end of this term and gets a job, like her mother did and like most of the kids at this school will do."

"So the prospect of her continuing her education, going to university, expanding her mind and having qualifications that safeguard her against the kind of insecurities you've faced, isn't even worthy of discussion?" the teacher asked, making no attempt to disguise the sharp edge in her voice.

"There's been a damn sight more discussion about her future than I ever got. At fourteen, they gave me a pit helmet, boots and a kick up the arse. The only discussion was to check whether I'd given me mam my wage packet on a Friday night. Now we need hers, whether I manage to find another job or not."

"So, she's to be viewed only as a source of financial support, is she? When the opportunity exists for her to do A Levels and go to university, without any expense to you personally?"

"I take that remark as a bloody impertinence. What is this? Some kind of inquisition? We've made our decisions. Naomi's got her obligations to the family and no out-of-touch schoolteacher's going to change our minds. This conversation is over," he shouted, rising to his feet to leave.

"Where do you stand on this, Mrs Nicholas? Do you agree with me or your husband?" asked the headmistress, undeterred.

Mrs Nicholas's eyes immediately darted towards the figure of her domineering husband, worried that she might say something that would lead to recrimination. Of course, she knew that Miss Wickham's proposals were obviously in her daughter's best interests, but she was the one left sharing a home with the tyrant that her husband had become. His class bitterness and his disillusionment now dominated their lives. Nothing would ever change him and she felt too old and tired ever to contemplate leaving him and starting anew.

"My husband speaks for us both, Miss Wickham. Indeed, he speaks for the family. That's the way it is with us," she replied meekly.

Mr Nicholas was nearly at the door when Miss Wickham played a card that amazed even herself. Her four decades in teaching had made her prudent and not given to impetuosity. She had met many fathers as class obsessed and selfish as this man. But, by some bizarre, genetic eccentricity, these two awful people had created a beautiful and talented child, whose entire future was about to be cast aside through prejudice and paternal tyranny. For the first time in forty years, Miss Wickham let her heart rule her head and resorted to a tactic, which might even lead to the loss of her job.

"Would you care to offer me an explanation for those deep bruises on the back of Naomi's leg, Mr Nicholas?" she asked, her voice trembling, as the words spilled out.

The man stopped dead in his tracks. His wife, already half out of her chair to leave with him, sank back into it with a sharp intake of breath, as she watched his face drain of colour and the anger glare from his eyes.

"Did I hear you right?" he spat out menacingly.

"You did," came the determined reply.

"Then I'm reporting you immediately to the Governors. You're accusing me of abusing my own daughter. I won't be the only one in this room out of a bloody job. Your mouth's just cost you yours," he raged.

"And when you report me to the Governors, they'll send Naomi to the doctor for a medical opinion on the possible cause of the injuries. Then they'll ask her other teachers if they've observed any signs of marks upon her over the years and the teachers will say that they've seen repeated instances of injury, some of which they have recorded. When they're asked why they've not taken the matter further, they'll tell the Governors that it was because Naomi begged them not to and, perhaps foolishly, they respected Naomi's wishes, probably out of sympathy because she'd lost her brother. Then, the Governors will ask Naomi to tell them the whole truth. Do you remain confident, Mr Nicholas, that Naomi will lie to the Board of Governors, knowing that her lies will cost me my job and cost her any chance of a successful future?"

"You can do your worst, you frustrated old cow," he bellowed. "Nothing changes. Naomi leaves this place at the end of term. You've no proof of anything, so if you open your big mouth outside this room, you'll have me to deal with."

"I don't understand exactly what kind of threat you're making, but frankly, it doesn't matter. The interesting thing is that you've offered no explanation at all for Naomi's bruising. Indeed, your every word suggests that you know only too well how the present injury and those over the past few years have been caused. I suggest you sit down, sir, for what I have to say to you next may have extremely serious consequences."

Since he was a young boy, no woman had ever stood up to him in this way and he realised that neither his fists nor the volume of his voice would deter her. Thoughts of what might happen to him, if ever the truth did emerge, raced through his mind, as she gestured towards the chair. Naomi was becoming increasingly wilful and he was not confident that she would lie to save him. This frail, bespectacled, old woman had achieved something no other woman had done since childhood. She had terrified him. He resumed his seat, head bent low, avoiding her eyes and those of his wife, who was observing these developments with increasing incredulity. Everybody in the room realised that the headmistress had now seized complete control.

"May I please spell out the position to you both," Miss Wickham began with surprising calm. "When this discussion concludes, I'll be making a full written record of what's passed between us. I shall seal it and place it in the school safe, where it'll remain unopened, unless and until I give instructions that it be sent to the Governors, the Social Services and the Police. If Naomi is never seen with injuries again, continues with her education, accepts the scholarship she'll undoubtedly be offered and proceeds to university and independence, then the question of your obvious physical abuse of her will never be raised by me again. Do we understand each other?"

"I'd deny any abuse…" he began lamely, before she interrupted him, with the sharpness of authority and control returned to her voice.

"I asked if we understood each other, Mr Nicholas. Do you think that a jury would believe you? Do you know what happens to fathers who persistently beat their children? They go to prison. And what treatment they're subjected to behind bars is a topic upon which you might wish to reflect, if you're ever tempted to vent your own frustrations on your daughter again. So, I repeat, do we understand each other?"

As the beaten man nodded and grunted his assent, the whole future of Naomi Nicholas opened up and the glittering prizes were moved within her grasp. Miss Wickham's brave victory had rescued an able child from a life of drudgery and wasted potential. Naomi was on her way.

CHAPTER 10

On a glorious, sunny summer's day she had graduated from Manchester University with a Class 2(1) Honours Degree in Law, missing a First by three marks, which had eluded her in Insolvency, a subject in which she had never had any interest. Most of the graduating students were accompanied by proud parents, who applauded this landmark day with unbridled enthusiasm, whereas neither her mother nor father had attended. Indeed, since she left home immediately after A Levels, her contact with them had been infrequent and strained. Since that week when the mock GCSE results had been announced, and her parents had been summoned to meet Miss Wickham, her relationship with them had been dramatically changed. Neither parent had ever disclosed what had been said inside that study to make them change their minds. Her father had stamped around the house, whilst her mother had made the bald announcement, without reasons, that, if she wanted, she could stay at school and apply for the scholarship to the High School. From that day onwards he had never struck her with his fists or feet again, but he had quickly identified another wounding weapon. Indifference. His life was lived as if she did not exist. Hardly acknowledging her, never showing any interest in any of her schoolwork or activities, he had carved out his own miserable path, reduced to menial jobs and friendless nights spent in the run-down local pub.

One supporter however, did make the journey north to observe Naomi walk up to the rostrum, where the Vice-Chancellor shook her hand and awarded her the rolled-up document, which epitomised such an enormous victory against the odds. Miss Wickham proudly clapped her all the way back to her seat as memories of that fateful confrontation in her study with the bullying miner came flooding back. All that she had ever said to Naomi was that, in most people's lives, there would probably come a time when they might have to take a big chance and, if they missed it, they might regret it for ever.

To qualify as a barrister, there now remained the one-year course in London, preparing for the Bar Finals, followed by a search for pupillage in a set of chambers. Struggling through university in Manchester had been a financial strain but the grants, student loans and awards had made it just about possible to survive. London, however, was a very different proposition.

The awards available were minimal, the loans were at their ceiling and the costs were prohibitive. After graduation, during the summer vacation prior to starting in London, her looks, poise and figure had earned her a temporary position with a Manchester modelling agency, which had enabled her to put away a sizeable sum of money. When she moved to London, it quickly became clear that these savings would not even see her through the first half of the course. A bedsit in Clapham had been the cheapest accommodation that she had been able to find, and even that was costing the earth.

As the last reserves of her savings dwindled away, Naomi looked for some modelling assignments that could be accommodated between her classes at the College of Law, but the timetable was so demanding that only the occasional job could be found. Eking out her last few pounds, she was delighted to be offered a job, one Saturday afternoon and evening, at a computer exhibition at Earls Court, for the biggest fee she had yet earned, which would certainly pay her rent for several weeks to come. Numerous software companies were exhibiting their wares and the hall teemed with thrusting, ambitious entrepreneurs, businessmen and designers, furiously seeking the elusive major break and the big money.

Naomi was modelling a three-quarter length, black highwayman's jacket, with a black stetson and knee-high leather boots, the heels of which made her stand well over six feet tall. The contrast with her blonde hair and fair skin was electrifying and heads turned as this tall, elegant beauty wandered from stall to stall, promoting the company that had hired her.

At one of the smaller, more modest stalls, sat an earnest young man, poring over his laptop computer, whilst a young female associate sat alongside him handing out their company brochures. As Naomi wandered down the aisle, she noticed with interest that the name of the company, set out in large, bold, green capitals on the advertising placard at the back of the stall, was "Naomi Mara Enterprises". Impulsively, she stopped at the desk and spoke to the young girl, whose hand had thrust a brochure in her direction.

"That's an unusual name for a high tech company," volunteered Naomi.

The girl had simply smiled in response and then let her eyes wander to the next passer-by into whose hand she might deposit a brochure, but the young man had lifted his eyes from the screen of his computer and immediately replied.

"It's my mother's name. Naomi means 'pleasant'. In the Book of Ruth, when Naomi's husband and sons died, she wanted to be called Mara, which means bitter. My company has established a worldwide accessible database, providing details of the incidence of any particular disease anywhere in the world, at any given moment. That is the bitter. We're now developing a similar database, identifying all known cures to these specific conditions and all plants and herbs, which might contain a curative property. That's the pleasant. So why did you ask the question?"

This answer had been delivered intensely but courteously in a rich, deep voice, with an accent which Naomi was unable to recognise. There was a hint of Eastern Mediterranean and an undercurrent of North American. The man's face fascinated her. The complexion was olive with a square chiselled chin and a Roman nose, which had obviously been badly broken at some time. The whites of the eyes were pure, making a dramatic contrast with the dark skin and the jet black hair, which shone with health under the overhead lights. Naomi had never seen such a handsome man before and a moment passed before she was able to gather her thoughts and answer his question.

"I asked because Naomi is my name, that's all," she replied with a smile.

"It is an inspirational name. Did you know its origin?" he enquired.

"I knew that Naomi was the mother-in-law of Ruth and I knew that they travelled from Moab to Judah together, after the death of her sons, but I confess I was unaware of the meaning of the name," she responded, watching his face with care and feeling a certain sense of pleasure, as his expression gradually began to register the beauty of the woman to whom he was speaking.

He got up from his seat and came slowly around the desk to continue the conversation but, just at that moment, the modelling agency representative walked by and called her away.

"Sorry, I must go, we're expected to keep on the move," she called out over her shoulder. "Good luck with the business." She could feel his eyes riveted on her back as she walked away.

By the time that the exhibition closed at nine o'clock that evening, she had been on her feet for over seven hours and, feeling very tired as she made her way to the Tube Station, she was startled when a hand touched her gently on the shoulder from behind and a voice spoke her name. Before she even turned around she knew that it was him.

"Naomi," he began hesitantly. "I didn't mean to startle you, but I spotted you leaving the Exhibition and decided to take a chance and ask you to come for a drink or dinner. Very pushy of me I know, but it was a case of now or never. I hope you're not offended." Whilst the invitation was delivered with great charm, the face did not smile and, although Naomi found herself instinctively attracted to this unusual man, there was an intensity about him which slightly troubled her.

"I'm flattered, not offended, by your invitation," she replied openly. "But I've had a long day and I'm tired. Besides, I'm not in the habit of going out with men I've hardly met before and whose names I don't even know."

"I apologise. I was far too forward, but sometimes one acts on impulse. Perhaps the world would be a poorer place if we didn't sometimes take a chance. Can I just give you my card and I'd be honoured if you ever called me. It'd be a great pleasure to spend some time in your company. Please phone me if you can but, if you don't, I fully understand. Good night." Urgently pressing his card into her hand, he turned on his heel and melted away into the Saturday night crowds. It was only when Naomi was sitting on the train, heading back to Clapham, reflecting upon his dark good looks, that she opened her hand to study the business card.

'Dov Karlenski. Naomi Mara Enterprises. Offices in London, Los Angeles and Jerusalem' it read, giving a series of telephone and fax numbers and email addresses. As Naomi slipped the card safely into her handbag, she had already decided that she would make the call, but in her own good time. She had learned the value of keeping men waiting for a while.

There were less than four months left to her Bar Finals and the last thing that she had wanted at this stage was some distracting romantic interlude, but the feeling of attraction had been more powerful than anything that she had experienced in the past. Moreover, she was absolutely confident that it was mutual.

For the next week she immersed herself in the dry intricacies of Contract Tort and Jurisprudence, deliberately suppressing all thoughts of Dov Karlenski. On the Friday afternoon she had made the call. Three hours later they were facing each other across the dinner table of the most expensive restaurant she had ever entered. His dark, brooding, good looks quite overwhelmed her and she knew that it was inevitable that they would end up in bed together that night, for she felt powerless to resist him and had no intention of trying.

Throughout dinner, as he disclosed more about himself, she realised that he was highly intelligent, wealthy and yet surprisingly modest. It quickly became very clear to her that, whilst the chemistry between them was so potent, there was unlikely to be any long-term future in this relationship. This was an eyes-wide-open surrender to base animal attraction, which would burn for a few weeks and then probably be over. His culture, circumstances, business interests, peripatetic lifestyle and family, would all conspire to make a lasting romance untenable and, to his credit, he sought to make no pretence to the contrary, indicating that he was preoccupied with achieving major commercial success.

Born in Jerusalem of a Jordanian mother and an Israeli father, he was neither Jew nor Arab. Naomi had never appreciated that there were many thousands of such relationships, where both sides of the political and factional divide, had learned to live in peace and harmony. Of course, there was no news value in this positive aspect of Middle Eastern life and it attracted little reporting. On the other hand, to the numerous extremists and fanatics on each side, a halfbreed of his make-up was regarded as an object of vicious hatred. Accordingly, his parents had decided that, after graduating from the International School in Jerusalem, he should go to college in the United States, where he had majored in Computer Science at Stanford.

Now, at twenty-nine years of age, he had been running his own software company for four years, splitting his year evenly between his three international bases, while keeping a home in Jerusalem. Family money had launched the company, but his level and rapidity of success had been such that venture capitalists were now clamouring to make funds available to him, so as to secure a piece of the action. His latest project, concerning the disease and cure databases to which he had referred at the Exhibition, had excited significant interest in the City and he believed that he was on the verge of a major coup. All of this information was relayed to her in the same intense terms that she had observed on their first meeting. He seldom smiled but, when he did, the eyes softened and a vulnerability surfaced, which made her find him even more desirable.

When she spoke of her circumstances and ambitions he had listened with genuine interest, although she had been careful to reveal only a very limited amount of her family circumstances and the hostility that she had encountered from that quarter. By the time that they left the restaurant and got into a taxi to take them back to the hotel suite that he rented during his time in London, they had both tacitly acknowledged that she would not be going home that night.

As she lay in the king-size bed, unable to sleep, she compared the darkness of his olive skin to the fairness of her own. They were opposites in almost every respect, yet the passion of the night had been more consuming than anything she had previously known, for Dov Karlenski was a man, where her other lovers had been but boys. The same intensity had dominated his lovemaking, but he was so gentle and appreciative of the beauty of her body. In his deep rich tones, he spoke to her of the mystique of the land from where he came, and the power and allure of a beautiful woman.

Eventually, she must have fallen asleep, for when she opened her eyes it was already morning and Dov, in a scarlet dressing gown, was seated at a desk in the bedroom, staring at the screen of his laptop. In the mirror she could see him react to sudden flurries of inspiration, which would send his fingers flying over the keyboard, as he beavered away at his latest project. Somewhere along the line he must have taught himself touch typing, she thought to herself. On the floor of the bedroom her clothes from the night before lay scattered in a trail across the red carpet from doorway to bed, reminders of the potency of the chemistry that had been at work. Perhaps she should feel a touch of embarrassment but, in truth, she felt none.

For three weeks the relationship had sustained its fervour and passion, undoubtedly distracting her from her studies and meaning that she seldom saw her own room in Clapham, other than the occasional flying visit to collect some fresh clothes. Each morning, by the time that she awoke to prepare herself for the day at the College of Law, Dov would already be in his customary place at the bedroom desk, working at the computer in his insatiable quest for the elusive material that would send his company into public flotation and conquer the international markets. Naomi knew very little about the true nature of Dov's work, save that he was becoming increasingly excited as some big deal was imminent and, at the end of the month, this would send him to Los Angeles for an indefinite period, thereby likely heralding an end to their affair. In one sense she considered that this might be a kindness to them both for already, on occasions, their fiery personalities had clashed and they had always known this liaison was not made to endure. Moreover, in the tests last week, Naomi's scores had dropped dramatically from the high standards she had hitherto managed to maintain. Nevertheless, the prospect of watching Dov head westwards and out of her life, at least for the foreseeable future, was a source of considerable depression.

Her mood was not lifted by the state of her finances, as the rent was due again in the next week and there had been no time to seek any modelling assignments to keep the wolf from the door. Dov had no conception of the parlous financial condition in which she existed, for her pride had dictated that he should not know. On any occasion that he had suggested picking her up, or dropping her off, in Clapham she had made a suitable excuse to keep him away from the run-down house in which her bedsit was situated.

Soon he would be gone, the hotel suite vacated and the lavish lifestyle to which she had been recently exposed, would evaporate. Any question of asking Dov to make her a loan to see her through to the end of the course had been rejected by her as, in her judgement, it smacked unequivocally of sex for money.

An early morning appointment with the bank manager had proved an acute embarrassment, as the dry, humourless man had spelled out the harsh realities with some force. Her overdraft was at its limit, her student loans remained unpaid, her grant for the duration of the twelve-month course was exhausted and there was no way in which he could possibly justify increasing her overdraft or any loan. Moreover, his Holborn branch handled the accounts of many students at the College of Law and he knew all of the relevant considerations affecting a career at the Bar. The next twelve months after qualifying she would have to spend in pupillage and, for the first six of those months, she would not be able to earn any money at all. At best, she might receive a small award from the chambers that took her on. She was obliged to concede that she had not even secured an offer of pupillage from any chambers in or out of London. Leaving the bank manager's office with her tail between her legs, she set off for the day's lectures.

In the early evening she had arranged to meet Dov in the Ship and Anchor just off Fleet Street and, as she walked from the College of Law down Chancery Lane and into the Strand, she became aware of a young man falling in beside her and trying to engage her in conversation. The streets were teeming with people making their way home after work and he did not seem to offer any threat to her, but she was alarmed at his persistence, which continued unabated, despite her ignoring him and quickening her pace.

Finally, as they passed a large shop doorway, she stopped and angrily confronted him. Looking directly at him for the first time, he did not appear at all aggressive or dangerous, but rather mild and unsure of himself. Standing at least three inches shorter than her; podgy, mid-twenties, fair hair, bespectacled and with a round, spotty face, he looked like an overgrown schoolboy.

"What the hell do you want?" she barked at him, as they both stepped out of the moving crowds and into the doorway.

"Sorry to approach you in the street, Miss," he began in faltering terms, "but I've been asked to give you a message and this was the only way that I could make contact."

"Who are you? Who asked you to give me a message?" she responded angrily.

"My name really don't matter. I'm just the paid messenger. If you spare me a minute or two I can pass on the message and then you'll be shot of me," came the enigmatic reply in a broad Cockney accent.

"Very well then. Just give me this message," she demanded.

"Here's the score. This geezer gives me your description, says your name was Naomi Nicholas and that you're a student at the Law…"

"How on earth do you know my name and what I do," she interrupted in a fury. The whole situation felt unreal and the idea that he knew her name and what she did was intrusive and deeply disturbing to her.

"I can't tell you who gave me any of this information," he continued, "'cos I doesn't know the answers myself. Look, I works for a bookie near the Elephant and a couple of days ago, just sitting having my lunch in the pub next door to our shop, I was approached by some geezer, out of the blue, asked me if I wanted to earn myself a grand, simply by delivering a message and giving him your reply. One thousand quid. Sounded a bit dodgy, of course, but when he explains the details, seemed like a piece of cake and I agreed. Just that they don't want you to see 'em or know who they are."

"Carry on," said Naomi with increasing incredulity.

"OK. This is the deal. The geezer says, you're meant to be seeing some foreign computer fella who's about to do business with a large, international corporation. Merger or takeover, summat like that. Your fella's meant to have a product which, if it's linked with this corporation, will make 'em all fortunes. The guys paying me need to know the name of the company your man's dealing with. The name. That's all they wants."

"You mean commercial espionage. You want me to steal a piece of information from a man who's my friend," Naomi shouted at him in contempt. "You can get bloody lost. And you can tell your contact that if I'm ever approached again I'll go straight to the police."

She turned on her heel to walk away from this little creep but, taking her by the arm, he pressed on insistently. "Just hear me out, Miss. Please just hear me out. Whether you says yes or no to the offer, or goes to the cops is then up to you, but let me give you the whole story," he pleaded. "I've got a grand riding on this already."

Naomi stayed in the doorway and roughly brushed his grubby hand from the sleeve of her coat intending to bring this bizarre and distasteful scene to an end but, despite herself, an element of curiosity was creeping insidiously into her mind.

Taking advantage of her momentary hesitation, he hurriedly continued. "There's four or five possible runners that your man may be dealing with. These geezers ain't sure which one of 'em it is. Once they suss the name, they'll buy up meganumbers of shares in that company. They're stymied as to buying into your fella's set-up 'cos he ain't public like, but they ain't got no doubt that the name on the other side of the deal is public."

"Insider dealing. Don't you know it's illegal!" she snapped angrily at him.

"I don't know nothing about that, Miss. But what I does know is that, if you coughs up this name, then they'll give you twenty thousand quid. In cash. No questions. No trace. Straight into your back pocket. The geezer says I gotta get across to you that your man's interests ain't at risk. His exact words was 'make sure she understands that the deal won't be jeopardised', or summat like that. Nobody'll be hurt financially. And, I'm to tell you that if you don't want to play, then they'll still be able to get the name through someone else, so you might as well have the money rather than her."

"Her," interrupted Naomi with an extra edge to her voice. "And just who is the 'her' supposed to be?"

"They don't give me no name, Miss. Just some girl he's got tucked away in Los Angeles who'll have the same chance as you to nick the info. So, if you cocks a snoot at the twenty grand they'll offer it to this other bird, 'cos he's meant to be going out there soon. But you'll know more about all that than me. 'The Yank'll grab our hands off,' is how the geezer put it, 'but with the English girl we get the name sooner.' My job's to spell it out that no one gets hurt or cheated, the deal won't be queered and if you doesn't get the name some other bird will, so you might as well have the money. Twenty grand, we're talking here. Twenty grand."

Naomi was still very angry and disturbed at this outrageous proposition but one part of her was hurt, yet not surprised, to learn that he obviously had a serious ongoing relationship with another woman. For just a fleeting instant, the realisation of how twenty thousand pounds would dramatically change her life, flashed through her mind. Cross with herself for even allowing the thought to have occurred to her, she set about sending this obnoxious toad on his way.

"Tell your people that I'm not interested and I never want to hear from you or them again," she declared coldly.

"Up to you, Miss. I've done my bit now. If you change your mind and want the twenty grand, then you've got 'til your man goes away to let 'em know. They've got your phone number, don't ask me how, 'cos I don't know. They'll phone you at six o' prompt each evening 'til he goes away to see if you want to play ball. The geezer says all you've got to do is access his laptop, take a gander at his correspondence files over the last couple of weeks, and you'll cop dozens of letters and faxes to and from this company, and you'll then get the name. If you're not interested, then don't answer your phone at six, 'til after he's gone to LA."

"And just how am I meant to access his laptop?" she heard herself ask.

"He goes nowhere without it and there's a password."

"So you may be interested then, Miss?" he observed with a sickly smile. "I don't know the answer to that, do I? That's up to you. Cracking that is how you'd earn your twenty grand. Anyway, if you goes for it, you're to tell the geezer on the blower that you've got the name and he'll give you a time and place for you and me to meet. Safe place. A boozer round here. One of their heavies'd be watching, 'cos I'd have the payout on me, like. You'd bring a piece of paper with the name on it and we'd swap. You'd have to sit there a bit while I went outside and the heavy checked it out on the blower. Then, if it's kosher, I comes back in, gives you the nod, you keeps the readies and I gets another grand. That's the whole story. Thanks for hearing me out, Miss. Twenty grand for one name. Take a bloody saint to say no to that, if you ask me."

Still in a sense of disbelief, she watched him slip away into the crowds and disappear from view. The most disturbing aspect of it all was that she knew, in her heart of hearts, she was tempted to do it. Of course, it was immoral and illegal but no one would ever know, no one would be hurt financially and Dov had another girl who would likely take the money if she didn't. Meanwhile, after all of the struggles she had been through to get a degree and to Bar School, she might well fall at the final furlong because she was broke.

As she walked along the Strand and into Fleet Street, Naomi found herself reflecting on that fateful day at school when Miss Wickham had somehow deployed a tactic with her parents that had changed everything and the words of the wise, old headmistress on graduation day echoed around her head.

"There will probably come a time in most people's lives, my dear, when they have to take a big chance. If they don't, they may regret it for ever." It was obvious that Miss Wickham must have taken a big chance on her behalf, inevitably involving some kind of threat to her father, and now it was Naomi's turn to weigh the odds.

When Dov awoke at dawn the next morning Naomi was already wide awake, having had hardly a wink of sleep all night, as her mind had been in turmoil ever since the meeting with that hateful little bookie's runner in Chancery Lane. There had been restraint in her sexual response to Dov during the night, brought about partly by the full realisation that she represented to him nothing more than a fleeting encounter. As her own thoughts were teetering on the edge of treachery and betrayal, she acknowledged that it would have been extreme hypocrisy for her to hold this against him, because he had never tried to suggest that the relationship was likely to endure. On the other hand, it would have been very comforting to find some reason to resent him in an attempted self-justification of what she was about to do.

In the corner of the bedroom next to the desk stood a full-length, mahogany cheval-glass mirror which swung on uprights and could be angled to suit the user's height and preference. Whilst he was having a bath the night before, she had adjusted the angle and direction of the mirror in such a way that, from her side of the bed, she could see directly on to the top of the desk, where sat the grey laptop computer, harbouring its crucial secrets. Now, feigning sleep, but in truth as alert as a huntress, she stared at the mirror, straining her eyes to watch his agile fingers key in the letters of the password that would persuade the computer to give up those precious secrets.

Although the light was not perfect, it was sufficient for her to see his hands and, as she already knew that he had taught himself touch-typing, her objective was to identify the particular fingers that moved as the password was entered. As her side of the bed was close to both mirror and desk, her expectation was that it should be possible, with two or three separate observations, to be sure of the fingers used. He was not due to leave for Los Angeles until the middle of next week, so there should be sufficient opportunity for her to study the movement and sequence.

As the beep of the computer being turned on softly sounded, she lifted her head a few inches off the pillow and concentrated on the fingers in that mirror, as if her very life depended upon it. Earlier casual observations had made her aware that he was fast on the keyboard but, for her purposes, it was only necessary to identify that first vital word which he would type in isolation and then await the Operating System's response before typing again. Her heart was pounding in her chest as if she had just sprinted a hundred yards.

The whirr of the hard drive coming on was just about audible to her. Then the shoulders moved. The head bent down. The wrists turned. He was off. Little finger right. Second finger right. Little finger left. Second finger left. Then a blur. Too quick. Probably two more letters, maybe three. She lay back. Elated and nervous at the same time, and amazed that her eyes had been sharp enough to absorb the first four movements at the first time of asking. Next time she could concentrate exclusively on the final two or three letters of the word. As she meticulously stored the sequence and finger of the first four letters in her head, she knew that she had already crossed the Rubicon and that the betrayal was now in progress. The worst of it was that she did not really feel like a rat. Nobody would suffer. Nobody would get hurt. Better that she should have the money than some woman six thousand miles away in America. Carpe Diem.

At the College of Law there was a computer room where the students had free use of the dozen or so desktops provided by the College. Naomi had hurried into that room as soon as the door opened that morning and located the touch-typing programme that was pre-installed. The various permutations for each finger were colour coded and set out on a chart. At this stage she had determined to concentrate only on letters, not on numbers or punctuation marks. The little finger on the right hand was used exclusively for the letter 'P'. Thus, if it was a word and not a series of numbers or a combination of numbers and letters, it had to start with 'P'.

The second finger on the right hand was either 'L' or 'O' whilst the little finger of the left hand was 'A', 'Q' or 'Z'. The second finger of the left hand identified 'S', 'W' or 'X'. She was on her way.

With considerable difficulty she applied herself to the tedious studies of the day although, periodically, her mind wandered to the possible permutations that the letters might produce and her notebook was littered with little columns of letters and variations. By six o'clock in the evening she was already back at Dov's hotel suite, awaiting his return. There had been no prospect of finding the laptop in its night-time position on the desk because, other than when he slept or bathed, he never left it unattended.

Her treachery had made her tense and nervous and she had no doubt that he sensed the differences in her responses to him, socially and sexually. Perhaps he put it down to his imminent departure and the mutual recognition that the excitement of the previous weeks was cooling, but he never invited or encouraged discussion on the topic. By the time they fell asleep, the mirror was precisely angled and her nerves were so on edge that her rest was shallow and fitful, although Dov slept deeply until his customary early morning computer session began, soon after first light. Naomi had been wide awake for over an hour before he had slipped from the bed and lifted the lid of the grey box and pressed the power button heralding the quiet, muted sounds of the drives self-testing.

Although she was lying in a comfortable bed, the tension in Naomi's body was so extreme that she could feel the muscles in her, neck, body and legs stretching and pulling, in anticipation of the critical few seconds that were now imminent. Telling herself over and over again to concentrate particularly on movements five and six, she stared into that mirror like a sniper taking aim at his target.

Little finger right. Second finger right. Little finger left. Second finger left. Then, probably, the index finger right and then the same finger as move three – little finger left. Then he stopped. A six-letter word for sure and confirmation of the accuracy of yesterday's observations. In addition, she was sure that the last movement was the same as the third, although there was some doubt about the fifth movement. With a little bit of good fortune, she just might have the material to identify the word and her impatience was showing as she hurried through her morning routine and set off early to the College and its computer room. Within a few minutes of researching the touch-typing programme again, she had drawn up her permutation chart and the choices were narrowing.

Her conclusions were that the word must begin with a 'P'. Then 'L' or 'O', followed by 'A', 'Q' or 'Z' and then 'S', 'W' or 'X'. Today's additions were possibly the right index finger, which was a problem as it raised a multitude of variables namely, 'B', 'J', 'U', 'Y', 'H', 'M' or 'N' and then a repeat of the left little finger which was 'A', 'Q' or 'Z'.

Naomi made her way to the first lecture of the day, which was Jurisprudence, but she digested little of the teachings of the great lawyer-philosophers of yesteryear, as she had a far more pressing task in hand. Assuming that the word was a proper word, and not a random sequence of letters, she felt confident that the third letter had to be 'A', because if it were 'Q' or 'Z' it would produce a combination with the fourth letter of 'QS' or 'QW' or 'QZ' or 'ZS' or 'ZW' or 'ZX' and she was unable to think of any word with that formulation.

Moreover, the last letter was 'A', 'Q' or 'Z' and, other than "topaz", which could be eliminated, she could not a think of a word ending in 'Z', nor could she identify any word ending in 'Q', leaving the overwhelming likelihood that the last letter, like the third, would be 'A'.

Thus, she reasoned, her choices could be set out as:

'P'

'L' or 'O'

'A'

'S', 'W' or 'X'

Uncertain

'A'.

By writing out the possibilities in column form, the solution hit her straight between the eyes and with such impact that she involuntarily jolted in her chair. Given the nature of the business and the logical way in which his mind worked, it was so obvious that the password would have a medical connotation. All that now remained was to check if the fifth letter, of which she was uncertain, but which she thought had been the index finger of the right hand, contained the missing ingredient. Checking her notes for the relevant finger producing the fifth letter, she went through the possibilities. 'B', 'J', 'U', 'Y', 'H', 'N' and there it was. 'M'.

'PLASMA'.

That had to be the password. Remaining cool was almost impossible and she thought that the lecture would never come to an end. In her excitement she considered how she would engineer a few minutes alone with the grey box from which he was seldom separated. For over thirty-six hours she had been addressing that particular problem from every angle and, now that she was armed with the password, she decided upon her course of action. If there was one pleasure that Dov insisted upon each night before bed, it was a long soak in a hot bath.

After lectures she went home to Clapham and did a couple of hours studying in an attempt to keep her mind calm. Sure enough, at six o'clock sharp, her phone rang. She counted the rings. Twenty, and then it stopped. She was not quite ready for them. Dov was working under enormous pressure at his office, as the complicated deal he was seeking to achieve approached its climax, but he still managed to take her out to dinner or to the theatre two or three times a week and she had not slept in her own bed for the last fortnight. Tonight he was working late, and they had arranged to dine separately and meet for a drink in the Bear and Staff, near to his hotel, at nine o'clock.

Dressed in a long black dress, with her hair up, little make-up and wearing small, diamond earrings that Dov had given her last week, Naomi looked quite stunning, turning many male heads in admiration, as she sat awaiting him at a corner table in the lounge bar. Arriving a few minutes late, Dov was in effusive mood, obviously stimulated by the encouraging developments in his business dealings and excited by her appearance and the attention she was clearly attracting. His high spirits and undisguised pleasure at being in her company gave her, for the first time, serious pangs of conscience at the treachery in which she had become embroiled. Naomi doubted that either of them was truly in love with the other but, apart from the immensely satisfying nights that they had shared, she really cared for him and believed that his feelings were the same. After some reflection over a glass of wine, she decided to ask him exactly where she stood, wondering whether it might have a bearing on whether or not her plan would be carried out.

"I haven't asked you this before, but I'm going to ask it now. You'll be gone for months. What's the story when you finally come back? Do we pick up where we left off or do we end up as strangers?" she demanded bluntly, carefully watching the effect of her words upon his expression.

"Strangers. Strangers. That's one thing we can't be," he protested. "You're a beautiful woman. How can I ever forget these last few weeks? The problem is that meeting you has coincided with a very testing time for me in business. This is a massive deal and I've got no choice but to work it from LA until it's completed or falls through. I've no idea how long that will take and, let's face it, we both know that you'll have your chances while I'm away. Am I supposed to ask you to say 'no' every time? Would that be fair?"

"That's the point. If you loved me then I wouldn't consider it unfair at all," came her terse reply. "But I'm not asking you to say whether you love me or not. You've never given me any reason to believe that this would be a permanent relationship. I've understood that from the beginning. What I'm really asking is whether you keep a girl in LA, another in Jerusalem and I'm just the London model?"

"That's not a fair question, Naomi," he replied uncomfortably. "Different situations arise. Circumstances change. Of course, I've had girlfriends in other cities. Sometimes the relationship survives my absences and sometimes it doesn't. Like you, I'm young and need the company of the opposite sex. That's the best answer I can give you."

"You're not really answering my question are you? You're just saying it's really a case of wait and see?" posed Naomi.

"I suppose that's right," he replied frankly, "but that doesn't prevent us from enjoying the present does it? After all, none of us knows what tomorrow may bring."

"I'm quite prepared to enjoy the present," she agreed with a smile, reflecting to herself that Dov's evasiveness had made her final decision much easier. "Shall we take a bottle of this wine back to your suite?" she added, taking his hand and moving closer to him. "There's a whole night ahead of us before we have to think of tomorrow."

Fifteen minutes later her elegant dress lay discarded on the bedroom floor and Dov sought escape from the pressures under which he was labouring in her arms. Conversely, Naomi was finding it hard to believe just how calculating she had become in her pursuit of the prize. As she had lain naked on her back, with her arms entwined around her lover's body, her eyes had been transfixed on the mirror in which she could see the reflection of a small grey box, sitting silently on top of the bedroom desk. Moreover, it had been deliberate strategy to excite and entice him into having sex and fully satisfying him before he took his bath. That way his bath would be relaxed, leisurely and unhurried.

As the moment approached, beads of sweat formed upon her brow and upper lip. Waiting until the bathroom door was locked and the sound of the water gushing from the taps was in full flow, she lifted the lid and pressed the power button. Her senses were so heightened that she could feel every ridge of the grainy, plastic exterior and the gentle vibrations from within, as it prepared to disgorge its secrets. Timing the activation of the power button precisely meant that, to anybody in the bathroom, the sound of the whirring of the drives was drowned out by the running water. Noting the exact point at which the manual volume control was set, she turned it down to zero so that, if she got into the system, the introductory music of the operating system would be unheard. Underneath the transparent nightie she was completely naked and, as the critical seconds of total betrayal neared, there was such sensual excitement in her treachery that, to her own amazement, she felt the beginnings of sexual arousal.

The black screen flickered and came to life. Her long, slender fingers, with their immaculately manicured nails, were shaking as she followed the instructions on the screen. Simultaneously pressing 'Control, Alt and Delete' as directed, the image changed and the box with the fateful command appeared.

"Enter User Name," the machine demanded.

No problem. Dov used his own name and, as the last user, his name had remained in the box.

"Enter Password."

The bath taps had been turned off, but she could hear the movement of the bath water as he lay back and reflected on the pleasures that she had just provided. Her breath was coming in short, sharp gasps.

PLASMA

Click OK.

Enter.

Two, three seconds. Jesus Christ, her mind screamed silently. She was in to the Operating System. Straight to " Documents Icon".

Double Click.

List of Files. Immediately, her eyes darted to the obvious candidate: "Mergers and Acquisitions".

Double Click.

Columns of correspondence, email and fax files. Chronologically listed. Scroll down to the last couple of weeks. Click on Monday of last week.

"Addressee: Naomi Mara Enterprises."

"Sender: "Catsclaw Research Inc."

"Subject: Proposed Acquisition."

Bingo.

Click out of that file.

Click last Friday.

"Addressee: Naomi Mara Enterprises."

"Sender: "Catsclaw Research Inc."

"Dear Dov,

Our accountants still wish to renegotiate some of the finer details of the share capital…"

Enough.

Click out.

Click yesterday.

"Memo from Catsclaw Research Inc., San Jose."

The sudden sound of the bath water rushing down the plug and of movement within the bathroom. Bare, wet feet on the tiled floor.

Click on File. Bring up Exit. Click.

Save Changes? "Yes or No." Click No.

Control, Alt, Delete.

Hell, he was coming. The door was being unlocked.

Hit the Shut Down button. Close the lid. The bathroom door was opening.

She dived on to the bed. Safe.

Exhausted, she lay back on top of the bed, feeling the sweat run from her brow. No conscience or guilt at all. That was what she couldn't understand. Even worse, the thrill and the danger of being caught had actually excited her. Had her father's abuse corrupted her into wanting to defeat men? Rubbish. She loved men. And she liked Dov. As he came out of the bathroom in his red, silk dressing gown he looked so handsome and she opened her arms wide as she called him over. "Come and help me out of my nightie," she whispered seductively into his ear, before consuming him again like a preying mantis.

Leaving College early the next afternoon, she had stopped by in one of the Cyber Cafés near Charing Cross, so that she could look up "CatsClaw Research Inc." on the Internet. The first search engine had thrown up the definition of Cat's Claw itself, describing it as "a popular herb among the indigenous people of Peru, where it is used to treat cancer, diabetes, ulcers, arthritis, infections, recovery from childbirth and as a contraceptive. Now under research as a promising treatment for viral diseases including AIDS, ulcers and various forms of arthritis".

A further search engine had led her directly to the "Catsclaw Research Incorporated" website. Based in San Jose, California they claimed to have major contractual agreements with a host of pharmaceutical companies and massive investments in medical research projects across the world. Their Board of Directors boasted the ex-chairman of one of America's largest banks and the Chief Executive of California's most prestigious hospital. Clearly, Dov was playing with the big boys.

By six o'clock that evening she was ensconced, alone, in her miserable little bedsit in Clapham, her phone lying dormant atop the scratched, cheap coffee table in the middle of the room.

With the punctuality of Big Ben, the shrill bell rang out on the old machine and she grabbed at it with unrestrained enthusiasm. Twenty-four hours later she was again alone in the same room, counting out twenty thousand pounds in used fifties, twenties and tens. One week later Dov had kissed her goodbye at Terminal 3 of Heathrow Airport, promising that he would be in touch. Naomi had hurried back into town for she had other things on her mind. Like finding a better flat. Ignoring the Tube, she travelled by cab.

* * *

By the time that the results of the Bar Examinations were published six months later, Naomi had received only the one telephone call from Dov, which came hot on the heels of the announcement in the financial press, that a small entrepreneurial software company by the name of Naomi Mara Enterprises, had been bought out by the acquisitive American predators "Catsclaw Research Inc.", turning one Dov Karlenski into a paper multimillionaire overnight.

Asleep in the double bed of her very much more comfortable flat in

Maida Vale, Naomi had been awakened by the sound of the phone. Dragging herself slowly out of bed and crossing the room to where the phone stood on the lacquered dresser, she fumbled in the dark for the plastic handset.

"Hello. Who is it?" she muttered.

"It's Dov, darling. I'm calling from LA. How are you?" that rich, deep voice on the other end responded.

"Fine, just fine. Congratulations, Dov. I saw the Financial Times. You're a genius," she enthused.

"Do you normally buy the Financial Times then, Naomi, or were you especially looking for something?" came the odd reply.

"No. I buy it occasionally, that's all," she answered defensively.

"It's because of the deal that I decided to call you, Naomi," he said, now with an abrasive edge to his voice that began to unnerve her.

"I really dislike the word 'bitch'. It's a horrible word. I've never called a woman a bitch before, but I'm calling you one now," he continued with increasing volume. "I knew someone had been into my computer. I was certain of it. I never have the volume control turned down to zero. I kept thinking about it. It had to have been someone who was so close to me when they were accessing it, that they feared I'd hear the start-up music, and I reasoned that it could only have been you. So I called to tell you that you are a calculating bitch. Was it a set-up from the start?" he snarled, now in a fury.

As he spoke Naomi had frozen in horror. With all the care that she had taken, there had been that mad hurry at the end and she must have forgotten to reset the volume control to its original position. How could she have been so stupid?

"Dov," she began nervously," I really don't understand what you are..."

"Cut the crap," he spat down the phone. "You're not dealing with a fool. I rechecked every file, every detail, nothing had changed. I had the accountants go over all the figures again, all the transfer arrangements. Nothing was different. The deal went through. All I could imagine was that, if you learned the name of the buyer, then you were going to buy some stock, but I don't believe that you had the kind of money to make it worthwhile. That's why I am asking you if it was a set-up from the beginning, that day at the Computer Show, had someone put some money up?"

"It wasn't like that at all. No set-up. I might've been able to really love you, if you hadn't made it so bloody clear that the best I could hope for was to keep your bed warm when you were working in London. I was on the verge of having to pack up studying for the Bar I was so broke. And you never knew anything about the struggle I'd been through to get as far as I had…"

"Spare me the sob story, bitch. I hear them all the time," he interrupted aggressively. "But I want to know one thing. And you owe me this explanation. How in hell did you get my password? How did you get your thieving hands on my fucking password?"

"Goodbye Dov, you don't come from the back streets where I was

brought up so you could never understand," she said softly, pressing the disconnect button, then unplugging the phone from the wall jack, before returning to that new, comfortable bed where she slept like a baby.

All of the distractions had taken their toll and her results were not quite as they might have been. Nevertheless, she had passed, obtaining a distinction in both Company and Criminal Law, although, if she had not had the affair with Dov at such a critical time in the course, she would undoubtedly have earned distinctions in at least two other subjects. Having discussed her results with one of the friendly young tutors at the College, he had advised that she seek a pupillage in a set of chambers that did commercial work, but also had some criminal practitioners, so that she could gain practical experience in both of the areas where she had scored so well in her Bar exams. Then, at the end of the twelve-month pupillage, she could take stock of her position, decide where her preferences lay and seek an appropriate tenancy. Asked his opinion, he would recommend that she make an application to Grosvenor Chambers in the Temple.

CHAPTER 11

On a Thursday evening, after a hard but extremely lucrative day in Court, Michael Hathington made his way back to Grosvenor Chambers, where he was due to chair a meeting of the Pupillage Committee. There were three prospective applicants to be interviewed that evening, two male and one female. In truth, having read the curriculum vitae of all three, Hathington doubted that any of them satisfied the criteria for Grosvenor, either academically or socially.

Hathington himself was one of the rising stars at the Bar, not yet in silk, but another couple of years and that should be remedied. However, despite a successful day in Court, he was not best pleased with life at the moment. His wife, Laura, was spending a week with her parents at their home on the outskirts of Brussels. Normally, this would have provided a golden opportunity for unfettered dalliances with some other female, but, in the last few months, opportunities to demonstrate his sexual prowess had been sparse on the ground and, last night, he had been reduced to an unsuccessful pursuit of the young office girl supplied by his instructing solicitor to take notes for him in Court.

Seated in the throne-like chair at the head of the Boardroom table in the Main Conference Room, Hathington directed sufficient questions to the first two male applicants to satisfy himself that they were not of a calibre acceptable to Grosvenor. Although the Committee also included two other senior male members of chambers, Hathington dominated the proceedings, paying little attention to their views in any discussion. By the time that the last applicant was shown into the room all three men were looking impatiently at their watches, anxious to call it a day.

When the elegant and beautiful figure of Naomi Nicholas walked into that room three pairs of eyes opened wide and all thoughts of an early evening evaporated. This young woman, now with maturity and street wisdom added to her repertoire, might have appeared more at home on a film set rather than in a set of chambers. Hathington was first to his feet, gesturing her courteously to her chair, and almost visibly slavering, as her skirt exposed a flash of smooth, inner thigh as she sat herself down. Inviting her to tell the Committee something of her ambitions at the Bar, his eyes wandered, observing the full, pink lips and the even, white teeth down to the voluptuous breasts which strained beneath the immaculately ironed, white, lace blouse. Her skin was so pure that he longed to lean across and run his fingers across it there and then.

Keen to impress her with his own intelligence, he referred to the very high standards that Grosvenor demanded, illustrated by tales of his own forensic successes. His two colleagues chimed in on occasion, but Hathington was now conducting affairs as if they did not exist, showing the girl who it was that called the shots, if she really wanted a place in Grosvenor Chambers. Naomi, well aware of the effect she was having on these three men, concentrated on her answers and believed that she had acquitted herself more than satisfactorily and with considerable self-assurance, in very demanding circumstances.

Promised by Hathington that she would be informed of their decision by letter next week, she thanked them for their time and wandered slowly out of the now deserted chambers and into the quiet lane within the Temple, leading up to the Strand. Before she had even reached the gate giving on to the main thoroughfare he had caught her up, trying not to sound out of breath as he appeared at her shoulder.

"Naomi," he declared, in a tone that sounded like they had known each other for years. "Awfully formal, those wretched pupillage interviews, I always think. You don't get the chance to know the applicant properly at all, do you? But you did jolly well, I must say," he added encouragingly.

"That's kind of you to say so, Mr Hathington," replied Naomi politely.

"No, no, my dear," he interrupted gently, laying his hand upon the sleeve of her black, tailored jacket and leaving it there far too long. "I know you're not quite a practising barrister yet, but you're nearly there. So it's either first names or surnames. No exceptions. You must call me either Hathington or Michael and I'd much prefer the latter. Similarly, I must call you either Naomi or Nicholas and I'd much prefer the former."

As he stood awaiting her response, his hand remained upon her arm, applying just that extra little amount of pressure, designed to pass a coded signal of a type with which she was only too familiar.

"I will remember that then…" she replied. And, after a second's hesitation she added, "…Michael."

"Not so difficult was it, Naomi?" he laughed. "The idea is that, whatever our experience, we're all equal, although, in reality, we aren't, are we? Still, I'm off to the wine bar for a glass of Pinot Noir before it's time for home. Why not join me? There may be some other members of chambers in there and you could meet them. All helps you know. You need every edge you can get, things are so competitive these days."

Naomi had no desire whatsoever to spend any more time in this unattractive and conceited man's company, but it was overwhelmingly obvious that her already slim chances of gaining a pupillage at Grosvenor Chambers would wholly evaporate if she declined and just might improve if she had a drink with him and met some of the other tenants.

"I mustn't stay too long as I have to meet someone later," she lied. "But a glass of wine would slip down very nicely."

Hathington chatted easily as they strolled up towards Fleet Street, before turning down a narrow walkway which, after a couple of hundred yards, led them to the Green Monkey. Once inside it appeared that there was a dearth of members of Grosvenor Chambers but, unabashed, he steered her towards a quiet corner table where he ordered a bottle of vintage Pinot Noir, which quickly arrived.

"Well, Naomi, have you always wanted to be a barrister?" he asked, taking repeated, quick little slurps of his wine, in a manner which Naomi found most irritating.

"Always. I suppose it started when I saw Charles Laughton in 'Witness For the Prosecution', but I hope the motive is slightly more realistic and less romantic now," she replied with a laugh, becoming acutely conscious of how he was leaning across the table, pushing his bearded face nearer and nearer to her own. At this close proximity, all of the thread veins in his cheeks became visible and the trimmed ginger beard could be seen for the obvious attempt it was, to conceal a blotchy and pockmarked complexion.

Mentioning Charles Laughton proved to be a serious mistake, for Hathington was amazingly well informed about him, and immediately launched into an expose of the actor.

"Wonderful film. Elsa Lanchester also appeared in that. They'd met when they were both in 'MrProback' in the West End and were married a couple of years later. He was born and brought up in Scarborough, you know, but they eventually went to California. What a barrister he'd have made, with that voice. Do you know that he used to read aloud to the wounded Allied soldiers in the war? He went to the hospital and read to them in that magnificent voice. Made them cry."

Naomi well appreciated that his sole objective was to overpower her intellectually and to impress her with his wit and knowledge. As he continued with his biography of Laughton, he edged ever closer, so that at times their knees touched and, pouring her a second large glass of wine, he took her hand in his.

"I do hope that chambers can offer you a place, my dear," he said earnestly. "You may rest assured that I shall do my best to persuade them."

"Are there any other members of Grosvenor here then?" she asked, taking the opportunity to turn in her chair so as to look around whilst, at the same time, moving away from him and extricating her hand.

"Seems not," he sighed. "Unusual. I'd normally expect to find a few of them in at this time. Never mind, we're managing without them, aren't we?" he asked in a patently suggestive tone, as he worked his way through his third glass of wine in those fast, irritating, little sips.

The rims of his eyes were pink and the more he unashamedly ogled her body, the more she was coming to despise him.

If there was any prospect of Hathington being her Pupil Master then she had already decided that, despite the outstanding reputation of the chambers, it would be impossible to stomach him on a daily basis. However, she reckoned that it was most unlikely that, as Chairman of the Pupillage Committee and being so senior, that he would actually act as a Pupil Master himself. Grasping the nettle, she asked him outright. "How do you allocate a Pupil Master to a pupil?" she enquired with a smile.

"We identify the particular field of practice and then work on a rota. For commercial work you'd be with Tom Kenyon. Top class performer. I have nothing to do with the criminal boys, if you went that way, but they're all sound. You need entertain no worries about that side of things, I can assure you."

Naomi breathed a sigh of relief. There was no prospect of being stuck with him and she would learn how to avoid him once she was installed.

It was now time, feigning regret, to escape his clutches. There was no doubt that he was smitten and that was the best way to leave it.

"It's been very kind of you to ask me along and to have the chance to chat, Michael, but I really must make a move as I'm late already. I'm sorry to break up the party. I've so enjoyed talking to you," she said, forcing a smile, whilst pushing her chair back and getting to her feet.

He was up in a flash, downing the remains of his glass and taking her arm in one practised movement. "I shall put you in a cab, my dear. I have made you late and cabs are not easy to get at this time."

"There's really no need, I can manage," she replied gently.

"No trouble at all," he insisted. "Besides, it's time I was also on my way."

Holding her arm firmly, as if they had known each other for years, he directed her across the bar to the door, out into the alleyway and the darkness of the night beyond, for it was now after eight o'clock. The lighting was poor and, as they began to walk back towards Fleet Street, he did not relinquish his grip upon her arm, chatting to her all the while about his views on the Law, actors and anything else that came into his head that he thought might impress her, overriding any attempt she made to speak or to slip her arm casually from his hold.

At one point there was a small junction where an even narrower alley led off to the left, giving access to the rear of an office building, now completely deserted. There was absolutely no one about and, for a second, Naomi had a fleeting attack of anxiety that Hathington, fuelled by the larger part of a bottle of potent wine, would try something on, before she dismissed such a possibility as absurd. A senior barrister molesting a female pupil applicant. She told herself to stop being so silly. As they were about to pass the junction on the left he suddenly stopped and swung her round, so that they both took a backward step, off balance, into the mouth of the adjoining alley.

Initially, she thought that he must have simply lost his footing but, in an instant, he had backed her further into the alley and up against a wall.

"Naomi," he breathed. "There's nothing in this life that I appreciate more than a beautiful woman. I can feel that we're attracted to each other. I know that I can offer you so much." As he spoke, she could feel the bristles of his grotesque ginger beard brushing against her cheeks as his wet, slobbering lips sought her mouth.

"For goodness sake!" she shouted. "Pull yourself together. Let me go and take a grip on yourself before this situation gets completely out of hand."

"I know when a woman wants me, Naomi. You don't have to pretend. Just relax, my dear," he whispered, as he nuzzled her cheek with his mouth and expertly slipped his hand inside her jacket, squeezing her left breast and beginning to breathe in short, sharp gasps."

Naomi struggled to break away from him, but he was leaning with all his weight against her and her back was now pinned to the dirty, brick wall of the building. "Get off me this minute, you lecherous bastard!" she screamed. All pretence at civility was now gone. Any prospect of a place in chambers was now history. This situation was serious. Still there was nobody about and there was no response to her shouting. "Get off, get off, you bastard!" she screamed again.

Completely undeterred, with his one hand still clutching her breast, she felt his other hand dart up her skirt and between her legs, fumbling to get inside her pants. Wearing stockings and suspenders her upper, inner thigh was bare and the feel of his fingers on that intimate skin and then actually within her pubic hair, made her retch and heave. At the same time, his wet mouth was on hers, trying to force his tongue into her mouth, preventing her from screaming out and she could feel his sexually aroused body pressing urgently against her stomach.

The daughter of a rough coal miner from the back streets of a tough town, Naomi Nicholas was no pushover and, at five foot ten and in heels, she was noticeably taller than Hathington. With one almighty lurch she brought her knee up into his aroused groin with all of her strength, then immediately brought the same leg down, with her size eight, high-heeled shoe on her long, elegant foot and smashed it down on to his instep. He crumpled to the floor, howling in pain and she ran, in a state of shock, out of the alley and away from this odious pervert.

When the cab dropped her home she was still shaking in fear, shock and disbelief. Her exquisite face was tear-stained and drawn. There was no one to whom she could turn for advice. She had to make an immediate decision on her own. Did she report him to the police? If so, it had to be now. Any delay until tomorrow and she would not be believed. Would she be believed even if she reported it now? He would deny it. Her clothing was not damaged. She was not injured. Should she report him to the Bar Council? Fat chance they would have of doing anything and her career would be blighted before it had even begun. The only decision that she could make was that she must get these clothes off. Then they would have to be destroyed, because she could never bring herself to wear again clothes that had been sullied by his filthy hands, get straight into the bath and attempt to wash away the sense of violation that she was experiencing.

Sobbing, she began pulling off her jacket, blouse, skirt and was about to run the bath when the telephone rang. It seemed that it was the middle of the night but, looking at her watch, she was amazed to learn that it was only a quarter to nine. Anybody could be phoning her. Walking into the sitting room she picked up the phone.

"Hello," she said, her voice still shaking.

"Naomi, this is Michael here. Michael Hathington," the voice at the other end announced, sounding perfectly calm and collected, as if he was phoning to have an everyday chat.

"How dare you phone me, how dare you?" she shouted. How on earth did you get my number, you filthy, filthy bastard?"

"Calm down, calm down. I've come back to chambers and your number was on your pupillage application. Now, let's just be calm and reasonable about this unfortunate misunderstanding," he said in patronising tones.

"Calm! Reasonable! Listen here, you bastard. You've committed a serious indecent assault on me. I'm just deciding who to go to first. The police or the Bar Council. You're finished. You go to jail for this," she raged at him, as the tears streamed down her cheeks, the sound of his voice coming down the phone into the sanctity of her home making her feel as if she would vomit.

"Stop the hysteria, my dear. Use your common sense. No one will ever believe you. Your own career'll be ruined, not mine. It was a misunderstanding. You gave out the signals. You wanted it and then you changed your mind. Let's just put it down to a misunderstanding, shall we," he continued in that same, cool, patronising tone.

"I gave out the signals? What kind of pervert, are you? This conversation is over. When I put the phone down I'm calling the police," she cried.

"Shut up," he barked. His whole tone had changed and the calm had been replaced by authority and menace. "Just shut up and listen. If you make any report to anyone, you'll be disbelieved. When you think about it with care, you'll realise that's right. Take this on board, you will not be believed. I have enormous influence at the London Bar. You will not get a pupillage in any decent chambers in London. I can and will see to that, should you be foolish enough to try. One word from me that you have a reputation as a cheap, untrustworthy, little tart and no chambers will take you. You're only a provincial scrubber anyway. Go back to the provinces, get a pupillage away from London. It's all that's left to you. If you do that, I shan't interfere."

"Go to hell," she responded.

"When you put the phone down you'll reflect on what I've said. You'll recognise that no one will believe you. You'll do as I've suggested. You never had a chance at our chambers anyway. We take firsts from Oxbridge, not seconds from somewhere in the sticks. Your motive for making a false sexual complaint against me, should you be foolish enough to try, will be that you were furious when I told you in the wine bar that you were bound to be rejected. So, if you ever want to practise at the Bar, get back to the provinces and stay off my patch. Good night."

There was a click as he replaced the receiver and Naomi was then physically sick all over her sitting room carpet. As she cleared up the mess and threw her smart clothes into the bin, she knew that Hathington was right and that she would not be believed. He had committed a serious crime against her, had got away with it and would sail on through life as if nothing had happened. There again, so had she, when she stole Dov's secret and sold it. Of all the untrue things Hathington had said he had, by chance, touched upon one adjective that had struck home. 'Untrustworthy.' That had hurt. Have no conscience and you will succeed in life. Was that the lesson to be learned? The realities were that the bastard would escape and that, for her, London was over.

* * *

All of that had been over a decade ago now, but as Naomi Nicholas drove back from Hull Prison towards her chambers in Leeds, the grotesque memories had come flooding back in depressing waves. As soon as Roger Sylvester had announced that Hathington was to be the Trial Judge, she had felt the blood drain from her face. After her enforced exodus from London, she had eventually obtained a pupillage, and subsequently a tenancy, in Leeds, where her career had flourished and Criminal Law had become her speciality. Hence, she never came across Hathington in his privileged, expensive Commercial world. Whilst it had disgusted her a few years later to see his name in the list of new silks, it had never occurred to her that a man with his personality flaw could fool the Lord Chancellor into making him a Judge, let alone a High Court Judge in the Queen's Bench Division, where he would be trying Crime. The filthy bastard must have pulled a favour in from somewhere to get that particular appointment. Now, the arrogant hypocrite would be trying men and sending them to prison, for doing to women just what he had done to her.

Immediately worried that it might be improper for her to remain in Trevors' Defence team, she had tentatively considered making some restricted and guarded enquiry of Cadogan. Given that he was so offensive and dismissive, such a course of action did not really appeal to her, but was, in any event, dispelled in an instant, when, at the gates of Hull Prison and well out of Sylvester's hearing, he had cornered her alone.

"Best that you understand from the outset," he had begun aggressively.

"I do cases without interference from the Junior. There's to be no questioning of my judgement or decisions by you. Either to me when we are alone, or in the presence of the client and solicitor. Do we understand each other?"

"Yes," came her monosyllabic reply, delivered in the full realisation that there could be no question of saying anything to Cadogan about Hathington. As she watched him laying down the rules it occurred to her that, whilst he was obviously more intelligent than her father, they seemed to share many of the same ugly characteristics.

"Another thing you ought to know," he added. "You're in the case because I demanded the best Criminal Junior at the Leeds Bar. Apparently, that's you. But I only wanted the best so that the Prosecution were denied the best. You're on this team only to remove the possibility of the opposition hiring you. You've no other role to play, although, now I've seen you, I suppose that you can sit there and look pretty." Without waiting for any reply, he had levered his enormous bulk into the back of the same, battered taxi that had earlier delivered him to the prison and disappeared without a backward glance.

During the long, bleak drive back to Leeds her spirits became increasingly lowered as she thought about the dreadful men she found surrounding her. Trevors, Hathington, Cadogan. All, in different ways, sharing similar flawed traits. Violence, bullying, control. Characteristics that brought back grim memories of her father. She'd only visited her parents twice since getting her tenancy in the Leeds chambers and starting to earn a good living. The first occasion had been an anniversary of Thomas's death and some kind of misplaced guilt complex had prompted her to drive over to the Council-run sheltered accommodation in Widnes where her parents now lived. There had been no warmth, no attempt at conciliation, just undisguised resentment at her success, but he had not been too proud to ask her for money.

"You're one of them now all right," he had begun. "With your new la-di-da voice and your posh black suit. Very nice. Shame you've done nowt for us since you left. Not a bloody penny."

The next day she had sent them a cheque for five hundred pounds but had never even received an acknowledgement, although the money had gone straight out of her account, and she had resolved never to see them again.

There had been a second visit however, when the note, scrawled in her mother's hand, in pencil on a lined piece of paper torn with ragged edges from a spiral notebook, had arrived in the post at her chambers. He was dying. They didn't have enough money for the funeral. Perhaps she'd like to help. If she wanted to see him again she'd better not leave it too long.

Seated in his armchair in the corner of the room he was shrunken and yellow. His bed had been brought in there. The television was on, showing the afternoon racing with the volume turned down, but he was displaying little interest. Even though his size was diminished he still frightened her. She had stared at those gnarled fists, the yellow skin now stretched thin over the bony knuckles, but still grotesque reminders of the pain they'd caused her. There had been a worn, grey blanket draped over his lap, leaving visible his lower legs in pyjama trousers, white and thin at the ankle without socks and heavily veined feet in old, beaten, plaid slippers, but she remembered those same feet in those terrifying, black, pit boots. His voice, though weak and hoarse, still overflowed with contempt and resentment. As if to conserve his strength he had reduced his sentences to short, vicious barbs, each delivered within one breath, followed by poisoned silence whilst he prepared for the next.

"Conscience brought you, has it?"

"Your kind's got no place here."

"Brought us nowt but bloody heartache."

"Betrayed your family… betrayed your class."

Those were the last words she'd ever heard him utter. Struggling to stay calm, not to answer back and risk saying something to a dying man that she'd later regret, the accusation of betrayal stung her into retaliation. It had not been a provoked, red-misted reaction but a cold, ruthless, lethal strike at a domineering, dogma-ridden bully who had sought to oppress and destroy her, just as he had succeeded in doing to his own wife.

"You're the bloody betrayer," she'd exploded, jumping to her feet and standing over him.

"You watched your own son die and felt only pity for yourself. You ground my mother into the dust under the heels of your filthy, black pit-boots. The same boots that you used to kick me so hard that my bones felt broken. And you dare accuse me of betrayal when you betrayed every principle of decency within our family."

She'd had some vague recollection of angry noise from his direction and her mother, in a state of alarm, running into the room, but she had continued unabated.

"Your class dogma is nothing but hypocritical envy. You weren't big enough to drag yourself out of the gutter so you've spent your life damning those who tried. Including me. You ruined any trust I might ever have in a man. You sullied my view of men and my understanding of trust. Oh yes, you damaged me all right, but you lost. Because I came through it. I've found a man I trust. I've got a job where I use my brain. I've bettered myself. You'll go to your grave as a hypocrite, a bully and a loser. Some epitaph, that is."

Her mother had hurriedly ushered her out of the room and, thrusting a cheque she'd previously written out for the funeral expenses into her mother's shaking hand, she had stormed out of the house, tears of anger and pent-up frustration streaming down her cheeks. He died six days later and she didn't attend the funeral.

These bitter reflections were interrupted by her arrival on the outskirts of Leeds where she decided that she'd had her fill of barristers for that day and, abandoning the proposed return to chambers, turned off the ring road and headed for Roundhay and her new house overlooking the park. With a bit of luck, Jack would be working from home on his latest article on the lack of trust between League Football Club Managers and Sports Reporters. How incredibly lucky she had been to find Jack, she thought to herself. All the terrible emotional damage wrought by her father had gradually been worn away by the genuine affection and respect of an honest and a decent man.

Making that call to Jack Farnham, after their chance meeting at the Charity Dinner, had heralded a contented and stable relationship for them both. Of course, he was appreciative of her looks, but he did not set out to impress her with his knowledge in his field or his strength, nor was he on some great ego trip which required a pretty blonde on his arm. Over the eighteen months they had been together, Jack's reputation as a broadcaster and reporter had grown in leaps and bounds, but his modesty remained intact. Not only had he earned a contract with a cable TV company, but his weekly article on the state of English football was now syndicated to a national newspaper and had become required reading for informed aficionados up and down the country.

From that first evening match under the floodlights at Elland Road, his manner had been kind, caring and open. Guided by his expertise, the finer points of the game had come within her focus and the excitement and fervour generated by a big match were now an important part of her weekly diet.

Nervous and apprehensive about embarking upon another relationship, he had simply taken their meetings one careful step at a time, which had suited her just fine because, as is the case with so many beautiful women, true romance had proved elusive. In Naomi's case, Hathington's assault, coupled with the earlier brutality of her father, had made her profoundly distrustful of men and two lengthy love affairs since she came north had both ended in tears and mutual recrimination. Accordingly, slow progress with a sensitive and caring man was welcomed and, in its own time, their contact had become intimate and fulfilling.

With a flourishing practice Naomi had decided, four months ago, to sell her small townhouse near to the city centre and invest in a four-bedroom detached house in the leafy and pleasant suburb close to Roundhay Park. Whilst they had both agreed that Jack should not yet part with his flat, it had seemed the natural progression that he should move some of his things in to her new house and, apart from the very occasional night when he went back to the flat, they now effectively lived together.

Despite the different demands and schedules of their respective jobs, they would spend many hours together. At six in the morning, whatever the weather, Naomi cycled to the gym on the far side of the park before returning home in time to make breakfast for them both.

As Jack's broadcasting was almost exclusively in the evenings and his writing could be done as well at home as in the office, he would often call in at Court to see her for half an hour at lunchtime. In the evening they invariably dined together and, at weekends, they were inseparable. Jack knew her as well as anyone ever had and she had no doubt that he truly loved her.

Right now, as she turned into her road, she felt that she really needed Jack. His judgement was sound and, most importantly, he cared so much. Obviously, it would involve telling him about the Hathington assault, which she had never disclosed to another soul hitherto, but she needed advice and Jack would instinctively know what was right.

With a sigh of relief she saw his faithful old XJ6 Jaguar parked outside the house as she swept into the drive and knew then that he would be in. Leaving her case with all the papers in the car, she hurried through the front door and into the dining room where Jack was working on his computer.

"You're back early," he exclaimed as she walked into the room, jumping up and kissing her cheek.

Naomi remained silent and unresponsive, desperate to seek his advice but fearful of the revelations it involved.

"What is it? What's happened?" Jack demanded, knowingly. The paleness of her face and the redness of her eyes told him that something serious must have happened.

"I've had a dreadful day and I need some advice," she sighed.

"Come into the other room and we'll sort it out," he said reassuringly, taking her gently by the hand and leading her into the sitting room where he sat her on the sofa, took her shoes off and lifted those long, shapely legs on to the plump cushions.

Seating himself in the comfortable armchair directly opposite, he urged her to continue. "Right, get it all off your chest and then we'll set about finding the answer."

"I had considered going to my Head of Chambers as it's really a professional matter," she began, "but, frankly, I don't want any member

135

of my chambers to know about it. It's personal and excruciatingly embarrassing. Anyway, thinking about it all on the way back from Hull, I realised that your advice would be just as good, if not better…"

"Let's get to the point," he interrupted. "It's not your style to flannel."

"OK. OK. Straight to the point. We had the conference. Trevors was the vilest person imaginable. Ruthless. Vicious…"

"But you deal with dreadful criminals, that's the job," he said, cutting across her. "You never let it get through to you."

"I know that. Trevors isn't the problem. That just sets the scene. The QC is offensive, conceited. Detestable. A bully boy, he reminded me of my father."

"Is he the problem then?" Jack asked.

"No. Although I'll hate working with him. He warned me not to question any of his decisions and just keep quiet. Said I'd only been briefed because I was the best Criminal Junior up here and he didn't want to run the risk of the Prosecution briefing me. His parting words to me were 'I suppose you can sit there and look pretty'."

"I get the picture," nodded Jack. "So come to what the real problem is."

"This murder is horrendous. It's very high profile. The policy today is often to select one of the new breed of Judges to try big cases. Recent appointment, thrusting for the top, brain like quicksilver, you know the type," she observed.

"I've heard your views on that before," Jack replied with a smile.

"You have. But this one, his name is Hathington. Michael Hathington. Knows nothing about Crime. Commercial silk. He's only been appointed two minutes. They're so bloody clever that they think they can pick up Crime overnight. They never understand that trying Criminal Cases properly is not about being clever, it's about knowing human nature."

"Come on. You're not responsible for the workings of the whole damned system. If the Judge blows it, then it's down to the faceless civil servants who appointed him, not you. I can't understand why you're getting so upset about it…"

"The reason I'm getting so bloody upset is because I know this Hathington. When I was looking for a pupillage in London I applied to his chambers and he manoeuvred me into going for a drink with him afterwards. When we left he indecently assaulted me, and I don't just mean he had a grope, he attacked me, he felt my breast, got his hand inside my pants, poking and probing with his fingers…"

Her voice tailed away, unable to continue, as, in her Leeds living room, ten years later, she relived those appalling few minutes, sobbing quietly to herself as Jack came over, put a comforting arm around her shoulders and let her cry it all out, suppressed as it had been, for over a decade. Gradually, her crying subsided and she turned her tear-streaked face up towards him, anxiously waiting for his reaction.

"I imagine that you're going to ask me if you should stay in the case or return the brief," he asked kindly.

"Of course," she whispered softly. "That's the professional dilemma. On the personal side of it, all I can do is despise him forever. But, can you grasp the extent of the hypocrisy involved? For him to sit in judgement on the actions of others?"

"Didn't you report what he had done?" enquired Jack in puzzlement.

"Until this day, I've never spoken to a single soul about what he did to me. As a man, it may be very difficult for you to understand fully what damage an experience like that can do to a woman. I could never have reported it and you're the only person I've ever been able to tell."

"But why couldn't you have reported it?" Jack insisted. "That's what I find so hard to understand."

"It was outside, just off a Fleet Street walkway, at 8 o'clock at night. I shouted and screamed at him, but no one heard or came. I wasn't hurt, my clothes weren't damaged and I didn't run to the police. I had to get home, get off my clothes and get into a bath. That was all that mattered to me at that time. Of course, that left me wide open to all the questions about why I hadn't gone straight to the police?"

Slowly, she forced herself to recount the details of Hathington's threatening phone call to her later that night and how, in effect, he'd hounded her out of London

"He said he'd spread it around that I was a cheap, untrustworthy tart. So I gave up. I couldn't face the fight," she acknowledged. "And, I might as well tell you everything. On one occasion in my life I had been untrustworthy and so when Hathington used that word, quite by chance and unknown to him, he'd touched a very sensitive nerve."

"Tell me, then."

"I really don't want to go into the details. Everything I've told you about Hathington is true. My own misbehaviour had nothing to do with him."

"If you want my advice, then you have to give me the whole story, not just a part," Jack pressed.

"The two incidents are entirely unrelated. I only mentioned it because Hathington happened upon the word 'untrustworthy'," she replied uncomfortably.

"Let's be having it. Spit it out and then it's done with. You know it'll never go outside this room."

Naomi's chin dropped on to her chest and her shoulders began to heave as the tears came yet again. Jack had never seen her look so awful and her distress was deeply upsetting to him but, as he comforted her as best he could, the confession tumbled out in pitiful little bursts of words.

"I was broke. Down to nothing. Stole some information. Off a boyfriend's computer. Selling his software company. Big public company buying. Someone wanted the name and I stole it. Off his computer. They gave me £20,000. The deal went through. Please, Jack, please. Don't make me tell you any more," she sobbed.

"Alright, alright," he agreed. "I've heard enough. You saw the ends as justifying the means. I think I can understand that. As to Hathington, I'm sorry you didn't report him. He bluffed you. Used his authority to menace you. In truth, he'd have been terrified that you were going to report him. Although you couldn't see it at the time, it's very likely that you would have been believed."

"But at what price?" she responded.

"There's the ugly reality," he answered. "Even a totally innocent woman can have her reputation sullied by being associated with such an incident. You may well have struggled to find chambers if all of that had come out into the open, so perhaps you did the right thing."

"Do you really think so?" she asked with a sense of relief.

"Probably. Anyway, it's ancient history now. Dead. As to the case. Although your client sounds to be a ruthless killer, I suppose the question you should ask is whether Hathington, because of what he did to you, can hold it against your client? Or, out of conscience, can he favour you and be unfair to the Prosecution? In short, is there any way Hathington's resentment of you, or his conscience, though I doubt the lecherous bastard has one, can influence the verdict, one way or the other?"

"You should've been a lawyer," she observed. "You've put your finger right on what matters and I'm sure that the answer to your question is 'no'. His actions towards me can't have any bearing on the verdict."

"There's your answer then. You do the case," he declared positively.

"You're right. It's a big case and I'm doing it. As best I can. To hell with Hathington. To hell with Cadogan. To hell with Trevors. I do the case, just like any other," she agreed, already feeling her spirits beginning to lift.

"The one who shouldn't be doing it is Hathington. He committed a serious crime against you. How can he be made a Judge? If he behaved like that towards you, don't tell me that he hasn't tried it on with other women. In a small circle like the London legal profession, word would get round. How the hell's he managed to get over that and make it to the High Court Bench?" Jack asked incredulously.

"Exactly what I asked myself," she nodded.

"I'll tell you this much. In football, two possibilities would spring to mind. Either it's a bung or a favour called in," he volunteered.

"More likely the latter in our game," she said. "Somewhere within the corridors of power, some politician, puffed up with his own importance, has put a pervert on the Bench, for a favour already owed or so that one day the debt can be collected."

"Another football analogy for you. Sometimes we used to get a referee that we didn't trust. Maybe he was biased or maybe he took a bung, who knows? Fact is we didn't trust him. You know what we used to do? Completely ignore him. Never let him get to us. From the moment he arrived at the ground until the moment he left, we treated him like he wasn't there. A pariah. Beneath contempt. On the pitch, when he swung a bad decision on us, we just accepted the decision and carried on. No protest. No histrionics. Just got on with the job. And, the funny thing was, as a result of all that, we always played out of our skins when we had him to deal with. Out of our skins."

"But football isn't quite the same as the Law, is it?"

"No. You're damned right it isn't. The Law's a much dirtier business," came the telling reply.

Naomi smiled at him, feeling much better now. She had known that Jack would get it right.

CHAPTER 12

Gordon Bertrand Haskitt QC rode to hounds. It was his passion and vital to his social standing. In his immaculately tailored, pink riding jacket, top of the range, black riding hat and boots, he considered that he cut a dashing figure. Tall and lean, with a long, cadaverous face and mousy, lank hair, he would blink through his rimless glasses at the gathered hunt, with a sense of great self-satisfaction. This year had seen his elevation to that much coveted, honourable position, Master of Fox Hounds.

Born to lead, he assured himself, as he headed the charge across the Sussex countryside in pursuit of the hapless fox. Two seasons ago had seen the blooding of his son, Laurence. A moment of enormous pleasure as the boy had ridden alongside his proud father, watched the hounds tear apart the exhausted and bedraggled fox, before the bloodstained brush had been smeared across Laurence's soft cheeks and then held triumphantly aloft. What a moment. What a day. Laurence was now in his penultimate year at Eton and undoubtedly Cambridge bound, where he would read Classics, before taking up the place at the Merchant Bank in the City which Bertrand had engineered through one of the members of the Hunt. Wheels within wheels. Favours done. Favours owed. Everybody knew that was how it worked.

He always referred to himself as Bertrand now. Gordon, his late father's name, belonged to another time, another world, when everything was very different and before Bertrand had ventured into the upper echelons of society and claimed his rightful place at the head of the Hunt, spending his time amidst people of real social standing.

Living in Tonbridge next door to Adam Glanville, Junior Minister in the Department of Education, had done him no harm either, producing an invitation earlier in the year to a box at the Gold Cup at Cheltenham, where he had rubbed shoulders with that excellent fellow, Roger Denstone, the Minister for Europe. The whispers in the box had been that Denstone would be Prime Minister before the year was out, so there was a contact to be nurtured. Michael Hathington had also been in the box, seemingly as thick as thieves with Denstone, and look what had happened to him in recent times. Only in his mid-forties and yet straight on to the High Court Bench.

Of course Haskitt envied him the appointment and, most of all, the knighthood and he had found himself wondering whether perhaps he had cut too many corners in too many cases ever to get the call. With his background, Haskitt had never been over concerned with all of the niceties, so long as he won. With victory came the next big brief and the next big fee. Nothing forced a fee up more than a high profile victory and even if, occasionally, one had to sail a bit close to the wind, it was all worthwhile when the cheque rolled in. Money was the key to it all. Money had bought him his six-bedroom, five-bathroom, mock Tudor house in Tonbridge, his Rolls Royce and a Range Rover for Angela. Money had bought him his place at the Head of the Hunt and a seat at the table at all of those wonderful dinner parties hosted and attended by the new elite. When he had started at the Bar he had waited months for his first proper brief in his own name, instead of just picking up the tiddler returns that others were too busy to do. Fifteen pounds had been that first fee. Fifteen pounds. Now, he wouldn't set foot in Court for less than fifteen thousand pounds.

The last couple of years he had cornered a very lucrative little corner of the market. Shipyard workers would pay their pound a week in Union dues and, when there was an industrial accident or when mesothelioma struck and litigation followed, Haskitt would represent the Union. Thirty thousand pounds, he told his clerk. Thirty thousand pounds to secure the services of Haskitt QC, and thirty thousand pounds the Union would duly cough up. Being a New Socialist helped get the briefs of course. They wouldn't want to brief a Tory. The calloused hands of the men, with their asbestos-stricken lungs and foreshortened lives, would dutifully hand over their hard-earned pound to the Union Treasurer and then it would wend its way into Haskitt's bank account to help pay for the Rolls and keep the boy at Eton.

What a far cry it all seemed now from those wretched days in Gravesend, where his father had worked for "Terminex", the local vermin extermination company. While he was at the Comprehensive school the word had got out and the taunting had begun.

"Haskitt, the ratcatcher's son". "Rat for dinner tonight, Haskitt?" They would form a circle around him, jeering and shouting. Sometimes they would encircle him when he was in his shirtsleeves and his green braces.

Then, they would pull and twang those braces, so that the elastic snapped back hard on to his thin, frail body, stinging his puny chest. How the girls would laugh at this, their shrill peals of laughter stinging him even harder than the spiteful elastic.

Once, in the melee, his National Health glasses had fallen off his face and landed on the playground concrete, from where Rosie Cranshaw had grabbed them like some prize, before thrusting them up her dress and down the back of her knickers. Rosie was the fattest girl in the class and took a fair bit of teasing herself, so it suited her admirably when the children found another target for their cruelty. Thereafter, Haskitt's glasses became the object of uncontrolled hilarity, featuring in crude little poems about where they had been and the similarities between Haskitt's face and Rosie Cranshaw's posterior. Eventually, when he could stand it no longer, he had deliberately broken the glasses, endured the anger at home and then managed to ensure that the replacements looked completely different and, at last, the jibes had subsided. How deeply these bitter memories were ingrained within his psyche and how much they still rankled. If only those cruel little bastards could see what he had done with his life thereafter.

Driven by an intense desire to escape this daily humiliation, he had applied himself to his books and discovered that he had an outstanding, natural aptitude for Maths. Brilliance at this subject took him to College and onwards to a Scholarship at Trinity, Cambridge. It was a remarkable achievement and, when he walked away with a First, they had offered him a Fellowship, which he was strongly tempted to accept. However, academic life would never earn him the money that he now coveted, whereas a switch to the Law might. With his mathematical brain, Fraud and Tax Evasion became his speciality, with spectacular results and silk came when he was still in his thirties. As a QC, he varied the diet with his shipyard cases and by chasing the best paid murders. Throughout this meteoric rise, he had never had a friend, except for Angela, whom he had met on a Forensic Accounting Course, where she was the administrator. Small and squat, where he was tall and thin, dry and completely humourless.

Tonight, Angela was dressed in her full-length sapphire gown, which had the one advantage of hiding her thick, shapeless legs, which ran from knee to instep without any discernible change in diameter. Remarkably, she was not the ugliest woman at the dinner table, for that dubious privilege belonged to Lady Laura Hathington who, with her husband, Sir Michael, was also present at the Glanvilles' soiree.

The major attraction however, was Della Montanari, recently promoted to second-in-command at the new BBC television channel. Just thirty, brought up above the family's fish and chip shop in Acton, very bright but rough as hell, with a skirt that left absolutely nothing to the imagination

142

and with a male partner who had no imagination. They had in tow a two-month-old baby called Chloe, of whom Della was plainly the mother, but whether or not the insipid, accompanying male was the sire was impossible to ascertain. Chloe was eventually deposited in a bedroom upstairs to sleep until, halfway through dinner she awoke crying and bawling at ear-shattering decibel levels. This development provoked mother Della to bring the child to the dinner table so that, under the full gaze of the entire gathering, she was able to produce her ample breast to feed the whining offspring. Haskitt observed the overtly lecherous manner in which Michael Hathington enjoyed this tasteless little spectacle. Thereafter, seemingly oblivious to the humiliation occasioned to his wife, Hathington fawned over Della, laughing hilariously at her off-colour jokes and cornering her alone whenever the opportunity arose.

At a late stage in the evening, when Della had excused herself to go and powder her nose, Hathington adeptly took Haskitt on one side in the hall.

"Just wanted a quick word in private, Haskitt," he began quietly. "I'm being sent up to Leeds soon to try a very serious murder. Very important case. Name of Trevors. Word has it that you've been instructed to prosecute, but we haven't had confirmation. Seeing you here tonight, just thought I'd check the reliability of our information."

"Yes, Judge, your sources are correct. I've been retained by the CPS. They thought it called for Leading Counsel from London to head the Prosecution team. Pretty tough one to throw at you so early in the judicial career, though, if I may say so. High profile. Very dangerous criminal. Needs putting away, or none of us is safe in our beds," replied Haskitt in solemn tones.

"Precisely, Haskitt, precisely. Requires a united effort, if you understand me. It'll be the first murder I've tried. I've been on the judicial course and I'm well prepared for it of course, but I'll be looking to you to ensure that nothing is slipped by me. You mustn't hesitate to intervene if it looks like I may be missing something. You criminal boys don't operate quite like us commercial fellows. We might have the intellect, but we can't be expected to pick up all the barrow-boy tricks overnight, can we? Worth a mention, I thought. Just worth a mention," he urged.

"So it's just a coincidence that Glanville invited us both to the same soiree is it, Judge, or is there slightly more to it than that?" asked Haskitt with interest and quite untroubled by the Judge's condescending words.

"I think that the Department may have had something to do with it," nodded Sir Michael with half a smile. "They like to give us new boys, who have changed disciplines, the chance for an informal chat with experienced Leading Counsel who are due to appear in front of us."

"I see," answered Haskitt provocatively. "So might you be having a word with Leading Counsel for the Defence in similar terms?"

"I'm not so sure about that, old boy. Anyway, we haven't been able to identify who's been instructed for the Defence. I was hoping you might be able to tell me," encouraged the Judge.

"Very strange, that. We know some local Junior from the Northern Circuit's been instructed but, despite repeated requests, nobody seems to know the name of Leading Counsel. That normally means that the villain has sacked the original choice and the solicitors are racing about trying to find some other silk to take the brief at short notice. Of course, all the decent QCs are booked months ahead, so the Defence may end up with some old has-been, often the way when there's a late sacking," came Haskitt's reply.

"Do you know that's what has happened here then?" the Judge enquired, much lifted at the prospect of a second-rater appearing for the Defence.

"Not for sure. But with a rogue of this calibre it's highly likely to be the explanation. He'll think that he knows it all. Will likely demand to run the case his way and his brief'll almost certainly disagree. Becomes a battle of wills. In the end, they often fall out. Been there myself more than once I can tell you," laughed Haskitt.

"Fingers crossed that you're right then. Enjoyed our chat. Just wandering back into the other room, if you'll excuse me," said Sir Michael, suddenly sidling away in the direction of the sitting room, as he observed the delectable Della Montanari emerging from the bathroom and heading in that direction.

"Della, Della," he called conspiratorially, "just a quick word before we rejoin the others. "I was wondering if you're in town next week. I've got a couple of theatre tickets and, quite unexpectedly, Laura is having to pop off to Brussels, so she can't use her ticket. It'd be great fun if you could make it."

"But what about my dear little man?" enquired Della mischievously, "what would he do without me for the evening?"

"He'd babysit, my dear, while I looked after you for a little while," replied Hathington, leaning over her as closely as he could, his eyes unashamedly peering down the front of her zebra-effect silk blouse as he spoke, transparently anticipating the moment when he could thrust his hand within and seize the luscious trophy he had seen on display earlier at the dinner table.

Haskitt was observing this offensive little mating dance from a discreet distance, but was absorbing every word, every nuance and storing them away, just like his father used to collect those bright purple pellets to poison the rats, waiting to observe where they fed before laying the trap.

CHAPTER 13

THE CROWN COURT SITTING AT LEEDS
R v GARY PETER TREVORS
PLEA AND DIRECTIONS HEARING
CORAM: THE HON. MR JUSTICE HATHINGTON

Half-open suitcases lay abandoned on the floor, spilling their ill-assorted contents in every direction. Collars, dirty shirts, black gowns and day jackets were tossed casually on the chairs and stools, while the tables were covered with a sea of red-taped briefs and wig boxes. A scene typical of any busy Crown Court robing room in the land, bustling with male barristers looking for their collar studs and females seeking their hairbrushes, all talking a penny to the dozen.

Within this maelstrom of human activity, Naomi Nicholas could be seen adjusting her bands in the mirror and ensuring that her wig was absolutely straight, preparing for her first contact with Hathington in over a decade and it was not a morning she had been looking forward to at all. Last night she had barely slept a wink, despite Jack's assurances that she would handle the occasion with dignity and style. Of course, it was most unlikely that Hathington had any idea that she would be appearing in the case, for the names of Junior Counsel in a case where Leading Counsel had been instructed were rarely handed in to the Judge. Moreover, in this case neither the Judge nor the Prosecution team had the slightest inkling about the identity of Leading Counsel for the Defence.

Her opposite number, Junior Counsel for the Prosecution, was Dickie Lampard, a genial local fellow who had been around a good few years and knew the ropes well enough, although his career had been slightly hampered by his inability to keep a confidence, thereby earning himself the sobriquet of "Singing Dickie". Almost as soon as she had walked into the robing room, Singing Dickie had sidled up to her in an attempt to learn the name of her Leader, so that he could relay the information on to Gordon Bertrand Haskitt, who was presently taking a cup of coffee in the Barristers' dining room, apparently very curious as to the identity of Leading Counsel for the Defence.

As was to be expected, there was no sign of Ronan Cadogan QC and the likelihood was that he would not make his entrance into public view until the case was called on in Court. Today was only a short, formal hearing in which the Defendant would be arraigned, the trial date would be confirmed and any preliminary issues, which might require a Direction from the Judge, could be raised. Today's list of cases were all of a similar nature and each was likely to last only a few minutes and, as the murder was the most serious case in the list and involved Leading Counsel on both sides, it would normally have been first in the list. However, at the instigation of Cadogan, there had been urgent telephone calls between the Court Listing Office and Arthur, his clerk, in which Arthur had insisted that the murder was listed second and not first, so as to allow his Governor sufficient time to get up from London, robe and be ready for the hearing. Eventually, the Listing Office had succumbed, but Naomi had recognised from the outset that if the case was first in the list, then Cadogan would have to be in Court before the Judge came into Court. On the other hand, if it was second, then Cadogan could make his grand entrance when the case was called on and when everybody else was already in place.

Easily sidestepping Singing Dickie's probings, she joined Mr Sylvester at the top of the stairs leading down to the cells and, together, they descended towards the rabbit warren below, to pay the required courtesy call on their client. After passing through the various bureaucratic and security hurdles, they found themselves in a poky cell in a distant corner of the custody area, behind three separate sets of steel gates. Trevors was a Category 'A' prisoner, the highest security risk of all, and was not even allowed into a normal conference room within the secured cell area. As he was ushered into the dingy cell where his lawyers now awaited him, Naomi felt that all-pervading sense of menace accompany him into the room. Four prison officers stood immediately outside the cell and refused to allow the cell door to be closed.

"We are entitled to privacy in our discussions," Naomi explained.

"Not with this one you ain't, Miss," replied the surly Senior Officer. "Our orders are that we're not to let him out of our sight. Ever."

Trevors, like most serious criminals, was very keen on observing the Prisoners' Courtroom protocol and, accordingly, was conservatively dressed in a black suit and collar and tie. The fabric of the suit was cheap and coarse, while the collar of the shirt, wholly unaccustomed to having a tie worn around it, was ill shaped and distorted. A thin, green, crumpled tie completed the attire, making him look like a pauper attending a relative's funeral.

"Makes no odds," sniffed Trevors. "The QC's not here and I only discuss the case with him anyway. Where is he, Mr Sylvester?"

"It's not his intention to hold any discussions with you today, Mr Trevors," replied the taciturn solicitor. "He phoned my office yesterday to inform me that he's ready for trial, today's hearing was only a formality and that he wouldn't need to see you until the trial was under way. He asked me to explain this to you."

"Well, you've explained it. And it ain't good enough. These bastards here," Trevors retorted, nodding in the direction of the four prison officers who were overtly paying more attention to Naomi's legs than to Trevors' mutterings, "…these bastards are saying that I've got to go into Court wearing handcuffs and I ain't standing for that. No way. I want the QC down here to sort that out now, before I go up. I want to…"

"I can assure you that Mr Cadogan won't be coming to see you today," interrupted Naomi in an authoritative voice. "He'll certainly not concern himself with inconsequential matters like an application for you to be handcuffed during today's hearing. I'll have to deal with that. Officer! Are you intending to apply for this man to be handcuffed in Court?" she fired at the Senior Official.

"Them's our orders, Miss. He's Category 'A' and viewed as a major security risk. If he thinks he can scarper out of that dock, then he'll give it a go," came the reply.

"Have you got any evidence or information to back this up?" she demanded.

"Evidence? Information? We don't need that kind of stuff to make this kind of an application with a villain like him," laughed the officer.

"Then I shall resist the application. Mr Trevors, you won't be in Court when that happens. You'll obviously know the result when you're brought up. You'll enter your pleas of 'Not Guilty', the trial date will be confirmed and Mr Cadogan will raise any matter of Law that he thinks appropriate. I doubt that the whole hearing will take more than a few minutes. Then, we'll see you again when the trial begins. We have done our preparation. We're ready," she explained carefully.

"I want to see Cadogan in the nick before the trial begins. I want to tell him exactly how I want the coppers to be questioned and how…" Trevors began to insist.

"You can forget all of that," interrupted Naomi. "He won't be coming to see you again. He needs no input from you as to how he's going to run the case. All of that was made absolutely clear to you when we had our conference with you in Hull Prison. You know that. If you don't like it, then you can seek a change in Counsel. Otherwise, leave it to him. You made that judgement in Hull, so let's not go over old ground."

Trevors lifted his head and looked at her in complete contempt for several seconds before making any response. "You know, I don't have to take that kind of shit off you or off any woman. But I'm going to let it go this time, because I've made my enquiries within the prison and the word is that Cadogan is the Man. At the trial though, I don't want you down here without Cadogan. Sylvester, you can come on your own but when I want to see the Brief, I don't want her on her own. Cadogan and her and you, or just you. Today, lady, we'll see if you're any good. You persuade that Judge no handcuffs. Get me back to my own cell!" he shouted at the officers, rising to his feet and shuffling to the door, from where he was led away down the corridor.

By the time Naomi and the solicitor had passed through the security systems in the other direction, the first case in the list was approaching its conclusion. Bertrand Haskitt was already in place on the front row reserved exclusively for silks and Lampard was tucked in behind him, doodling on the cover of his blue notebook. The Honourable Mr Justice Hathington, in scarlet gown with large ermine cuffs, was flanked by the High Sheriff to his left and the Chaplain to his right. As Naomi took her seat in the second row, the Judge's head was down, studying his papers and, disturbingly, there was still no sign of Cadogan.

Once Naomi had arranged herself, she fixed her gaze upon the Judge, awaiting the dreadful moment when his head would lift and his eyes met hers. Her heart was pounding but her face was determined and resolute as the dreaded confrontation approached. In the present case the Judge was only being asked to confirm that a Defendant should remain on bail but he seemed to be taking an unnecessarily long time in coming to his decision, thumbing through the same papers over and over again. Eventually, he appeared to have resolved the matter.

"Stand up, Wayne Deeley," the Judge declared, beginning to lift his head and look into the well of the Court. "I have decided that it is appropriate er, er..." he began, before stuttering to a complete halt mid-sentence as his eyes met those of Naomi Nicholas who was staring uncompromisingly straight at him. The laser force of her glare seemed to force the Judge physically backwards into his enormous, throne-like chair as he visibly sought to regain his composure. Slowly and hesitantly, averting his eyes from Naomi, he somehow managed to find the words to send Wayne Deeley on his way, earn a few minutes' respite before the next case was called and recover from the shock of seeing a ghost from the past.

Haskitt had observed this bizarre faltering by Hathington and the remarkable exchange of looks between him and the attractive Junior whom Singing Dickie had informed him was the Defence Junior in the murder. "Something very rum there," thought Haskitt to himself, as he got slowly to his feet to deal with his case, recollections of Hathington leering at Della Montanari floating though his mind.

"My Lord," he began, "I appear for the Crown in the case of Trevors. Mr Lampard appears as my Junior and the Defendant is represented by Miss Nicholas. I am presently unaware of the name of Leading Counsel for the Defence who, presumably, is not attending today's merely formal hearing. Before the case is actually called on and the Defendant is brought into the dock, I must inform Your Lordship that application is made for Trevors to be handcuffed to prison officers during this hearing. He is a Category 'A' prisoner, known to be a high security risk and there is reason to believe that he may be violent. We would be grateful if Your Lordship would make the appropriate order which is becoming increasingly common in serious cases of violence such as this."

Naomi Nicholas was on her feet before Haskitt had fully resumed his seat. Her voice was firm, her poise was absolute and her words were fluent. She was in complete control of the situation whereas she knew that Hathington was not, as his face still displayed the shock of seeing her again after so many years. As she spoke, his eyes could not hold her stare and he was smiling nervously in her direction, as if making some pretence to acknowledge an old acquaintance, whilst underneath it was obvious that he was badly shaken.

"It may be becoming increasingly common to handcuff prisoners in other Courts," she began sharply, "but if so, those Courts are in error unless there are powerful reasons, supported by reliable evidence or information, to back up the allegations made. Trevors has no previous convictions for seeking to escape from custody. Ever. Anywhere. There is no information or evidence to suggest that he is planning to escape. If there is, and I expressly submit that there is not, then I respectfully demand that Your Lordship be shown it now in writing. If it is confidential I do not mind. I do not ask to see it. I ask for Your Lordship simply to be shown it. Now. This, I suggest will not happen, because it does not exist. In Courts on this Circuit, judicial and administrative decisions are made on hard material. No such hard material exists in support of this application and I ask Your Lordship to reject the application for handcuffs unless my learned friend satisfies the test I have referred to."

As Naomi resumed her seat she felt a sense of elation. Holding her back straight and never allowing her eyes to stray from Hathington's troubled face, she knew that the Judge was so rattled by her appearance, her seizing control and by his own inexperience in dealing with this kind of application, which was essentially peculiar to the criminal jurisdiction, that he was likely to find in her favour.

Whether or not Trevors appeared in the dock today in handcuffs was a matter of total indifference to her, however much Trevors might whine about it afterwards. What mattered was confronting Hathington, rocking the authority that his position gave him, showing him that she was a force to be reckoned with, was dangerous to him and then making him accept her submission. Haskitt would not have a shred of evidence to back up his application and her discussions with Jack about the Hathington incident had taught her an invaluable lesson. Jack had impressed upon her that bullying men like Hathington are, in their hearts, cowards. If ever she had the chance to face him down, she must take it and then he would show his true colours. Here was the first chance, albeit only in a small way, to test Jack's theory.

"I do not have to provide written material to support this application," blustered Haskitt. "This is a case of murder. The Defendant has previous convictions for violence. Your Lordship is entitled to draw appropriate inferences if the prison staff express anxieties about such a man. We ask for handcuffs."

Throughout these exchanges Hathington had remained totally silent, occasionally looking to his left and right as if seeking guidance from the uniformed dignitaries accompanying him on this first High Court Day of the new Legal Term. In the still silence, their faces remained completely expressionless and Hathington was left alone, exposed and unsure what to do. Nervously shuffling through some of the papers he suddenly cleared his throat and spoke a few words. Although the word 'handcuffs' was audible none of the barristers had heard the rest of the sentence as it was so mumbled and indistinct.

"Would your Lordship be so kind as to repeat your decision?" invited Haskitt, before adding the cosmetic lie. "There was some movement in the Court while Your Lordship was speaking."

"I stated that handcuffs could not be justified," replied the Judge, swallowing as he spoke, before burying his head again in his papers as the matronly Clerk of the Court formally called on the case of the Crown against Gary Peter Trevors.

No sooner had she called the name than there was a tremendous hustling and bustling at the back of the Courtroom, as the imposing double doors were thrust open and a procession marched into the well of the Court. At its head, strode the enormous figure of Ronan Cadogan QC, towering over everybody and feigning to acknowledge glances of recognition and admiration from the press benches and the public gallery, although, in truth, it was surprise that he was attracting, not recognition.

Behind him, weighed under by the armful of files containing Cadogan's brief that he was struggling to carry, scuttled the elderly figure of his Senior Clerk, Arthur Helliwell. In turn, behind Arthur, the young Junior Clerk, just a boy, hurried along, hugging the rest of the brief to his chest and his Governor's folded, carved lectern which was carefully opened and placed on the QC's desk as the great man took his seat, looking about him for signs of appreciation. Arthur and the boy briskly laid out the files on the desk and lectern, before withdrawing discreetly to the back of the Court.

The Governor had had him up here since six this morning, commandeering a private room from the Court staff, with its own key, where Cadogan could get robed alone and in secret, away from prying eyes in the ordinary robing room. It had taken Arthur an hour, and a twenty pound note, to get an audience with the security officer who had arranged for Cadogan to be admitted to the Court Building by a private side door, so that there was no chance of him being seen and the grandeur and surprise of his entrance in anyway thereby diminished. Of course, as Arthur knew, the whole design was to devastate Haskitt but, at the same time, he found himself acknowledging the fact that, bastard though he was, Cadogan certainly had style.

Naomi Nicholas had never before seen an entrance like this in her professional life. Without speaking a word, Cadogan had seized full control of the proceedings. His size and physical presence now dominated the whole of the Court and the Judge, peering down from his raised bench in disbelief at the spectacle being enacted below, had already been reduced to a bit-part player.

However, the greatest impact of all had been upon Gordon Bertrand Haskitt, whose jaw had visibly sagged from the second the formidable figure of Cadogan had first loomed into view. Naomi's gaze passed from the Judge, to Cadogan, to Haskitt, back to the Judge and then again became transfixed on Haskitt. His mouth was still open, displaying yellow teeth, his already cadaverous face had gone deathly white, a pulse was beating frenetically on the side of his long, scrawny neck above the starched, wing collar and she could clearly see that his heavily veined hands were actually shaking. Cadogan's entrance had provoked a reaction in him that was quite staggering and, despite her loathing of the giant, this performance had truly been an act of pure brilliance.

As the atmosphere in the Court became still again, Naomi was surprised to see that Trevors had appeared in the dock, his arrival completely unnoticed and overshadowed by Cadogan's scene-stealing. However, it was apparent from Trevors' face that he had caught at least part of the virtuoso performance because his thin, mean lips had spread in what passed for a smile, as he observed his Brief's opening number and he nodded his head in approval. As he caught Naomi's eye he held up his hands, wrists held apart to show her that he was unmanacled. This was a promising start, his look acknowledged.

"Gary Peter Trevors, you are charged upon an indictment containing three Counts. On the first Count you are charged with murder in that you murdered Paul Michael Checkley. Do you plead Guilty or Not..."

"Not Guilty," snapped Trevors before the Clerk could finish her question.

On the Second Count you are charged with Aggravated Burglary in that, you entered Blossomfields, Alwoodley as a trespasser and with intent to steal therein and, at the time of such entry, had with you a knife. Do you plead Guilty or..."

"Not Guilty," came the interruption

"On the Third Count you are charged with wounding with intent in that you wounded Sarah Checkley with intent to do her grievous bodily harm. Do you plead Guilty..."

"Not Guilty."

As Trevors took his seat between the two largest prison officers of the four in the dock with him, Cadogan rose imperiously to his feet to introduce himself, whilst Haskitt seemed temporarily to have lost the power of speech.

"If it please your Lordship, my name is Cadogan. Ronan Cadogan. Queen's Counsel. In this case I lead for the Defence. I would expect that Your Lordship has already been informed of the names of other Counsel in the case."

Hathington nodded, looking anxiously in the direction of Haskitt and reflecting on his empty assurances at the Glanville's dinner party that the Defence were currently scraping around for some second-rater, some has-been. This Cadogan was a complete pro who would know every trick in the book and then some more. As if being brought face to face with that female pupil he had tried to crack all those years ago wasn't enough. Now he was faced with a titanic struggle to handle a difficult case and a dangerous, formidable Defender.

"I can tell your Lordship," continued Cadogan, "that this trial will last just over one working week. We have notified the Prosecution of our witness requirements. The Defence are fully prepared and ready for trial, which is scheduled to start before Your Lordship in this Court three weeks from today. We ask for confirmation of that date."

The Judge looked over towards the Prosecution end of Counsel's Row.

"Mr Haskitt. I take it that the Crown is ready?" he asked.

"Well, much as I would like to give that assurance, there are certain matters that I still wish to be investigated and it is by no means certain that we can be ready," replied Haskitt, taking everybody by surprise, including the Crown Prosecution Service and his own Junior.

"What's he talking about?" whispered David Nathan, the CPS solicitor to Dickie Lampard. "Of course we're ready. You and I have been running around to make sure of that. The witnesses are all lined up. He's never said a word about any matters requiring further investigation."

Lampard tugged on his Leader's silk gown and leaned forward, making it impossible for Haskitt to ignore him. "We are ready, Bertrand," he insisted, in what was meant to be a whisper but, in his urgency, echoed around the Courtroom for all to hear, including the Judge.

Cadogan smiled. "Cold feet, Haskitt?" he asked across the Bench, making no attempt at all to keep his voice down.

"What matters were you specifically referring to?" posed the Judge, in a state of ever-increasing consternation. Perhaps if the flustered Haskitt came up with some decent excuse, for which he was obviously desperately searching, then the date of the trial could be changed and Hathington could avoid trying it, leaving someone with more Criminal Trial experience to handle Cadogan and Naomi Nicholas.

Haskitt stood speechless, struggling to come up with something, before eventually turning round to look at Lampard for some inspiration. All that emanated from that quarter was a puzzled shake of the head. After a moment's acute embarrassment, Haskitt fixed on an idea. "We were hoping to do some more DNA tests," he volunteered. "New techniques are being developed and they may assist in securing more conclusive results."

"I see," observed the Judge. "Yes, that would be of great value in this trial. I do see your point."

Cadogan stood up with a smile and beamed along the Bench at Haskitt.

"My learned friend must have inadvertently overlooked Page 352 of the papers, My Lord. And, it must be that, if Your Lordship professes to see Mr Haskitt's point, then Page 352 could not have found its way into Your Lordship's bundle. May I therefore read directly from it. It is the Witness Statement of Miss Jane Bewley at the Forensic Science Laboratory, who is the DNA expert relied upon by the Crown in this case. Having detailed her findings and the statistical conclusions that it is safe to draw from the scientific evidence in this case, she states:

'This is only a partial profile. The crime sample obtained was in such miniscule quantity that only a partial DNA profile was obtained. This has two main consequences. Firstly, the match probability produced represents weak evidence. Secondly, for a variety of technical reasons, the remainder of the sample, such as it is, will not be susceptible to any of the new DNA profiling techniques currently emerging.'

I assume that your Lordship was missing that page?" enquired Cadogan mischievously.

"It somehow seems to have been misplaced in my paper," replied the Judge, staring directly at the relevant page and the deadly quotation that had just been read out to him.

"Very well," continued Cadogan, with an understanding nod of his head. "May we therefore confirm the trial date? Three weeks today? In this Court? Before Your Lordship? Mr Haskitt prosecuting?"

"Confirmed," replied the Judge reluctantly, without affording Haskitt any further chance to put on public display the fact that, for some reason, he was running scared.

"One further matter, My Lord," added Cadogan. "We hereby put the Prosecution on notice that we shall be submitting that the evidence of the Voice Identification Parade is inadmissible and we shall be asking Your Lordship to exclude it as a matter of Law. That is all I wish to say at this stage."

"Mr Haskitt, do you wish to respond?" asked the Judge, bewildered at what point Cadogan must have dredged up about the parade.

"Not at this stage," came the weak reply from the humiliated Haskitt. "The parade is, we submit, faultless," he added feebly as the Clerk of the Court was already calling on the next case.

Leaving his lectern and papers for Arthur and the boy to gather up, Cadogan hurried towards the doors of the Court, beckoning Naomi to follow him. In the corridor, just beyond and to one side of the double doors, he silently positioned himself awaiting his quarry, offering no explanation to his intrigued Junior. Haskitt was now getting a taste of what it felt like to be the fox and, still inside the Court, he was making urgent, whispered enquiries as to whether there was an alternative exit from the Courtroom. As his Junior and Mr Nathan became increasingly anxious to leave, Haskitt eventually collected up his papers and prepared to sweep out through the doors and use his speed to scurry away from any ambush that may be awaiting him.

Bursting out of the doors he walked straight into the barrel chest of all 6 foot 5 inches of Ronan Cadogan, who backed him straight up against the adjoining wall. In front of the Juniors and the solicitor from the CPS Cadogan spelled it out, without any pretence of propriety or civility. This was to be a street fight.

"Try and back out of this, Haskitt, and your name will stink all the way back to London, you'll be unemployable," he threatened.

"How dare you make such an accusation? How dare you speak like that in front of Junior Counsel and my instructing solicitor..." blustered Haskitt.

"It's your solicitor that I particularly want to hear it," replied Cadogan knowingly. "He's the one that would have to find a last minute replacement if and when you funked it."

"Your remarks are actionable, Cadogan. I shall consider..."

"Then sue me, Haskitt. Sue me. Have a bleat to the Bar Council. But, for the moment, just shut up. Shut up and listen," interrupted Cadogan, forcing his bulk upon his opponent and leaving him no room to escape from the small circle that Naomi, Lampard, Nathan and Cadogan himself had inadvertently formed around the beleaguered silk.

"This is a big case. All of the pressure is on you. If he's convicted, who cares? But if he's acquitted, then a dangerous killer is on the loose. And, if he's acquitted because you make a mistake, then it's on your head. And, I'll be trying to make you make that mistake. I've been waiting a long time for this. So, don't funk it, will you, old boy? Just reflect on my words each night when you go to bed and think about the Voice ID Parade, there's a dear. And, by the way, that last case we were in together, the mother I represented, you remember, she's still inside. Risley Prison. The recommendation was that she served fifteen, so only about ten to go."

Turning on his heel, Cadogan headed for the stairs that led to the private changing room arranged for him by Arthur. It was only just after eleven and he had already achieved an excellent morning's work. Now, it was back to London and keeping the barristerial ear close to the ground as he waited for Haskitt to make his inevitable move. It was amazing how much you could learn just by turning up at a Court where you were not known and asking a few questions of the press and the local Juniors. That fellow Dickie Lampard for example, "Singing Dickie", they called him up here. Perhaps Naomi Nicholas might be useful after all, keeping up with the news in the Prosecution camp, courtesy of Singing Dickie.

CHAPTER 14

Outside the Golden Eagle, on the outskirts of the town, the Hunt was gathering for its Saturday morning Chase. Just over one week remained before the trial was due to begin and the Master of Fox Hounds had not been sleeping well. Cadogan had taken him completely by surprise with his staged entrance in Leeds and that subsequent ambush outside Court, but Haskitt had been assuring himself that, once the initial shock had passed, he could handle it. Besides, he found himself acknowledging, Cadogan had cornered him so effectively that, barring illness or death, it was virtually impossible for him to avoid the confrontation.

It was a crisp morning. There was still a sharp frost on the ground and the breath of the baying hounds froze upon the air. Somewhere out there the fox was straining its ears, listening for the sounds of the pack and the clattering hooves and feeling for the vibrations through the ground that threatened a wretched, agonising death.

As they approached the old railway line to the west of the village, the hounds picked up the scent and the big hunters broke from their lumbering canter into a full-blooded gallop. Over the small hedge marking the perimeter of Galloway Field and then the ground fell away down to the brook, before the steep ascent up Monument Hill. At this point the speed necessarily dropped and, if the chase broke to the right, there was a small stone wall, no more than three feet high, which the beasts would take easily in their stride, before looping down the other side of the hill and into Morgan's Copse. The Master of the Hounds had taken a leisurely walk, alone, over this route last Sunday afternoon and could be seen lingering for many minutes in the area immediately before and after that three foot stone wall, repeatedly testing the firmness of the ground on each side with his heel.

Today, as the hunt lumbered up the hill, Haskitt was up and out of the saddle, keenly waiting to see which way the hounds broke, left and away from the copse, or right, towards and over the stone wall. Two or three of the more skilled horsemen had taken up the lead but there was plenty of space on each side. Haskitt wanted no one behind him at the critical time. It was difficult enough already without the added risk of another rider or horse falling on top of him.

"Tally Ho! Tally Ho!" came the cry from one of the leaders, veering suddenly to the right and away towards the wall and the copse. Pulling firmly on the reins, Haskitt reduced his hunter's pace as much as he dared, deftly slipped both feet from the stirrups and then, as the stone wall raced nearer and nearer and his steed's front feet left the ground, Haskitt released the reins, sliding neatly backwards off the left rear of the saddle, crying out as he fell.

Landing on his left side and shoulder, all of the breath was knocked out of him and he felt like he had been struck in the stomach by a battering ram. He had not been winded since he had cowered on the wing in enforced rugby games during his schooldays and the nausea and shock reminded him of those dreadful times. Lying deathly still on the grassland near to the stone wall, he felt sickened by his own act of profound cowardice whilst, at the same time, discreetly testing each limb, satisfying himself that nothing was broken. Now, badly winded, aching and desperate, he was unable to deny to himself how much Cadogan terrified him. The source of the fear was not simply that Cadogan was capable of tearing him physically from limb to limb, nor that intellectually and in Court, Cadogan was naturally superior. The real fear stemmed from the recognition that Cadogan knew that he, Gordon Bertrand Haskitt, had cheated in that trial five years ago and that he was responsible for an innocent woman being sentenced to life imprisonment and a guilty killer going free. All of these ghastly thoughts flashed through his mind as he lay in the dirt, awaiting rescue.

"Huntsman down! Huntsman down!" rang out the cries. Keeping his eyes tightly closed, he let them all fuss round him, reach for their mobile phones to send for the ambulance and, in due course, carry him down the hill to the road, where he was driven off to the local hospital.

At five minutes past nine on the following Monday morning, Mr Nathan of the Leeds CPS, received an anguished telephone call from Haskitt's clerk, expressing his deep regret that the QC was now extremely doubtful for the murder trial starting next week. Unfortunately, it was explained, there had been a riding accident and the hapless barrister was presently lying in a hospital bed in a private hospital in Six Oaks, having been transferred there from the Tonbridge General yesterday evening. No details of the injuries were available, but Mrs Haskitt had been in touch with a message from her husband that, whilst he would try to drag himself to Court, it was all looking pretty bleak and a new QC should be instructed.

Mr Nathan, still reeling from the events that he had witnessed when the case was in Court for Plea and Directions, remained a touch sceptical and was quickly on the phone to Dickie Lampard. By lunchtime, Singing Dickie had spread the story all across the Leeds legal world and, by three o'clock that afternoon, Naomi Nicholas was obliged to carry out Cadogan's parting instructions at their last meeting.

"If any word reaches your ears that he's trying to funk it, then you phone me, on this mobile number, at the double, day or night. Understood?" he had snapped at her, as he walked away after that amazing attack on Haskitt outside Court.

By four o'clock Cadogan knew the name and phone number of the hospital and the name of the doctor overseeing Haskitt. Sitting in his room in chambers with his feet stretched out across the desk, he placed the call.

"Dr Harmer, please," he asked

"Who is calling?" enquired the receptionist.

"This is Sir Michael Hathington," came the curt reply. "Please put me through to the doctor."

"I'll have to bleep him, Sir. It may take a moment or two," was the respectful reply.

Thirty seconds later the line clicked and a young voice came on.

"Harmer here. Who is it, please?"

"Dr Harmer, this is Sir Michael Hathington. I'm one of Her Majesty's Judges. You have a patient called Haskitt. Fell off his horse. I need a professional, up-to-date medical report. Now, if you please."

"I can't do that, Sir Michael. Not without my patient's consent. You aren't family, are you?" the doctor replied, with a singular lack of authority in his voice.

"I'd better make myself very clear, Dr Harmer. Very clear. Your patient is not dying. He does not have some incurable disease which calls for sensitive handling. I am a High Court Judge. Haskitt is a barrister. He is due to prosecute a murder trial in my Court next Monday. At 10.30 sharp. I need to know that he is going to be there. This is a trial of public importance. Your report is required by my Court to arrange a murder trial. Now, what is his condition?" demanded Cadogan.

"Mr Haskitt has particularly asked that no bulletins be issued. Indeed, he insists that there should be no bulletins," came the timid response.

"Dr Harmer, do you know how many tens of thousands of pounds it costs to set up and hear a murder trial? Do you know the extent of my powers as a Judge if anyone obstructs the running of such a trial? I asked for information. Provide it. Now," commanded Cadogan.

"Well, I think it's in order for me to tell you that his condition is satisfactory," replied the doctor meekly.

"And?" snapped Cadogan.

"And he's fit to be discharged this evening or tomorrow morning at the latest," he added reluctantly.

"I want the facts, Dr Harmer. Does he have any concussion?"

"No concussion, Sir Michael."

"Does he have any broken bones?"

"No broken bones."

"Any internal injuries?"

"No."

"What injuries does he have then, Dr Harmer? My patience is beginning to wear thin."

"He has some slight bruising to the left shoulder, the left outer thigh and buttock and he suffered some degree of shock."

"Is there any medical reason why he cannot prosecute the case in my Court, next week?" demanded Cadogan.

"No, Sir. He will be medically fit to return to work by then. I have no doubt about that," conceded Dr Harmer, reluctantly.

"Very well Dr Harmer. Will you kindly tell him, immediately, that I have phoned and that you've assured me that there is no reason, no reason at all, why he should not present himself for duty next Monday. I shall ensure that everybody involved is informed that he's fully recovered," insisted Cadogan.

"I shall go and see him right now and pass on your message, Sir Michael," the young doctor agreed.

"Thank you, Dr Harmer. Excellent news. Please be sure to send him my regards and tell him that I look forward to seeing him on Monday, by which time I trust that his left buttock will be fully recovered. Good afternoon."

Cadogan replaced the receiver and, throwing his head back, he started to laugh. A great raucous sound, starting from deep within his belly and bursting out of his chest so that the whole room was filled with the cruel sound. The hunter had become the hunted.

CHAPTER 15

Unless you knew that, just under two years ago, Charles Jardine had been diagnosed with a very serious form of leukaemia, then it would have been quite impossible to find any logical explanation for the dramatic and extreme deterioration in his behaviour.

Until he was twenty-one he had lived a blameless, respectable and industrious life. His mother had died young of a similar condition when Charlie was still at school and, as an only child, life at home had been emotionally bare, as his father spent most of the week away on business, leaving the boy in the hands of a succession of housekeepers.

In the summer holiday before he went up to Manchester University to read Geography, there had been a monumental fall-out between Jardine Senior and his son. Every decision the boy tried to make was challenged by the father and his attempts at independence were persistently demeaned. It had always been his intention to take a gap year and travel to South America. However, his father, now chairman of an international engineering combine, but who had come up the hard way, refused to countenance what he termed "a waste of a year and a waste of good money". The row had simmered in the weeks leading up to the A Level Examinations and had exploded into full-scale warfare when the results came out and decision time arrived.

On one dreadful Friday night they had rowed in the kitchen and eventually had come to blows, when Graham Jardine struck the boy across the face, causing Charlie to lash out in retaliation, cutting the father's lip with his fist. In a fury, Jardine Senior had ordered him to leave the house the next morning. When morning came, the fury had been replaced by a cold and resolute contempt. A small monthly payment was to be made if the boy abandoned his plans and went straight up to university.

A distraught and humiliated Charlie accepted the offer of meagre payment and set off for university, where he studied with enthusiasm, but became completely estranged from his father. There was no contact, save for the monthly standing order into Charlie's bank account.

Dealing admirably with the situation, Charlie was already in the running for a First Class Honours Degree by the end of his second year at Manchester. By the middle of his third year he was in prison.

The symptoms had begun manifesting themselves just before exam time during that second summer. It had been a marvellous year. He'd met Alice at the Art Gallery and they had been going out together for six months. His tutor had told him that he was in line for a special award next academic year and he had the best batting average in the University Second Eleven. At first, he had believed the symptoms to be no more than a nervous reaction to the impending exams but, from the first visit to the Medical Centre, to the ultimate diagnosis at the City Hospital, had taken less than two months and his world was shattered.

Alice was wonderful to him, but he could not cope with her kindness. When he had the treatment and his resistance was at rock bottom, he would become wholly consumed with bitterness, resentment and envy of people who were in ordinary health. He could hear his own vicious jibes, thrown in despair at those around him, but was powerless to make himself stop. Gradually, his friends fell away, including Alice, until there was no one left to shout at. The doctors had insisted that, with appropriate treatment and the right attitude, there was a reasonable chance that he could complete his studies and embark upon his career. Of course, they were unable to give him any long-term guarantee but, if he soldiered on for another three or four years, there was every reason to hope that medical advances would keep the disease at bay.

Charlie had not believed a word of the platitudes because he knew how he felt and he did not expect to see twenty-five. Turning up at the Faculty on odd occasions when he was feeling a bit brighter kept his place open, but he never looked like he would come through the emotional, let alone the medical, crisis.

After four debilitating months of intensive treatment the appointments had been reduced to every fourth Tuesday, so long as he religiously took all of the prescribed medication each morning and evening, with a major review in another three months. Faced with these kinds of prospects, the depression deepened by the day.

It had started with cannabis. He had no idea what effect it may have on his medication but he didn't care. Five pounds a throw. It was easier than buying a bottle of milk. The sellers were everywhere. In the pubs and clubs and a couple actually came on to the campus, wandering about the cafeterias and bars, openly offering their wares. He was amazed that he had never even noticed them before. Back in his miserable room, he would sit alone and quietly inhale the thick, sickly-sweet smoke and all of that bitterness would gradually evaporate, until nothing really mattered very much. For those few minutes he could no longer feel the pain and he didn't care about the future. After an hour or so, grim reality would begin to return and he would need another draw, which meant yet another five pounds. The habit was beginning to make heavy demands upon his limited resources and the need was growing by the day. In the absence of any communication with his father, the meagre payment remained at the same level and the father remained in ignorance of his son's condition.

Within the squalid subculture that he had now entered, the large-scale suppliers were constantly seeking out the vulnerable and the weak to carry the risks of their operations. The most valuable asset that they sought was a person, preferably female, without any previous criminal convictions. Such a person had the best chance of passing through the Customs unnoticed as a packhorse for a consignment of illegally imported drugs. Charlie's supplier, a rodent-faced druggie himself, explained all of this to him one evening in the King's Head, as he watched the familiar pattern of the boy struggling to come up with the cash for his latest score.

"There's just a chance that I could offer you a trip, mate," the dealer suggested. "They had a black bird lined up. Scouser. Travelling with a baby, which they like, less suspicious, but last I heard she'd cooled off."

"What's involved?" asked Charlie.

"Coke. It'll almost certainly be coke. I can get the details if yer interested, mate. But don't piss me about. These guys turn nasty very quick."

"I need to know what's in it for me. If it's enough, I might be interested," came the cautious reply.

"Stay put. I'm going outside to make a call," said the dealer, pulling out a mobile phone from his inside jacket pocket.

Within five minutes he was back. "They need info. Have you ever been nicked for anything? Anything at all?"

"Nothing. Never."

"Got a current passport?"

"No problem."

"What stamps has it got on it?"

"Well, last year I went to the Costa Del Sol. The year before that I went to Ibiza. That's the lot."

"Yer seems quite a smart lad. Yer speak nice. What's your dad do? He ain't a copper or nothing like that, is he?"

"He works for an electrical company," lied Charlie.

"They might give yer a run when they hear all of that. I'll let you know by the weekend," the dealer concluded.

"I need to have some idea of how much I stand to get," urged Charlie. "I'd be taking all of the risks. You know what they pay, so tell me."

"It changes, mate. Depends on what yer bring back. From where. In what form. Where yer stay. Varies. See yer at the weekend. I'll know more by then."

For the rest of that week Charlie had felt better than he had in a long while. On two days he had attended lectures and by the weekend the prospect of engaging in a serious criminal drugs operation had lost much of its appeal. During the times that he was not feeling ill, he found it hard to believe that he could ever have contemplated an act of such lunacy. Despite this, on Friday and Saturday night he had wandered down to the Kings Head for a drink, expecting to see the druggie and still half-curious as to what the offer would have been. As it happened, there was no sign of him and on the Sunday lunchtime, when Charlie felt the need for another draw, he had to go down to one of those sleazy amusement arcades in the town to do an expensive deal with a stranger.

By mid-week he had felt really ill and his supply was gone. He spent the whole day in bed and only got up in the evening to go to the campus cafeteria for something to eat. Just as he was finishing a dreadful example of mass-produced cottage pie, the slimy little pusher slipped into the chair opposite.

"Three grand, mate. Three grand in it for you. Interested?" he mumbled.

"Can I score tonight?" asked Charlie. "I'm out."

"What about the big deal?" was the reply.

"First things first. Can you deal now? I've got ten quid on me."

"OK. OK. What about the other?"

"You're very keen for me to run the risk, aren't you? What's your cut?"

"In this game, mate, you learn what to ask and what not to ask. You don't ask nobody what you just asked me. Have you got that?" the dealer retorted, with more than a hint of menace in his voice.

"What's the deal then for three grand?" Charlie enquired.

"I can't give yer much detail. You'd speak to them on the phone, though I'd take the delivery and pay yer out. I'm the only one you'd ever meet. You'd be out the country less than a week. Long journey. Coke, I'd guess. That's all I know. Three grand. Take it or leave it. They only offer once. You only do it once. Second yer get a stamp on your passport from a particular place, yer no use no longer."

Charlie leant back and thought hard. What was he doing getting involved with people like this sordid, grubby, parasite sitting opposite him?

On the other hand, what did it matter? His studies were going nowhere and, after only a couple of days of feeling better, his decline had quickly resumed. Drugs offered some relief and there was no legitimate way that he was going to be able to lay his hands on three thousand pounds.

"I'll speak to them," he snapped. "But I don't have a mobile. Don't have the funds. Now give me the ten quid's worth and arrange the contact."

"They'll speak to yer on my phone. Meet me in the King's Head tomorrow around nine," he said, pushing the small package into Charlie's hand under the table, whilst deftly palming the ten pound note.

"Do I try and negotiate a better pay-off?" asked Charlie naively.

"Negotiate! Don't talk crap," sneered the pusher. "You just listen to what they say. You say yes or no. No negotiating nothing. D'you know who these people are? They run the Manchester scene. They carry guns. They pull the triggers 'n all. They've got coppers on the payroll. Little nothings like you and me just do as we're told. See yer tomorrow."

During the night Charlie had suffered a prolonged attack of sweating and had stayed in bed until lunchtime to try and catch up on some sleep. When he eventually dragged himself out of bed and looked in the cracked bathroom mirror his face had no colour at all and his gums were bleeding heavily. His head was hurting with a dull, relentless ache and, as he pulled on his jeans and the same shirt he'd been wearing for three days, he saw the bruising had appeared all up the inner aspect of his left arm. Forcing the tablets down his throat, he remembered that the hospital had warned him of the likelihood of these particular symptoms, but he'd never had them as badly as this before. He felt so isolated, lonely and, above all else, frightened.

Not yet having the strength to walk up to the campus, he'd called in for some lunch at the café in the supermarket, where the brighter lights and the hustle and bustle of the shoppers had helped to revive him. Stealing a puff or two on the nub end of one of yesterday's reefers as he walked across the car park, had lifted him further and, by the time he had reached the bar in the Union, the terrible attack of fear had subsided and his headache was almost gone.

One of the girls on his course came over and sat with him for half an hour, chatting about yesterday's tutorial concerning Antarctica and he had made the right noises now and again, until she offered her excuses and wandered away to find somebody else to talk to. Few people at the university knew of his condition and he much preferred it that way.

Spending the rest of the afternoon over a single drink, he mulled over the chance to put a few thousand pounds in his back pocket, weighing up the extent of the risk factor. It was obvious to him that he was never going to graduate but, if he were caught on this escapade, then he'd get a heavy prison sentence. Prison was a topic about which he'd never even thought before. Of course, he'd seen those old Victorian piles on the television, with landings and grills, but they were just meaningless pictures without any sense of reality, for he'd never been inside a prison, never heard the noises, smelt the odours and seen the dregs of humanity within. Thinking calmly and rationally about it, he realised that, even contemplating this trip was both wicked and crazy but, the real problem was, when the depression set in again, when the head ached and the hopelessness returned, then nothing mattered anymore and he was quite capable of just letting it happen.

By eight o'clock he was discreetly tucked away in a quiet corner of the King's Head, taking occasional sips from the half-pint of bitter which had soon gone flat and tasteless. Surprisingly, the mean-faced pusher was early and, even more surprisingly, he bought the drinks.

"My phone'll ring at nine. I'll answer it and then you take it outside. Then it's down to you, mate," he explained, as soon as he returned with the drinks.

"How safe is this?" asked Charlie.

"If it were safe, mate, they wouldn't be paying yer three grand for a week in the sun, would they? All I know is that they're well organised. But, you're on risk of getting nicked. You makes the choice knowing that."

"And what happens if I'm caught?" Charlie demanded of him.

"That's easy. Your tickets will have been bought through a London bucket shop for cash. Untraceable. Your only contact will be me. You don't even know my street name and besides, you won't see my arse for dust. Depending on the value of the load you'll get around seven or eight years, serve about four. Can't tell you straighter than that, can I?"

Just at that moment the dealer's mobile phone rang and, pressing it to his ear, he mumbled secretively into it before handing it over to Charlie.

"Take it out into the street and make sure no one hears you," he directed. "This is when you piss or get off the pot, mate."

Grabbing the phone in its well-used, cheap plastic case, Charlie walked out of the side door of the pub into the quiet, unlit alley. Checking that there was no one around, he furtively spoke into the mouthpiece.

"OK. What's involved?" he asked, trying to sound tough, but feeling increasingly terrified, as the point of no-return loomed ever closer.

"Before we talks, I's just telling you we got your face and name. We got where you study," intoned the threatening, disembodied voice in a strong, black, Manchester accent. "D'you get me, Charlie, boy?"

"I get you."

"A week on Saturday. Manchester to Kingston. Bus into town. Stay at Jerry's Boarding House. Single room. Paid for. Thursday morning, on your bed, two pretty packets of Bath Salts. Wrapped in their boxes. Cellophane sealed. Present for your ma. Get me? Back on the Thursday night flight. Arrives Friday morning. That night meets up with the man. Give him the boxes. Three grand for you. Easy-peasy. D'you get me, boy?"

"What's in the boxes?"

"You don't need to know. Bath Salts is all you know. Your man will give you the tickets next week. You get two hundred spending money in the same envelope. In US Dollars. Get me, Charlie?"

"OK," grunted Charlie, "I understand."

"You knows not to cross a Zulu, don't you, boy?"

"A Zulu?"

"Zulu. A warrior. Didn't the man say? Sometimes we shoots. Sometimes we wets. Sometimes we cuts your balls off."

At that the line clicked and went dead. Charlie walked back into the pub and, resuming his seat, returned the phone to the pusher with a knowing nod of the head.

"What's he mean 'sometimes we wets'?" Charlie asked

"To wet, mate. It's their Zulu lingo. Means 'cut, stab', then you bleeds and gets wet. If you've given 'em the nod, then you'd better go through with it, 'cos he'll have told yer names of places."

"He said I do it all through you," muttered Charlie.

"Take some advice, then. When you comes back through. Wear a jacket. No jeans. No backpack. Stash the stuff in your case. Not in a carry-on bag. Yer a mule now, mate. A muffin. They say one in three gets pulled."

At that, the pusher started to laugh, reminding Charlie of an old witch's cackle. He was still cackling quietly to himself as he wandered off into the bleak night beyond.

* * *

Ironically, the few days in a decent climate seemed to be doing Charlie some good. Jerry's Boarding House was just like something out of an Ernest Hemingway novel. White clapboard construction, with the paint of decades peeling off every visible strip of timber. Run-down and constantly cracking and creaking under the fierce sun. The downstairs area was open across the whole of the ground floor. An antique fan swished around from the ceiling, its vibrating so out of synch with its motion, that Charlie expected it to hurl itself from its chains at any moment and smash its way around the room, crashing uncontrollably into the dilapidated armchairs and sofas distributed around the perimeter. Late in the afternoons, these seats would fill up with elderly toothless Jamaican men and vastly overweight, laughing, overpowering women. Any exit or entrance made by Charlie would be treated with hoots and peals of laughter as they poked fun at the whiteness of his legs and the incongruity of his presence in a dive like this.

Kingston was frenetic and Jerry, the owner, had warned him on arrival that certain parts were no go for a white man, in particular Trenchtown, which was the area where Bob Marley had once lived, now reduced to a dangerous slum, where drug slayings were an everyday occurrence and the police hardly bothered to pick the bodies up, let alone look for the killers. Charlie reflected sombrely that this was the culture in which some of those Manchester boys had been brought up. Despite this warning, he had wandered along Harbour Street in the original waterfront area safely enough and, on two afternoons, had made it by bus to the public beach where, despite being in a minority of one, nobody had troubled him.

With a population approaching three quarters of a million the contrasts were quite staggering. In one section stood massive new tower block constructions whilst, but a stone throw's away, hundreds of wooden one-room hovels were homes for entire families. As the latest gleaming Cadillac glided its way towards Beverly Hills, Kingston down the middle of a wide boulevard so, on the opposite pavement, did a young boy lead along his herd of assorted goats. Shanty town or Tinsel town. Kingston had them both.

So far, this part of the deal was proving easy. His medication was working well and, somehow, he had forced the real reason for his presence to the back of his mind. The Boarding House was situated on the edge of Lizard Town, just below Torrington Bridge and, once you passed "Below the Bridge", you quickly learned to tread with care and, accordingly, Charlie did not stray far at night. Fortunately, immediately adjacent to the Boarding House stood a rum shop called "Jerry's Rum Place", which endorsed Charlie's initial reaction that Jerry seemed to have his fingers in a multitude of pies. In Jerry's Rum Place you could purchase virtually any variety of Caribbean Rum and have it mixed into cocktails and punches that would put most able-bodied men straight on to their backs. Just as readily available was a constant supply of "ganja", which could be bought over the counter for next to nothing. On this island it had the value of the common weed that in reality it was, and he indulged himself without fear or inhibition.

On the Thursday of his departure, whilst he was in the disgusting, communal bathroom at the end of the corridor, two floral packets appeared on top of his narrow, unmade bed. Each was about the size of an average paperback novel, sealed in cellophane paper, quite light in weight and with the name "Delilah" cheaply etched on the cardboard surface. They sent a shiver down his spine, lying there in such apparent innocence, yet they had the capacity to lock him up for seven years. Not ganja. Too small. At least cocaine, maybe worse. Carefully finding a place for them amongst his socks and handkerchiefs in the battered, brown suitcase that had once belonged to his mother, he dressed himself in his crumpled sports jacket and brown canvas trousers, before setting off on the bus to Norman Manley International Airport, thirteen miles to the far side of the city. Traffic choked the streets and the day was particularly humid. Unable to eat, he forced his tablets down with a can of warm Pepsi, occasionally glancing at the numerous billboards which lined the road, screaming out their warnings of the dangers of travelling this route at night. Robberies, assaults, shootings, car hijackings.

As the bus came within the boundaries of the airport, Charlie could taste the heavy aroma of the aviation fuel and his senses were intermittently bombarded with the deafening roar of the aircraft turbines, as the monsters careered along the runway before rising into the blue skies and heading off towards some distant Customs Hall.

Inside the Departures Terminal he espied notices that had not attracted his eye on arrival. Clear warnings about the carrying of firearms and the exportation of all controlled drugs which, the signs emphasised, included marijuana. Realising that its visitors would have seen the weed being openly traded like tobacco, this was Kingston's polite but sharp reminder that other jurisdictions were not so liberal.

Modern airport terminals had all been reduced to a lowest common denominator. A frozen capsule in space; timeless, weightless, one-dimensional, where one set of canned human cargo was sent out while another was brought in. British Airways was late and he was early. By the time you eventually slumped into your seat for these flights you were already exhausted and another seven or eight empty hours stretched ahead, he reflected to himself. His mind was instinctively operating as if he was on a genuine, ordinary flight, allowing himself the mental comfort of complaining about the frustrations and the boredom. In truth, his anxieties would not begin until he collected that suitcase from the carousel and walked the gauntlet of the Green Channel.

Cruising at thirty-three thousand feet and averaging five hundred and twenty knots an hour, his appointment with inevitable disaster was hurtling towards him with the speed of a bullet. Each moment added to the despair as certainty of discovery began to take over his mind. Up until now, he had somehow succeeded in not really thinking about what he was doing. Never giving his brain more than a fleeting second to pass over the thought processes, not allowing any lingering or concentration on the realities. Now, imprisoned in a giant, metal cigar tube, the impact had struck at last. His disease was debilitating and this kind of strain quickly drained his meagre physical resources. When the stewardess went round with landing cards for the foreigners, he had actually endured a panic attack, which necessitated him putting the blanket over his head and forcing himself to perform deep breathing exercises until he had regained his composure.

Whatever the differences with his father, he came from a respectable family and had received an excellent education. All right, he had been diagnosed with an awful illness and it was tough, but he didn't have to give his neck. He didn't belong in a world of dirty packages stuffed between his socks and hankies. In his mother's old suitcase, for goodness sake. He was a stranger in the realm of "wetting" people, mules and "Zulus". Spending his few pounds on dope bought from a snivelling, unwashed pusher. Why hadn't he seen all of this before now? Pressing his sweating forehead against the thick perspex of the porthole window, he prayed to survive the Customs Shed. If those packages had been in his carry-on bag he would have rushed straight to the bathroom and emptied the evil contents down the lavatory. Was that the reason that the bastard had told him to pack them in his checked-in bag? He had thought it was because the Customs Officers might be more likely to look inside carry-ons and that it was advice to improve his chances. Now he realised that it must be part of the mule syndrome with which the pusher was well familiar. In the airborne hours immediately before the critical time, the mule would likely panic and dump the cargo. With the stuff in the hold he was cornered. The next opportunity he would have to get at the packages would be in the Customs Hall itself, where they watched through one-way glass and where there was nowhere to dispose of the goods.

Early morning. Manchester Airport. Dry, windy and cold. The first of the Transatlantic Jumbos had already lumbered on to the grey runway and the Far Easts would be rolling in within the hour. Like behemoths at the break of day, emerging from the mists, as they all congregated at the watering hole. American Airlines from New York and the British Airways from Kingston landed within a few minutes of each other. Baggage handlers scurrying around in their tough little vehicles, unloading and loading all the useless bits and pieces that people insisted on dragging along with them, as they criss-crossed the continents.

The endless walks through those soundless, characterless corridors from the plane to the Immigration Desks. Just carrying the small sports holdall as hand luggage. Couple of books, washing kit, bottle of rum. Long queues as the foreigners waited for the paperwork to be checked and the same questions repeated, time and time again. The pink cardboard passport holders straight through, on a quick flash of the photograph, into the lion's den, grabbing the metal trolley and waiting for the carousel belt to stutter and lurch into action before regurgitating its innards from below.

"Charles Jardine, Ellerton Rd, Manchester M13, England. "

Yellow label on brown suitcase. Only one Charles Jardine with that address and a case like that. Forcing the arm out to grab the handle, pull it off the belt and swing it on to the trolley. Straighten it up. Turn the awkward little wheels to the right and head for the Green. Just the right pace. Know that there's beads of sweat across the upper lip. Can feel it. Everybody must be able to see it. Four, five, six of them, standing around on each side. Smart black jackets, fresh white shirts, gold braid. Some with hats, some without. Don't look them in the eye. Don't hurry. Don't wipe that sweat away. Over halfway through. No sign of interest. Three quarters there.

A dagger thrust straight into the heart. Cold steel ripping deep into the vital organs.

"Good morning, Sir. Which flight were you?"

Young. Male. Angular. Dark hair. Unattractive complexion. Greasy and damp looking. Just short of six feet. Eyes taking in everything about the traveller. Jacket. Trousers, not jeans. Can't miss the sweat. Pallid anyway, after a long flight through the night on top of the condition and the pills. Speak. Stay calm. Polite. Speak. Don't smile.

"British Airways from Kingston." Sounded like somebody else's voice. Far away.

"Business or pleasure, sir?"

"Pleasure. Got a girlfriend out there. She's teaching for a year. Went to stay with her," came the practised response.

"Are you familiar with the restrictions on the amount of spirits and tobacco you are allowed to import to the UK, sir?" the officer enquired, his eagle eyes watching everything. Behind him, all the other passengers were just wandering straight through unimpeded. Why had he been picked out?

"Yes. I've just got one bottle of rum."

"Are you familiar with the prohibition on the importation of firearms and controlled drugs?" probed the young man.

"Sure."

"Do you have any?"

"No."

"May I see inside that bag, sir. The small holdall," he said pointing at the hand luggage.

Placed the bag on the desk. Slow unzipping. The bottle of rum, wrapped in blue tissue paper. Unwrapped it. Seal checked. He'd heard in Kingston that they were shipping cocaine in liquid form, suspending it within another liquid. That's why he's double checking that seal. Walkman and a few tapes. Toilet bag. Opened. Good look inside. Wet and sticky in there. Fingers in. Couple of books. Putting them all back inside. Zipped it up. This was it. Now, the suitcase.

"Thank you, sir. No need to hold you up further. Good morning."

The officer's eyes wandering away to new faces, new trolleys, new cases.

Charlie Jardine put his holdall back on his trolley and wandered casually to the automatic doors and out into the main terminal building. All the drivers waiting, holding up their little placards with passengers' names. Taxis, buses, ticket desks. This mule was free.

* * *

During the bus ride home he was on an adrenalin high. All of the tiredness of an overnight flight and the nervous exhaustion caused by the enormity of the risk he had run, just evaporated into thin air. Never again would he put his freedom at risk but, on this solitary occasion, he had tasted real danger and had been stimulated by it. Back in his room he unpacked his few belongings, slipping the two floral packages under his pillow while he took a long, leisurely bath. "Delilah" was safe. Lunch at the café and then an afternoon sleep, before setting off for the King's Head in the early evening, confident that the pusher would show.

Sure enough, not long after eight and before the pub had got very busy, the mean face appeared in the doorway, spotted its prey and headed directly over, collecting a drink en route.

"Good trip, mate?" he enquired.

"No problems. Went well. Have you got the cash?" replied Charlie coming directly to the point.

"Cool it. Cool it down, mate. The hard part's done. Take it easy, now."

"Does that mean you haven't got the cash?" Charlie insisted.

"No, it means that this place is known for dealing, so we don't get over-excited and draw any attention to ourselves. I've got what you were promised."

"How do we do this, then?" asked Charlie.

"Not in here. We finish our drinks. Takes our time. Then we leaves separate. Me first. Meet up in the doorway of the butcher's on the corner. Have you got the stuff here?"

"Yeah."

"There's two questions you have to answer, then. One. Have you opened any of the wrapping, removed any of the cellophane?"

"I've undone nothing. The cellophane's intact," came the swift reply.

"OK. Two. What's the name on the boxes? To check we've got the right one, mate."

"The name's Delilah," he answered.

"Sounds good to me," responded the dealer, swigging down the last of his half-pint of beer and rising to his feet. "Getting busy in here now. See you by the butcher's in a few minutes mate."

Charlie forced himself to wait five minutes, timed by the second hand on his watch. Well aware that he couldn't trust this pusher any further than he could throw him, it would also be the case that the slimy creep would be highly suspicious of him. The opportunity for a double cross on either side was obvious. At least the corner where the butcher's was located was well lit and well frequented at this time of night.

Looking about him as he left the pub and headed for the rendezvous, Charlie saw nothing to cause him concern. A few pedestrians, mainly students, walking between the local pubs and a steady flow of cars in both directions. The pusher, now sporting a grubby Nike baseball cap was leaning on the butcher's shop window speaking into his mobile, his eyes fixed in Charlie's direction as the boy approached the shop. On reaching the doorway Charlie stopped and waited for the call to finish.

"Time to deliver, I think," the dealer demanded, now taking up a position directly alongside Charlie inside the alcove.

"No," snapped Charlie. "I've taken all the risks so far. It's your turn now. You give me the money. I'll count it in this doorway. You can block my exit. As soon as I'm sure it's all there, then I deliver."

"Yer do know you're being watched by the big men, don't you mate?

174

You and me, both. They won't let me out alone with three grand of their money or risk you trying to pull something."

"I guessed you'd have some company. Where are they?" replied Charlie calmly.

"I don't know exactly where they are or what they look like. But they're out there. So don't play the Lone Ranger or the coppers'll be scraping you off the pavement," warned the dealer thrusting a brown McDonalds' paper bag into Charlie's hand.

Charlie ducked right into the far corner of the shop doorway. The light was sufficient to see a thick wedge of notes within. Pulling the whole bundle out he counted them, clumsily but effectively. Thirty fifties, fifty twenties, fifty tens. Straight deal.

"All there," he breathed. "Here's the Delilah," he muttered, pushing the two packets into the man's hands. "Check it out. Cellophane intact. Unopened."

The dealer looked carefully at the packages, meticulously inspecting the sealing points of the cellophane, before slipping them into the deep inside pocket of his jacket. "Done and dusted, mate. We're out of here," he grunted, moving away and down the road as he spoke. Charlie Jardine walked briskly off in the opposite direction, three thousand pounds to the good. Just ten more minutes would see him safely back in his room where he could relax, secure in the knowledge that he would never risk such a terrifying and foolhardy enterprise again.

The heavy hand descended on to his shoulder like a steel vice. It came from simply nowhere out of the night. No sound or movement had preceded it. The grip of the fingers bit into the cartilage of the shoulder joint and the element of surprise was so complete that Charlie was stopped, literally, dead in his tracks.

"Police!" a voice shouted. "Police. Stand completely still. Don't move your hands from your sides."

Moving round from behind him, but not relaxing the vice-like grip for one second, the tall figure of a man in his late thirties loomed into view, pushing his head on its long neck right into Charlie's face, so close that, even in the cold, night air, Charlie could smell the sourness of his breath.

"Detective Sergeant Ronald Perry. Northern Regional. You are under arrest on suspicion of conspiracy to import Class A controlled drugs," spat out the voice in triumphant tone, brandishing a wallet containing his Warrant Card and photograph, which he quickly returned to his pocket.

"Drugs?" protested Charlie. "I don't have any drugs on me."

"Shut your mouth. Put your hands behind your back. Now. Then turn round. Slowly," ordered Perry, producing a pair of handcuffs from his belt. As Charlie, still in shock, obeyed the command, the grip on his shoulder was released for a couple of seconds and the cold metal of the cuffs closed almost instantaneously around his wrists.

"That's got you nicely, trussed up," snapped Perry. "Now I'm going to search you under the powers conferred on me by the Police and Criminal Evidence Act. I wonder what little goodies I might find. What have you got for me, Charlie? Do you want to volunteer it or shall I have to put my lily whites into your dirty dealer's pockets?"

"How do you my name?"

"My little secret, pal, my little secret."

Charlie stood silent while Perry went straight for the pocket in his anorak where the cash was sitting in its brown bag.

"Been for a Big Mac and fries, have we?" sneered Perry as he pulled the prize from its hiding place. "I'm very partial to a Big Mac myself. Plenty of onion, I hope. Let's take a little peek," he continued, as his fingers flicked swiftly through the thick wad of notes.

"I can explain…" Charlie began, but was immediately interrupted.

"Just shut it, kid. Keep your poxy mouth shut until I tell you to open it. You've heard the caution on the box. Consider yourself cautioned. You're on your way to hell, courtesy of Sergeant Ronald Perry." Pulling out a mobile phone he dialled a number which was answered before it rang twice. "I've got mine trussed up like a chicken on a spit. How about yours? Good. Two pieces of shit off to the sewer. Send a car, now."

"How was the pussy in Kingston, kid? Hope you made the most of it, 'cos you'll not be seeing none again this side of thirty," he laughed. "The car'll be here in a couple of minutes. D'you want to tell me the Manchester names now, the big boy names, not the shit you met in the pub? Tell me now. Here. Off the record, rather than on tape? You'll find it easier if you do," he said in a completely calm voice as, without a hint of a warning, he grabbed the boy by his lapels bringing his knee up into Charlie's groin with all the force he could muster. As Charlie screamed and collapsed Perry just continued to hold him up by the lapels, thrusting his face right into Charlie's.

"Names, kid. Names. Give me the names. Now," he demanded.

Hardly able to speak Charlie mumbled, "I don't know names, don't know 'em." As he spoke a large white police car came speeding round the corner with its blue light flashing and screeched to a halt. Two uniformed officers leaped out of the front, and, seizing an arm each, frogmarched the miserable boy into the back of the car.

"You had your chance to tell me off the record. We'll continue our chat a little later on tape, Charlie. I'll join you at the station, boys. Got my own car up the street. Take him away," directed Perry, before sauntering off to collect his own vehicle.

* * *

MANCHESTER POLICE (Ringway)
<u>RECORD OF INTERVIEW</u>
<u>PLACE OF INTERVIEW:</u> Manchester Central
<u>PERSON INTERVIEWED:</u> Charles Eric Jardine
<u>INTERVIEWING OFFICERS:</u> Detective Sergeant Ronald Perry;
Detective Constable Richard Welford
<u>OTHERS PRESENT:</u> None
<u>Tape Reference:</u> BG/496/81
<u>SUSPECTED OFFENCES:</u>
Importation of Prohibited Drugs (Class A)

Perry:

This interview is being tape-recorded. It may be tendered in evidence if your case is brought before a Court. You will be provided with a copy of the tape. We are in an Interview Room at Manchester Central Police Station. I am Detective Sergeant Ronald Perry.

Welford:

And I'm Detective Constable Richard Welford.

Perry:

Please confirm your full names and age Mr Jardine.

Jardine:

Charles Eric Jardine. Twenty-one.

Perry:

You're entitled to have a solicitor present. One can be arranged if you ask. Do you want one?

Jardine:

No.

Perry:

You've been arrested on suspicion of conspiracy to evade the prohibition on the importation of Class A controlled drugs into the United Kingdom. I shall now caution you.

You do not have to say anything, but it may harm your defence if you do not mention when questioned something which you later rely on in court. Anything you do say may be given in evidence. Understood?

Jardine:

Understood.

Perry:

You said you were twenty-one?

Jardine:

Twenty one. Nearly twenty-two.

Perry:

And you're a student at the University.

Jardine:

Yes.

Perry:

Our records indicate that you have never been arrested before.

Jardine:

True.

Perry:

Then why not have a solicitor?

Jardine

Because I'm guilty of what you said. There's no point in having a solicitor. I did it.

Perry:

We know you did it. We tracked you. We've got your accomplice. What we want off you are the names of the big boys.

Jardine:

I know no names. I only met the one dealer. I don't even know his name.

Perry:

We'll come to the details shortly. Firstly, do you want your father told?

Jardine:

Absolutely not. He is not to be informed at any stage.

Perry:

You told the Custody Sergeant that you are on strong medication? Do you require a doctor to attend?

Jardine:

The only reason I would need a doctor is because in the street, as you well know, I was…

Perry:

The question was if you wanted a doctor. You may think it wise to think about what you are going to say with some care. Do you want a doctor or not?

Jardine:

No.

Perry:

What's the condition for which you take medication?

Jardine:

I have leukaemia. It's an extremely serious illness.

Perry:

Does it, or your medication, affect your ability to answer our questions now? We're prepared to wait.

Jardine:

No.

Perry:

We've arrested your accomplice. He had two packets in his possession, disguised to look like bath salts. A field test shows them to contain cocaine, a Class A prohibited drug. Forensic analysis'll confirm this and tell us the degree of purity, but we're confident that this consignment has a street value of many tens of thousands of pounds. What do you know about this?

Jardine:

I'll tell you the truth. I'll only say it once. I'm guilty of bringing those packages into Manchester Airport from Kingston. I dealt only with the dealer you've arrested. I know no names.

Perry:

We don't believe that you don't know names. It may encourage you to be more frank if I tell you that you were observed returning through Manchester Airport this morning and have been under surveillance ever since.

Jardine:

Why should that encourage me to give names?

Perry:

Because you're at university, aren't you and I'd expect you to have some intelligence. If we knew about your plans, and I knew your name, then isn't it obvious that others have named you?

Jardine:

Not really.

Perry:

Listen, I'm a Yorkshire officer. I'm in Manchester because one of my informants gave me, personally, information that a student would be coming through Manchester this week from Kingston with cocaine. That comes from a leak higher up the chain. You get the picture? Now, let's have the names you dealt with.

Jardine:

I only dealt with the man you have. I spoke once to another man on a mobile phone who gave me my orders.

Perry:

How?

Jardine:

On the dealer's phone after they'd already made the connection. What's the dealer's name you arrested?

Perry:

Mount. Derek Mount. But I believe you already know that.

Jardine:

No. I never called him by any name. The man on the phone, who, from the dialect I am sure was black, gave me details. Mount gave me the tickets and spending money and did the exchange on my return today.

Perry:

Who did you deal with in Kingston?

Jardine:

No one. I stayed at Jerry's Boarding House in Lizard Town. My bill was prepaid, as were my tickets. Cash in a London bucket shop I was told, so an untraceable source. The packets were deposited on my bed on my last morning. That's the whole story.

Perry:

I want names.

Jardine:

I never knew any.

Perry:

When you were arrested you had in your possession a brown McDonalds' bag containing fifty twenties and fifty tens. Fifteen hundred pounds. Where did this money come from?

Jardine:

Fifteen hundred? That's not right. I had…

Perry:

I arrested you. Listen to me very carefully. You'd got fifteen hundred pounds. We have to form an informed judgement of the level of your involvement. The bigger your pay-off then, of course, the higher your level of involvement. Do you follow the logic, Mr Jardine?

Jardine:

Oh, yes. I follow it now all right.

Perry:

Good. Downstairs, booked in as an exhibit, is the fifteen hundred pounds that I recovered from you on arrest. Does that represent your total pay-off?

Jardine:

Yes.

Perry:

Why were you picked?

Jardine:

Because I'd developed a cannabis habit. I was down, because of my illness, and I was broke. That's why. I've answered all you've asked and I'm now beginning to feel unwell. Can we stop?

Perry:

Of course.

INTERVIEW TERMINATED.

"Thank you, Detective Constable Welford, I'll take Mr Jardine back to the cells and check whether he needs the doctor. You carry on," declared Perry, opening the interview room door to usher the junior officer out.

"Jardine," he continued when they were alone. "We're off tape now. You're going down for a long time. You're a fucking loser all ways round. The less the Judge, and the Prosecution, think you were paid, the better it is for you. Do you get my meaning?"

"Loud and clear. You stole my money. You're as guilty as I am."

"Big words. No one'll ever believe you. You're a drugs courier. A muffin. Your word is worth shit. You have no voice. Any more than Mount if he wants to back your story up. A couple of crackhead dealers. So, take a tip. You got paid fifteen hundred."

"Take me back to my cell. I don't care any more. And yes, I do want the doctor. I'm going to be sick," Charlie declared.

"One final piece of advice. A smart, nicely spoken kid like you in the nick, will have enough enemies as it is. Don't make an enemy of me. My tentacles reach behind bars. You already know how much a knee can hurt, don't you? That would rank as just a taster. Do we understand each other?"

"Get me back to the cells, please."

"Like I told you before, you're on your way to hell, courtesy of Sergeant Ronald Perry."

"And like I asked you, get me back to the cells."

"Certainly. Enjoyed our little chat. No need for any more interviewing. We're all sorted."

CHAPTER 16

It was a very busy time for Detective Sergeant Ronald Perry as the Mount and Jardine drugs case was now due to be heard at Manchester Crown Court on the Tuesday and the Trevors murder case was listed to start on the following Monday at Leeds. Insisting that he remained as officer in charge of the drugs case had the advantage of ensuring that he stayed in sole charge of the entirety of the paperwork, which was very useful in the event of any difficult questions being raised about the amount of cash recovered from Jardine's brown bag. On the other hand, it had involved numerous trips backwards and forwards across the Pennines, seeing the case through to the final furlong in the Crown Court. Hopefully, today's trip to Manchester would be the last, because all of the indications were that both Jardine and Mount would be pleading guilty and so, by the end of the day, they would be tucked up in Strangeways starting a nice, long stretch.

This was Mrs Justice Gaynor's last week sitting in Manchester Crown Court. Usually she sat in the Family Division, but there had been a serious arson trial which had to be expedited because the Defendant was only thirteen years old, and so the Lord Chancellor's Department had despatched her up to Manchester to try it. Fortunately, both Counsel had got on with the job and the trial had finished four days earlier than scheduled.

Now the Listing Office had found her a short drugs importation case to fill in the rest of the week, although, on looking at the papers in the Lodgings the night before, it appeared pretty obvious to her that it would resolve into pleas of guilty. Jardine had already made a full admission and Mount was simply playing games and she had little doubt that he would plead guilty at the eleventh hour. If all of that happened then they would have to find her something else to hear for the rest of the week at Manchester, before she set off for a month's sitting at Leeds Crown Court where she would resume her normal Family work. Regrettably, that new appointment, Hathington, was presently up at Leeds, trying the Crime, and she would have to share the Lodgings with him. The gossip on the Bench was that Hathington was proving to be very unpopular. Full of himself. Thought he was God's gift. Appointed in the wrong jurisdiction because he didn't want to wait his turn in the Commercial Division and quite unbearable socially. Had some top level connection which he was not coy about broadcasting.

Living in Lodgings when you were out on circuit was the most depressing feature of the job, she reflected to herself, relaxing in the back of the chauffeur-driven limousine as it delivered her to Court that wet Tuesday morning. Most of the resident cooks were unemployable anywhere else and the butlers were more interested in prying and officious organising than buttling. The bedrooms were invariably tired and stuffed with sixties, utilitarian matchwood. But the real aggravation stemmed from some of the Judges you ended up sharing a roof with. The old brigade, steeped in the obsolete protocol, insisting on every last, pitiful part of the dining and entertaining ritual. Who picked up the right fork at the right time. Who sat where at the table. When spouses were allowed to come and stay. Which old duffer from the locality was to be invited to dinner. On the other hand, the new brigade were no better. Thrusting and ambitious. Absolutely no style. All hustle, bustle, down to business, no presence, no weight. Eye to the main chance. Smiles at breakfast and knife in the back at dinner. Apparently, Hathington managed to combine the worst features of old and new, so a month with him promised to be a lot of fun.

Eventually, the limousine swung into the secure yard at the rear of the Court building and came to a halt by the Judges' Entrance. As the bored uniformed police officer opened the car door, her clerk, in his out-of-date morning suit, scurried round to the boot to collect her canvas bags containing the case papers. Straight through the doors, on to the red carpet and into the lift. Up to the second floor and into her chambers at the side of the Courtroom. This was how she lived during the working week. Never seeing the light of day. Never breathing the fresh air. Never touching reality. In Court, all the empty pomp and false courtesy. My Lady this. My Learned Friend that. Miserable, dead faces in the dock, waiting to see what hammer blow life was about to deliver next.

There was still half an hour remaining before the drugs case was due to begin and so, over a cup of fresh ground coffee from the cafetiere that she always took to Court, she re-read the reports on the two wretched specimens that she would doubtless be sending off to jail before the day was through. Until you saw them in the dock, staring across the void, they were only names on pieces of paper. Reduced to psychological and sociological data. "Chances of reoffending." "Previous convictions." "Attitude to offence." "Risk to the public." "Employment prospects."

Then, in the dock, for a few moments, they became real people, until her sentencing words sent them back into the statistics pile.

Derek Mount. On drugs since he was fifteen. Father unknown. Mother didn't care. Never worked. Twelve previous convictions, all for drugs offences. A complete no-hoper. Nothing would ever change his lifestyle. If she gave him ten years or ten months it would make little difference. He'd hang his head, do the sentence, with big chunks of it knocked off by the system, so that he never served anything resembling the sentence actually imposed; then, he'd be released and return immediately to the same lifestyle that had gone before. Maybe, for the first few months after his release, while the State was keeping him in some hostel or halfway house at vast public expense, he would stay off drugs but, at the first crisis, he'd slink off to his old haunts, willingly succumb and the cycle would begin anew.

Charles Jardine. A university student. Very successful father but presently estranged from son. Mother dead. Leukaemia at twenty-one. Sucked into running drugs for the barons that never got caught. And now she was supposed to send him down for seven or eight years when he might not even survive that long. What a disaster. A knock on the door interrupted her reading and the Court Usher appeared, indicating that the Court was now ready and, apparently, both Defendants were intending to plead guilty. On with the wig. On with the day.

Forty-five minutes of Prosecution opening was followed by a dreary mitigation on behalf of Mount, which had little to commend it, and made not a shred of difference to the sentence that she had already jotted down in her notes of the night before. Fortunately, despite Jardine's resignation to his fate, he had eventually asked for a solicitor when he was charged. The solicitor had instructed an extremely able young barrister by the name of Paul Dickinson, who had just delivered one of the most eloquent and moving mitigations that she had heard in a long while. Both Defendants had sat silent and motionless throughout the proceedings, heads bowed and hopelessness written in every line of their bodies. Mount looked like the dealer stereotype. Thin, drawn, dirty and disinterested. Jardine just looked ill. His face was the colour of parchment. Now it was her turn.

"Stand up, Derek Mount and Charles Jardine", the Judge directed. "You have both pleaded guilty to a conspiracy to import cocaine, a Class A controlled drug, into this country. The amount involved, at a purity level in excess of fifty per cent, would give the consignment a street value of at least fifty thousand pounds. You each played your parts at different stages in the operation, occupying differing places in the hierarchy. You, Mount, were plainly much closer to the big men at the heart of the scheme. Men who you chose not to name or give the police any help at all in identifying. While such men can rely on your silence, the Courts are left with only one recourse, namely, to punish dealers such as you, so fiercely that you, and others tempted to behave like you, are deterred."

Perry had found himself a seat at the side of the Courtroom alongside the press bench which gave him a clear view of the two wretched faces in the dock. As soon as he heard the Judge refer to a deterrent sentence his lips parted in a smile of anticipation.

"Could make double figures here mate," he whispered excitedly to the hack next to him as the Judge continued with her sentencing remarks.

"I am satisfied that you recruited Jardine and that you were to be paid a sum of money in excess of the fifteen hundred pounds that was to be his reward for taking the real risks. You are older than Jardine with numerous previous convictions relating to drug dealing. Indeed, you have already served one sentence of five years' imprisonment for supplying heroin. Your eventual plea of guilty came at the last moment and, in truth, given that you were arrested with this consignment of cocaine in your pocket, you had no chance of escaping conviction. The appropriate sentence in your case is one of eight years' imprisonment. Take him down."

As Mount turned and shuffled his way down the staircase leading to the cells below, Perry, visibly angry that the Judge hadn't dished out ten years, stared hard at Jardine, hoping to see signs of the terror that eight years inside should induce in him. However, Jardine's white face was expressionless and empty.

"I now turn to your case, Charles Jardine," the Judge announced. "You became embroiled in a drug dealing culture to which you were hitherto a complete stranger. In the hands of the kind of men who run these operations you must have been like putty. Your good character was your appeal to them so that, as a courier, you had the best chance of smuggling the drugs into this country undetected. You sold your name, your future, your freedom, all for the sum of fifteen hundred pounds. The sentence that should be imposed on you is measured in years, although significantly reduced by your immediate confession and immediate plea of guilty. However, I am deeply troubled by the state of your health."

When the Judge mentioned the word 'health', Perry's expectations of

Jardine also picking up eight years dropped like a stone. "Maternal instinct, bloody women Judges," he muttered quietly to himself.

"You have been on strong medication for leukaemia," the Judge intoned. "Prison for you, a dreadful experience even if you had your health, will be even more harrowing, given your condition. I am not satisfied that I have sufficient information about the prognosis, the treatment as administered within the prison regime and the actual state of your health at this time. Accordingly, I direct that a full medical report covering these aspects is prepared immediately. And I mean immediately. Next week I shall be sitting at Leeds Crown Court. I want that report before me by ten o'clock on Monday morning at Leeds. You will be transferred to a prison convenient to that Court and brought before me there on Monday. Mr Dickinson, you must attend please, although I shall take the case at a time during the day to suit your convenience. The Prosecution need not attend. Adjourned until next Monday at Leeds for sentence. Take him down."

* * *

Through the rush hour traffic on a Friday night, eastwards across the M62, cooped up in a metal cubicle inside a prison van, like a pig being taken to market. From Strangeways Prison, Manchester to Armley Gaol in Leeds. Perry was right, he had been consigned to hell. Eight years for Mount would normally have produced the predicted six or seven for him, but Charlie hoped that the Judge's concern for his health might yet reduce his sentence. In prison he had quickly learned the key factors that affected the release date, particularly the crucial significance of the four-year threshold. If you were sentenced to four years or more, you would have to serve two thirds before you were released on licence. However, any sentence under four years and they let you out after serving half. As he bounced along the M62, Charlie allowed himself to wonder if there was any chance of the Judge coming down below four. It would all depend on the contents of the doctor's report which had been finalised that afternoon, hence his transfer to the Leeds Prison so that he was on hand for the appearance in Leeds on Monday.

The prison staff had taken some pleasure in informing him that bad as Strangeways was, Armley was considerably worse and that the overcrowding in the decaying institution had reached chronic proportions. When the van eventually arrived at the towering gates and the humiliating prisoner reception procedure was about to begin, it transpired that the notification of his transfer had not come through on either the Armley fax or computer, and a row had promptly broken out between the Leeds staff and the Manchester staff, culminating in an order for him to be taken back to Manchester. Steadfast refusal to comply with the order led to the Assistant Governor being summoned from his office just as he was about to set off for home.

"Right," he declared angrily, having listened impatiently to the claims and counter-claims, "we've got'em hanging from the rafters in the convicted wing, so either he goes back to Strangeways or he spends the weekend in with the Category 'A's."

"Then bang him up with the Cat 'A's," snapped the Senior Officer from Strangeways, "do the bugger good and we ain't carting him back to Manchester tonight."

"Move your arse then, Jardine," grunted the Assistant Governor to Charlie, who had been seated, in handcuffs, on the low, wooden bench which ran the length of the grim reception area, watching this spectacle of bureaucratic incompetence. "You'll be booked in on the wing. Don't come complaining to me if you get a rough ride in there. The inn is full."

Endless corridors, flights of narrow stone stairs, iron gates, venomous glares and hostile spitting. That dreadful prison stink of sweat, urine, commercial disinfectant and hundreds of men's bodies, laced with that indefinable odour that years of human misery can actually deposit into the fabric of a building. Arrival in the Category 'A' Wing heralded further cursing and mutterings, as the policy in housing the dangerous men in that wing was to maintain one man per cell and every cell was occupied.

"Send the bastard back to Strangeways," the Senior Officer on the Landing declared after he had checking the details on his clipboard.

"We're one man to a cell with the nutters we get on this Landing and there ain't none spare."

"We've been through all of that crap in Reception, Mr Jenkins," answered the officer who had escorted him up from downstairs. "They had the Assistant Governor down. He's told us to bang him up here over the weekend and sort it on Monday."

"What am I meant to do? Spirit a bloody cell out of thin air? Or put him in with some nutter who might strangle the bastard in the middle of the night?" came Jenkins' reply. "I 'spose I can shove in him with Madman Miller, he'd make him welcome. He's already doing life for three rapes and he don't care what gender."

"Well, it's your problem, mate. I've delivered him up here. Take him home with you as far as I care. I'm off," declared the escort as he set off back to his little corner in Reception.

"It ain't my problem, it's his," Jenkins shouted after him, "he's got to survive the night. Murderer or rapist is your choice. Jardine. We gets a good class in this nick. Park your arse here while I gets you checked in by the quack and fixes up a nice, comfy bunk. Does sir prefer lower or upper?" he queried, chuckling to himself.

After a further half hour of foul-mouthed grunting and paper shuffling, Jenkins led the way down the landing until he came to the last cell on the left. The door was ajar and Jenkins kicked it fully open, revealing a table upon which stood a pile of papers, and a wooden chair under the high grilled window. A grimy lavatory was located in the right hand corner. Any occupant was obscured by the door.

"Trevors," he shouted, "you've got company for the weekend. Hope you're looking your best. Get yourself in there, Jardine. Lock up for the night is in one hour. I'll bring your washing gear before then," he said as he wandered away back to his desk on the landing to complete some more paper-pushing.

Charlie Jardine walked apprehensively into the forbidding cell, immediately looking behind the door at the two-tier bunk beds with their grey, coarse blankets. On the lower bunk, stretched out on his back, lay the figure of a man in prison issue blue and white striped shirt and blue jeans. His hands were folded under his head as he stared unwaveringly upwards at the metal springs of the bunk bed above him. The absence of a collar on the shirt disclosed on the right side of the neck a large, jagged scar which seemed inflamed and pulsating. Not turning his head even one degree towards Charlie, and neither speaking nor making the slightest noise, he exuded such menace and hostility towards the newcomer that Charlie's hands were shaking in fear. Not daring to climb on to the upper bunk which would have involved putting one foot on the lower, Charlie shuffled the couple of steps to the battered wooden chair, pulled it away from the table and lowered himself nervously on to it. Six desperate months on remand had taught him some of the basic rules of survival, but so sinister was the atmosphere created by this man's resentment of the invasion of his territory, that Charlie could not even look in his direction and he sat, staring at the wall, in complete silence. The pile of papers stacked on the far corner of the table could now be seen to be Court case papers in the same font and format as his own.

'Regina v Gary Peter Trevors.

Committed for trial at Leeds Crown Court.
Murder of Paul Michael Checkley
Aggravated Burglary
Wounding with intent of Sarah Checkley
CPS Solicitor: David Nathan.
Officers in Charge of Case: DCI Ernie Noble and DS Ronald Perry'.

Charlie closed his eyes and then read the names again with care. Ronald Perry. Detective Sergeant. It had to be the same bent copper. Same name. Same rank. Same region. The bastard had said that his tentacles reached behind the bars.

After several minutes of battling to regain some composure, he steeled himself and half turned the chair so as to speak to the recumbent prisoner who, in the meanwhile, seemed not to have moved a muscle. From this position Charlie could see how white the face was, with eyes set deep in the sockets, still staring straight upwards.

"I'm only here until Monday, mate. Cock-up in the paperwork," offered Charlie nervously.

There was no reply, no movement, no acknowledgement.

"Is it OK if I climb up on to the bunk?" Charlie asked

Silence.

Charlie turned back towards the wall and sat with his head in his hands, the wooden seat growing harder by the minute and the brooding animosity of Trevors filling him with dread.

There was very little noise on the Landing. All of the inmates seemed to be in their cells and it brought a sense of relief when Jenkins appeared with the small white flannel, wafer thin bar of soap and tiny toothbrush and tube of toothpaste that would have to last him indefinitely.

"Get yourself down to the washroom, Jardine. Ten minutes and I call lock up," ordered Jenkins from the doorway.

As Charlie collected the package and headed on to the landing a hard, dry north-eastern voice spat out the one word "Jenkins".

"What you want, Trevors?" muttered Jenkins

"I want him out," shouted the voice, suddenly erupting into a fury. Trevors leaped up from the bed and came out on to the Landing where Charlie had stopped en route to the washroom.

"I want the bastard out. I'm Cat 'A'. Own cell. I'm too dangerous to share. That's the fucking rule. Get him out."

Now Charlie could see the broad shoulders, just under six feet tall, pinched, vicious, pale face.

"It's only 'til Monday. Orders from the Assistant Governor. There's nowt I can do," replied Jenkins with a singular lack of interest.

"My case starts on Monday. I'm going over the deps. I don't want no distractions. I'm telling you, get him out or you'll be carrying him out," threatened Trevors.

"So? We'll carry him out. Who cares? And you'll be in solitary with no privileges just at the time when you're on trial. No shaving. No showering. You'll look really good, mate. And you'll stink like a badger's set. Use your loaf, Trevors," responded Jenkins wandering slowly away. "Ten minutes, Jardine. Move!" he shouted over his shoulder.

Two black men were in the washroom, stripped to the waist, revealing powerful, overdeveloped upper bodies. One of them nodded in Charlie's direction, while the other carried on washing in that sullen silence that seemed to dominate this Landing.

When Charlie returned to the cell, Trevors was sitting on the lavatory, filling the air with his foul smell; like an animal marking out its territory with its waste. Charlie stood outside until Jenkins reappeared with the keys, gesturing for Charlie to go back in. When Jenkins reopened the door Trevors was perched on the wooden chair, now poring intently over the pile of case papers.

"OK if I climb up now?" asked Charlie tentatively.

Silence.

Charlie slipped off his shoes and, very deliberately, put one foot on the metal frame of the lower bunk, studiously avoiding standing directly on Trevors' blanket and, as he was about to hoist himself up on to the upper bunk, a hand snaked out and a grip like steel was applied to his left ankle. The arm had moved so fast he had never seen it coming and the pressure was biting so hard into the ankle that he could not move the leg an inch.

"Never put your fucking foot on my bed. Never." he shouted, suddenly pulling on the ankle so that Charlie's support on the bed was removed and he crashed to the floor. The officers outside were bound to have heard the shout and the noise of the fall. No one responded.

Lying on the floor, with Trevors standing above him, he waited for the onslaught. This animal was facing a murder charge. He was likely psychopathic and probably had the capacity to kill with his bare hands. The first kick was straight into the ribs and sent a pain directly to the heart that felt like a knife. Charlie rolled into a ball and tried to steel himself for what was to come, closing his eyes tightly and tensing his muscles.

Nothing happened immediately. Then, sensing a quick movement, he opened one eye and saw Trevors sitting back down in the chair, presumably reading the case papers again. Resigned to Charlie's presence during the night, he seemed to have made his point and then suddenly lost interest.

Gingerly getting to his feet, pressing the heel of his hand into the area of the ribs where he had been kicked, testing to see if anything seemed to have been broken, he quickly grabbed the metal bar of the upper bunk and lifted his bodyweight up with his arms, levering himself on to the upper bunk without in any way standing on the lower. As he stretched himself out on top of the thin blanket, he could see that Trevors had turned his head to check that his orders had been obeyed, then, satisfied, the head had resumed its position poring over the papers. Eventually, Charlie fell asleep, counting the endless hours until Monday morning when he might escape from this evil lunatic. Periodically during the night he awoke, always to see that the dim cell light was still burning and the head was staring at those papers, going over them time after time after time. Obsessive. Violent. Territorial. The psychiatrists could have a field day with this one, thought Charlie, drifting back into an uneasy sleep, as the murderer started again on page one.

When Charlie awoke a few rays of morning light were filtering through the narrow cell window. Although the cell light still burned, Trevors was no longer at the table and the case papers could be seen in their neat pile on the corner of the table. Presumably, he was asleep on the bunk below, but there was no sound of breathing or movement. Not daring to look for fear of the reaction, Charlie lay there, awaiting the unlocking of the cell door or some sign of activity from below.

"What you done?" demanded that hard, rasping voice, suddenly from below.

"Drugs," Charlie replied with a sense of relief that some form of communication was taking place.

"Supplying?"

"Importing."

"What?"

"Coke."

"How?"

"Did a run from Jamaica. Got through Customs at Manchester Airport but the coppers'd been tipped off."

"You fight it?"

"No, I pleaded. I was caught with the cash in my pocket. The other guy was caught with the coke. No choice."

"There's always a choice. Golden rule. Never plead. Never. Don't give the bastards the satisfaction. If nobody pleaded we could clog up the whole fucking system," Trevors declared.

"Too late for me now. I get sentenced Monday."

"Why ain't you sentenced before in Manchester then?"

"The Judge wanted reports and she was coming here."

"What kind of reports. You a nutcase or something?"

"No. Ordinary sentence report," lied Charlie, not wanting to tell Trevors he was ill. His kind of mentality would see any kind of illness as contagious and the incentive to kick him out of the cell might be revived.

"How much you stand to make on a run like that?"

"Three grand."

"Three grand. Peanuts. You're working for peanuts," sneered Trevors.

"Truth is I was shafted anyway. Copper here in Yorkshire got a tip-off. Came over to Manchester to do the business. Nicked me in the street on his own. Seized the three grand and booked it in as fifteen hundred. Then warned me off," volunteered Charlie, wondering whether to reveal Perry's name.

"Cute bastards, ain't they?" sighed Trevors. "Yorkshire copper, you said. Name?"

Charlie hesitated. What was he letting himself in for here? Who knows what had gone on between Perry and Trevors in his case?

"Name?" snapped Trevors. "Bent coppers don't advertise."

"Detective Sergeant Ron Perry," Charlie replied

Trevors was out of his bunk in a flash, standing alongside Charlie and grabbing him fiercely by his T-shirt. Stripped to the waist and wearing only a torn pair of white boxer shorts, Charlie's eyes were drawn to the tattoo on the left shoulder of a spider's web and a hideous scar on his inner arm where a whole chunk of flesh seemed to have been torn off.

"Are you taking the fucking piss, 'cos if you are, I'll batter you so your own mother don't recognise you," he shouted.

"That was his name," stuttered Charlie. "Ronald Perry. I'll never forget it. Said he was sending me into hell and if I ever complained no one'd believe me and he'd make things even worse for me inside."

"You seen that name on my papers and giving me a wind-up?" challenged Trevors.

"Perry. Ron Perry. Tall, thin, sharp featured. They call him 'The Peril'. He's a liar and a thief. Do you think I made it up? Do you think I'd go all the way to Jamaica, run that kind of risk for fifteen hundred quid? Perry, he's bent," Charlie responded.

Trevors' mean face was screwed up in concentration as he absorbed every word, weighing up the use to which he might be able to apply this information. This pathetic kid was a complete novice. He was terrified out of his wits and wouldn't have the street nouse to dream any of this up and, more importantly, it would be obvious to any jury that he was telling the truth. If this kid could give Cadogan the ammunition to smash Perry, then the whole Prosecution case against him would be undermined. All of the various ramifications were teeming around Trevors' brain as he stood transfixed to the spot, still clutching the kid's T-shirt.

After an interminable silence Trevors decided upon his plan of campaign.

"Get your arse into that chair," he ordered, half pulling Charlie from his bunk.

Positioning himself on the edge of the lower bunk he fired a stream of questions at the boy. As he spoke Charlie could see the upper section of a tattoo of a naked girl running right across his stomach and down towards his crotch, the blue black of the tattoo ink making a distasteful contrast with the unnatural whiteness of his skin. There was another tattoo on the outside of the right, hairless, leg. A long, narrow stiletto-type dagger in its sheath.

"How long had you had the three grand before he nicked you?"

"Five minutes."

"Who gives it you?"

"The dealer. Derek Mount. He got eight years. He's in Strangeways."

"Can he say it was definitely three grand?"

"Yeah, but he won't say who he got it off."

"Was Perry alone when he nicked you?"

"Alone."

"How was the money made up?"

"Thirty fifties, fifty twenties, fifty tens."

"What exactly did he take?"

"The thirty fifties."

"Did he book the money in?"

"Booked in the fifteen hundred in tens and twenties."

"Did you make a complaint?"

"Started to in the interview. He warned me off."

"Did you tell your brief?"

"No."

"Did Mount tell the coppers that he'd handed over three grand?"

"No idea. I never read his interview. In court they said he was the go-between and hadn't named any names."

"On Monday, after you've been weighed off by the Judge, my brief's going to be down in your cell. You're my star witness. You got that?"

"I don't want to…"

"What you want ain't worth shit. But it ain't going to affect your sentence anyway."

"No, but Perry said if I ever made a complaint he'd reach me inside and I'd pay."

"You listen, kid. I can have things done to you in any nick in the land. I can have your fucking head caved in for a pack of fags. Your legs broke for a few Rizlas. But, if you plays ball, I can sweeten your time."

"OK. OK. Whatever you say."

"You're learning. We'll start right now. You sits at that desk and scribes out everything you just told me. The whole bloody shooting match. Then I gives that to the brief on Monday. I'll be down the boozer by Friday night."

CHAPTER 17

Arthur Helliwell's second entrance to Court One at Leeds Crown Court was noticeably less dramatic than his first. The arena was benign and deserted except for one elderly lady cleaner, who paid little attention to Arthur, as he erected the Master's lectern and set out all of the case papers along his section of the row reserved for Queen's Counsel. As always, the same tradition prevailed, whereby the Defence had to be located nearer to the jury than the Prosecution. How empty the stage seemed without the players, Arthur mused to himself, as he laid out the small piles of coloured notepaper and fluorescent highlighters that Cadogan invariably used nowadays. No doubt the unpleasant giant was indulging himself in a King's breakfast at his 5 Star Hotel, after a comfortable night's sleep in his top of the line suite. A big improvement on getting up at four in the morning to catch the early train from King's Cross, lugging all the files and law books, which was the fate he had imposed on his clerk. By 9.20 a.m. Arthur had completed his tasks, including commandeering the private robing room, courtesy of the same security officer as on the previous occasion, and was walking through the still slumbering building, en route for the cafeteria and a bacon sandwich, awaiting the arrival of his Governor and the barrage of orders that would inevitably follow.

Within the secure side yard, the van from Armley Gaol had disgorged its cargo of misery and the prisoners had been led to cells deep in the bowels of the building, waiting to be brought briefly to the surface for the red robes and ermine to put them back down for another chunk of their three score and ten. From the special Category 'A' security cell Trevors was demanding that a message be communicated upstairs that his solicitor and counsel come and visit him in the cells as a matter of urgency. In the ordinary cell area Charles Jardine lay out on the hard wooden bench, anxiously waiting for his case to be called on at some stage, when Mrs Justice Gaynor would pass sentence and, to make the day even more traumatic, Trevors' lawyers were bound to come down and interview him about Perry.

Cadogan was in a foul mood as nothing had gone to plan. Having arranged to come up to Leeds on the Sunday and settle into what was reputed to be the best hotel in the city, he had discovered that the suite they had given him was located immediately above some roadworks. The incompetent contractors were working until late on the Sunday evening, trying to fix a burst water main and it was nearly midnight before they had eventually finished their drilling. Predictably, sleep had not come quickly thereafter. Breakfast had been a major disappointment. It was served buffet style and all of the cooked dishes were kept warm under those powerful heating lamps, with the result that the eggs had spent the last hour swimming in their own grease, the bacon was limp and tired and the tomatoes had imploded. These were not good omens for the difficult day that lay ahead.

As Naomi Nicholas had been getting increasingly apprehensive at the excruciating prospect of at least a week appearing before Hathington, coupled with working alongside an offensive bully boy, Jack Farnham had insisted upon driving her to Court and carrying her robes and brief into the robing room. Finding that there was still no sign of Cadogan even after she had robed, Naomi suggested that Jack came upstairs and had a coffee with her, before departing for his own day's work. Seated alone in the far corner of the cafeteria, Naomi espied Cadogan's clerk tucking into a large bacon sandwich and immersed in the back page of the *Sun*.

"Arthur," she called across, "can I get you another cup of something?"

Lifting his eyes from the match reports of last Saturday's games, Arthur immediately recognised the Governor's Junior, although Cadogan had never deigned to introduce him to her when they were all here for that momentous Plea and Directions Hearing. What a stunner she was, thought Arthur. Real style. Elegant and classy. Shame she wasn't in our chambers, he reflected with a rueful smile.

"Love another cup of tea, Miss," he shouted. "Two sugar. Go down a treat."

When she brought the tea over to his table a few minutes later, Arthur observed that she was accompanied by an athletic-looking male whose appearance seemed very familiar.

"Morning, Miss Nicholas how are we today?" enquired Arthur kindly as he got to his feet. "Come and join me, there's no sign of Mr Cadogan as yet. Mind you, he likes timing his entrances," the clerk added with a knowing chuckle.

"Thank you. We'll join you. May I introduce my fiancé, Jack Farnham. Jack, this is Arthur Helliwell, Ronan Cadogan's Senior Clerk."

As the two men shook hands Arthur was staring intently into Jack's face and, as soon as they all sat down, he spoke.

"Jack. Jack Farnham. I knew it. Soon as I looked at you I knew that you were familiar. You played for Northampton Town, didn't you? Back four. That's been my team since I was a lad. Used to be a regular down at the County Ground. Can't say I like it so much since they moved to the new ground, mind you," enthused the old clerk.

"Been a while now, Arthur. Lot of water's passed under the bridge. I went to Port Vale and then Rotherham after that, but I've only fond memories of 'The Cobblers' and the old County Ground. The town treated me well."

"Saw you score a goal once. Always remember it. You being a defender I s'pose. Stands out when a defender scores. What a goal it was," Arthur reminisced, shaking his head.

"And I bet I know which one it was. Everyone always talks about that one. Third round of the Cup, right?"

"That's the one. And you know why people remember it? 'Cos you dived down amongst all those flailing boots and headed it in. Your chin must've been in the mud. Sheer guts, that's why. And it nearly saved the game."

"Nearly isn't good enough though, is it?" said Jack. "In football or in Court. Naomi's always telling me that it's do or die in her game."

"Not quite a fair analogy," interrupted Naomi. "You can always draw in football. For us it's a straight win or lose."

"Ah, but you get paid the same, whatever the result, Miss. Playing for 'The Cobblers' in the days we're talking about, the basic wage without the winning bonus wouldn't have taken you very far. Am I right about that, Jack?"

"You're absolutely right. Anyway, enough talk about me and football. Naomi told me about your spectacular performance the other week when this case was in for Plea. She said you should've been given an Oscar," smiled Jack.

"Well, the Governor has had me pull that stunt more than once, I can tell you. But, there's a history between him and Mr Haskitt, made it really matter. Best I don't say too much, but you'd have got a flavour of it last time, wouldn't you, Miss?" observed Arthur in Naomi's direction.

"Hard not to, but I'd like to know exactly what…" Naomi began, only to be interrupted by the sudden arrival of the already robed Ronan Cadogan himself, looking singularly displeased with life. Instantly spotting Arthur and his Junior in the corner, he marched purposefully towards their table, scowling as he approached.

"We're wanted urgently in the cells and I couldn't find a trace of either of you, or the solicitor, Sylvester," he barked. "It's time for work, not coffee and sandwiches."

"Sorry, Mr Cadogan," mumbled Arthur, jumping up and scurrying towards the door, abandoning his cup of tea and the remains of his sandwich. "I'll find Mr Sylvester and send him straight down to the cells."

Casting a resigned look at Jack, Naomi Nicholas picked up her laptop and the selection of case papers that she had brought up with her and prepared to head for the cells.

"I've been here quite some time, Ronan," she offered defensively, "and apparently Arthur has been here since the crack of dawn. We must have just missed each other. Goodbye, Jack, see you this evening."

Cadogan paused to look down at the seated male figure, openly weighing him up in a flash, in exactly the same way he used to assess his wrestling opponents. Looked like he'd been a serious sportsman, still retaining that competitive gleam in his eye. Tough guy with a determined jaw line but predictable. The sombre suit complemented his powerful frame but no amount of tailoring could compensate for the conservative fabric, with the Marks and Spencers' blue shirt and matching tie. Obviously screwing Naomi. Couldn't blame him for that, but not my sort. The snap judgement formed, Cadogan made no attempt to acknowledge the man, but rudely turned on his heel, calling for Naomi to follow at once.

"Don't they say 'Good Morning' down in London then?" Jack shouted after him as he strode from the room, with Naomi hot on his heels.

"Depends on the company," parried Cadogan in reply, without even turning his head or breaking his stride as he hurried to meet his contemptible client, wondering what dirty little schemes the killer had been dreaming up.

Once again the prison officers were refusing to allow Trevors out of the special secure area, although they had not indicated any intention to apply for him to be handcuffed in Court after their failure on the previous occasion. As the lawyers passed through the various steel gates towards the inner sanctum, Cadogan was complaining bitterly to Roger Sylvester about the shortcomings of the hotel. Arriving at the cell door, it became clear that it was almost impossible to fit three adults, including one of Cadogan's dimensions, into the eight by eight cubicle.

"We need a bigger room," Cadogan demanded of the officer who opened the door, revealing Trevors within, wearing that same awful, cheap, black suit.

"There's not one in this section of the cell area, Sir," came the disinterested reply.

"Then, you'll have to move him to another section where there are proper conference rooms. This man's on trial for murder. He's entitled to speak to his lawyers and we can't all get into that shoe box," Cadogan insisted.

"Your choice, Sir. That's all you get. Take it or leave it," was the bored response.

"Get me the Senior Prison Officer, then," shouted Cadogan in a fury. "You're denying this man a fundamental right and I won't stand for it. I'm quite prepared to take this before the Judge."

"I'm the Senior Officer here. Trevors is violent, dangerous and he's on our list of escapers. He stays here. Them's the orders. Tell the Judge, it makes no difference to me."

"Put a man in uniform and reason is the first casualty," Cadogan muttered to himself as, still grumbling, he was obliged to squeeze himself into the cell and sit alongside Trevors, leaving Naomi and Sylvester to stand in front of the bench, half closing the door behind them.

"This is the best we're going to get, Trevors, so you'd best come straight to the point," remarked Cadogan as he shifted his bulk further into the corner. "What is it you want to see us about?"

"I've got you a piece of dynamite. Enough to blow Perry out of the water," Trevors announced triumphantly. "Pure dynamite, I'd say."

"Well, let's be having it then, before I suffocate in this black hole," came the impatient reaction.

"Read this little beauty," replied Trevors, producing Charles Jardine's handwritten statement with a dramatic flourish from his inside jacket pocket. "Feast your eyes on that, Mr Cadogan. It's dynamite, I tell you."

There was a long, tense silence while Cadogan meticulously scrutinised the document that Charlie had recorded in their cell in Armley Gaol. It was written in an educated hand, the English was of a high standard and it undoubtedly had the ring of truth about it. Cadogan well knew that drugs couriers wouldn't do that kind of run for fifteen hundred pounds and, unless Trevors had established some hold over this boy, there was no motive for him to invent such an allegation against Perry. He had pleaded guilty and had not even sought to raise the matter in the course of his own case.

"The boy's here. In the next corridor. Speak to him yourself. He can do for that bastard Perry and, once we does for Perry, then it makes their whole case stink," Trevors declared with conviction.

Cadogan passed the document to Naomi who, with Mr Sylvester leaning awkwardly over her shoulder, read it through word by word. She knew something of 'The Peril's' reputation, but nothing had ever been made to stick. However, like Cadogan, the whole feel of the document and the circumstances, persuaded her that Jardine was probably telling the truth.

"So, you'll have the solicitor see him and then you'll be calling him?" enquired Trevors, impatient for Cadogan to make some response and show his appreciation of this piece of gold dust, but Cadogan did not speak.

"It's kosher, mate. The lad's genuine. Take my word for it," Trevors continued. "He's my star witness. Perry's going to fall."

"One thing is for sure," announced Cadogan eventually. "Jardine won't be your star witness. Jardine won't be called to give evidence for the Defence. Jardine won't set foot in the witness box."

Despite the crush in the cell, Trevors jumped up from the bench in his anger and surprise at this outrageous announcement, knocking clumsily into Naomi without apology.

"Have you lost your bottle or your marbles?" he shouted. "Or probably both. I'm telling you, this is my case. You call him. You call him, do you get me?"

"Explain it to him, Naomi," replied Cadogan calmly.

"It's evidence as to credit, Mr Trevors. The Law states that a party cannot call evidence whose design is simply to damage the credit of a witness. There are a few exceptions, but I doubt that any will apply on the facts here," Naomi patiently answered.

"You lot are all copping big money on this case. You're representing an innocent man. Now I've come up with dynamite and you sound off that you can't use it. You'd better start earning your money, Mr QC. You make it become one of them fucking exceptions. You're paid to deal with problems like this, so deal with it or you're out on your arses, the lot of you," he insisted angrily.

"Sit down, Trevors. Just sit down. I'll explain it to you in words of one syllable but, first of all, let's be clear, that's the last time you threaten me with the sack. Next time you so much as hint at it, I withdraw. If you want to be rid of us, then do it now. I don't have to put up with your little tantrums when things don't go the way you like. So spell it out, once and for all, do we stay or do we go?" challenged Cadogan aggressively.

There was a long pause as Trevors struggled to keep his temper under control before he slumped back down on the bench in resignation.

"You stay," he grunted. "But I want to follow this. How's it work?"

"It works like this. In cross-examining Perry I'm entitled to ask him if he took fifteen hundred pounds from Jardine. Obviously, he'll deny it.

I'm then bound by his answer. This is because it doesn't go to a direct issue of fact in your case, it goes exclusively to the credit, the credibility, of a witness. So, when he denies it, I can't call Jardine to contradict him. Have you grasped that?"

"It's crap," sneered Trevors.

"It may be crap to you, but it's the Law. And I haven't finished. There are exceptions. Such as bias. For example, if we could show that Perry has acted out of some existing bias towards you and had fabricated evidence because of this bias, then it just might be admissible but, at present, there's no suggestion of any such bias," explained Cadogan. Also, there's a recent case where efforts by a crooked police officer to secure a conviction by fabricated evidence tempted the Court of Appeal to say evidence of his alleged malpractice in another case should become admissible. But, I see little prospect of that working here, for we've no actual evidence of Perry fabricating evidence against you."

"And that's crap as well," interjected Trevors angrily. "He verballed me and you know that Voice Identification Parade stinks to high heaven."

"So you say, so you say. But on the question of this allegation of pocketing fifteen hundred pounds it gets even worse. If I suggest that to Perry then he will undoubtedly deny it. It's clear that I will have attacked his character. Then, when you give evidence, the Prosecution will apply to the Judge for leave to retaliate and attack your character. They'll seek to cross-examine you on your previous convictions. In my opinion the Judge will give them that leave. Once the jury hears of your previous they'll be only too delighted to convict you of murder," Cadogan continued.

"What if I don't go into the box?" Trevors astutely enquired.

"That way I'll have raised the matter with Perry. He'll have denied it. My questions aren't the evidence. His answers are the evidence. So, the only evidence the jury will have heard will be Perry's denials. Full stop. My questions on that topic will have no evidential value. Then, I will drop the bombshell that you're not giving evidence. The Judge will ask me, with the jury sitting there watching, if I've advised you of the consequences and I shall say that I have. The Judge will then tell you that, in due course, the jury may draw such inferences as they think proper from your failure to testify."

"You mean they can decide I'm guilty and can't answer the questions that'd be coming my way," Trevors declared.

"Exactly. So you'll have avoided the jury knowing of your previous but, the price you'd pay, would be for them to smell such a rat from your silence that they'd convict you. All for the fleeting satisfaction of asking Perry if he'd pinched fifteen hundred quid, which he would have denied. The question would probably die on the wind and you'd have snookered yourself. Give evidence and in go your previous. Guilty. Or, don't give evidence, avoid your previous going in, but get the Judge's warning about silence. Guilty."

"I'm buggered either way. I ain't got no chance. It stinks. That Perry's a crook and the jury don't get to know. He's stitched me up and he nicked fifteen hundred quid. And I can't use Jardine. You call that justice?" Trevors whined.

"Not absolutely accurate. Firstly, as your previous convictions establish, you're also a crook, but the jury won't know anything about that either. Secondly, I said we couldn't call Jardine. I didn't say we might not be able to use Jardine. There's a difference between the two. Sometimes there's more than one way to skin a cat," Cadogan replied enigmatically.

"What the hell does that mean? In ordinary English," enquired Trevors.

"You'll just have to wait and see. When I've decided, I'll let you know. Jardine has put an extra card into my hand. Whether I can ever play it or threaten to play it, depends on which way it all breaks," responded Cadogan.

"Bluffing. You're talking bluffing. Right?" Trevors concluded.

"I prefer to call it strategy," Cadogan corrected him.

"OK, so what's this strategy?" Trevors demanded.

"Firstly, we wait until Jardine is sentenced. That will probably be first off at half past ten in Mrs Justice Gaynor's Court. Then the strategy kicks in. It starts with disclosure. We disclose Jardine's statement to the Prosecution in open Court. We tell the Judge what we're doing and that Jardine, now sentenced, is in the cells available for immediate interview by the police. It's important that he's sentenced so that he can't be accused of making this claim in the hope that he might get a reduced sentence. But that's the strategy, disclosure."

"So, your idea of strategy is to show them our bloody cards. Sounds very impressive, very impressive, like Churchill giving the Germans our secret codes," came the sarcastic retort.

"Jardine's lawyers will have to be told," continued Cadogan, ignoring Trevors' whingeing. "That's your job, Mr Sylvester. They'll want to sit in on any interview. The police'll also have to try and interview Mount in Strangeways. My guess is that he'll refuse to see them and, when he's tucked up in HMP, he can refuse, unless they have reason to arrest him. This enquiry would give them no such power of arrest. So, the police will just have Jardine to weigh up. Then we'll take stock," explained the QC.

"Do I have any role to play in this strategy?" Naomi asked, unsure as to what Cadogan hoped to achieve by all of this.

"Oh yes. You have a few tasks. One, you go upstairs and ask the Judge's clerk to allow us an extra half hour. Tell him we've just received some very important instructions that need consideration. Second, you type out Jardine's statement on that laptop you carry around. Next, you'll see my collection of coloured notepaper in Court. Choose the electric blue coloured paper and print out a dozen copies of Jardine's typed statement on that coloured paper. Finally, when we know that Jardine has been sentenced, give two of those copies to the Prosecution Junior with the loose tongue. I forget his name. One for his Leader and one for him. As you give them to him, tell him that Cadogan thinks there's some skulduggery here. That's all you need say."

"Right. Dickie Lampard is his name," she responded.

"Yes, Lampard. May all come to nothing, Trevors, but we'll try and make some use of it. But we're not risking your character going in and we're not risking you failing to give evidence. So, whatever happens, we won't be damaging your case. Understood?" asked Cadogan, getting to his feet.

"I understand some bits, not others. All I know is that somehow Perry has fitted me up. His grubby prints are all over that phony ID parade and he's verballed me. He's a fucking crook, just like Jardine says."

"Yes. I think you've mentioned all of that before," Cadogan remarked.

"One other thing before you go. I've not seen the forensic photos. The body and the injuries to the woman and all that. I want to see 'em."

"What on earth for? Your defence is that you weren't there. Why do you want to see post-mortem photographs and photographs of Mrs Checkley's hideous wounds?" Cadogan asked with unmasked contempt.

"'Cos it's my case. I'm entitled to see it all, not just what you lot choose," he responded.

"Mr Sylvester, will you stay down here while he ploughs through them?" asked Cadogan, shaking his head in disgust.

"If you say so, Mr Cadogan. I've got a set here in my briefcase. But I have to say I see no purpose in it," Roger Sylvester replied.

"Just hand 'em over. I'm entitled," repeated Trevors.

Leaving Trevors salivating over the gruesome photographs, visibly excited by the glossy photos of the male body on the mortuary slab and Sarah Checkley's butchered torso, Cadogan and Naomi Nicholas headed out of the cell.

"All the symptoms of the psychopath. Actually proud of his

handiwork," Cadogan muttered to Naomi. "Well, while you do your bit, I'm going to have a coffee with Arthur before I despatch him back to London." Then we'll have the pleasure of seeing old Haskitt again. I do hope he's recovered from his nasty fall."

"There's little doubt that he funked it, is there? You put the fear of God in him. What's it all about?" Naomi bravely asked.

"Dirty dealing. Few years back. Time for revenge. What goes around, comes around," he answered. "Tell me, you're a local, does 'Perry the Peril' have a serious reputation up here? Trevors is right about one thing, I've always smelt something fishy about that Voice Identification Parade."

"Oh, yes. Despised by all and sundry. Nothing's ever been proved, mind you, but I imagine that his wallet was looking pretty fat after he'd arrested Charlie Jardine," she answered.

As Cadogan passed through all of the steel gates en route for freedom and the cafeteria, he reflected on this latest development. It was obvious that Jardine was telling the truth. Unfortunately, the chances were that there wouldn't be a way whereby he could use any of it, but he could certainly make Perry sweat and, just as importantly, he could fluster his opponent. Haskitt was already frightened. A sweating copper, coupled with a frightened and a flustered Haskitt was just what the doctor ordered.

CHAPTER 18

M r Justice Hathington had travelled up from London to Leeds on the Monday morning and taken a taxi directly to the Court, bypassing the Lodgings until the limousine took him there for lunch. Having studied the papers in the murder case with the utmost care, he felt rather more confident to help steer it home to a conviction, so long as Haskitt made a decent job of it. His performance at the Plea and Directions Hearing had been pitiful and that fellow Cadogan would take some handling. No doubt Haskitt had simply had a bad morning but would be well up to speed for the actual trial.

Arriving early at the Judge's entrance, he had been efficiently ushered into his chambers and supplied with a coffee whilst he awaited the arrival of his clerk who was bringing his robes. Sipping his cup of coffee whilst he re-read *The Times*, he was disturbed by the unexpected ringing of the telephone on the large, modern desk at which he was seated.

"Yes," he stated abruptly, as he picked up the phone.

"Michael. Good morning. It's Roger, how are you?"

"Roger, how splendid to hear from you, is all well with you?" replied Hathington, instantly recognising the voice of the Minister for Europe.

"No complaints. Working hard as ever. Is Laura up there with you?" enquired Roger Denstone.

"No, I tend to come out on circuit on my own. The Lodgings at these places are pretty grim, you know. One of the downsides of the job, I'm afraid."

"Plenty of up sides, though, I hope. It's all been worthwhile, I trust?" responded Denstone, by way of oblique reminder of the influence that he had wielded in securing the appointment.

"Very satisfactory so far," came the reply, immediately recognising that this was the code which prefaced a request for a return of the favour.

"Are you alone?" enquired Denstone.

"I am."

"Have you met Mrs Justice Gaynor yet? I understand that she's up there in Leeds as well."

"No. I travelled up this morning and won't see her until the car takes us back to the Lodgings at lunchtime. Never met her before. She's Family

Division, you know, so our paths have never crossed. Is she a friend of yours then?"

"No, I've never met her either. Bit awkward really, but just thought you might indirectly be able to pass on to her a bit of character reference," said Denstone, as he adroitly moved nearer the true purpose of his call.

"What kind of character reference?" probed Hathington gingerly, the warning bells sounding. The return of the favour was going to be particularly sensitive.

"Normally, of course, it would go in writing to the Judge, but it's a touch tricky in this situation, old boy, so I'm wondering if you could just have a word," continued Denstone, edging ever nearer to the crunch. "You see, it's just been brought to my attention, in the last hour in fact, that she's about to sentence a young lad for bringing some drugs into the country. Poor boy's got leukaemia, otherwise he'd never have got into this mess."

"Yes?" came the hesitant response.

"Well, the Government has a major project in mind. European dimension and all of that. We're busy raising the necessary, talking to the big commercial operators. And I mean big. One of them is the father of this lad. They'd become estranged and he only learned last week that his boy was in trouble. Saw a report in the paper. Apparently, there'd have been a lot of character references available if he'd had proper notice, but he's just called me in a bit of a panic, asking if I could let the authorities know that, normally, the boy is honest and trustworthy and this venture is completely out of character. All due to him having leukaemia and being depressed. Just a word needed, if you understand me."

"I understand you all right. But hellish tricky. I don't know this Judge from Adam. Could easily be misinterpreted," replied Hathington uncomfortably, knowing only too well that this was nothing to do with a character reference. It was a quid pro quo which could never be done openly. The message he had to carry to Mrs Justice Gaynor was a clandestine Government directive to reduce the sentence."

"Yes. I realise that. Always a risk of misinterpretation, of course. And I'm afraid that we can't allow you to use names, including mine. But you are at liberty to say that the father is doing a great deal for the country and his efforts are appreciated at a very high level."

"She'll ask me who I spoke to. What shall I say?" asked Hathington. "That's where we can rely on your discretion, can't we? We all have to learn how to deal with that type of question. So glad I can count on you. The boy's bound to go down, but let's hope the Judge can see a way to keep it reasonably short. You must bring Laura round for dinner when you're back in town. We don't see enough of each other, do we?" concluded Denstone, safe in the knowledge that he had demanded the return of the favour and that Hathington was obliged to try and deliver.

"Yes, we'd like that. But, on the other matter, you do realise that I may not be able to make any difference. You know that I'll try, but absolutely no guarantees," Hathington emphasised.

"Of course, of course. Just a character reference, that's all. No more than that. Up to the Judge. Not interfering. Entirely up to the Judge. Just a character reference. Jardine's the name. Charles Jardine. Look forward to seeing you soon, old boy. Bye."

The phone clicked, as the receiver was replaced on the call that had never taken place, leaving Hathington faced with a dreadful dilemma. He had always known that, sooner or later, the debt would be called in, but he was being directed to influence a Judge in the length of a prison sentence. A Judge he'd never met. She might decide that he should be reported to the Lord Chancellor. Well, if that happened, Roger would just have to bail him out. Looking anxiously at his watch, he realised that it was nearly ten o'clock and she was bound to have arrived in her chambers. Better get on with it before it was too late.

Looking at the Court List on his desk he saw that she was sitting in the Court immediately adjacent to his own, so presumably, she was accommodated in the adjacent chambers. Walking slowly along the empty corridor, he observed the fine paintings, loaned by the City Art Gallery, lining the walls. Old landscapes, modern industrial panoramas, fading portraits. Picures of the High Sheriffs and Deputy Lieutenants of the County from over the years. All the grand trappings of this pleasurable life style. Fitted in so nicely with the knighthood and the limousine. Yes, he supposed, the return of the favour was justified. He knocked boldly on the door and went in.

"Good morning. I'm Michael Hathington. As we've never met I thought I must come and introduce myself," opened Hathington with great charm to the neat, silver-haired lady seated at her desk, reading the medical report on Jardine that she had ordered to be prepared for today's hearing.

"Helen Gaynor. Please sit down. Let me pour you a coffee. I always make my own. Really can't abide the dishwater that the Courts serve up," she replied, pointing to a half-full cafetiere on a tray. "Spare cup, there we are. How are you finding life on the Bench, Michael?"

"Most agreeable, most agreeable," answered Hathington, as he launched easily into the small talk at which he had always been so accomplished. After allowing five or ten minutes of gentle exchanges to pass, he started to probe for the right opening, as it could not be very long before the court staff started to come knocking on her door.

"I understand that you're doing a criminal case here today," he began.

"Only for a few minutes. It's a sentence that I've brought with me from Manchester. Then I'm straight back into my Family work. Far prefer my own territory, you know," she smiled.

"I don't know anything at all about your criminal case. Nothing about the facts or the appropriate sentence, but I did learn that the poor boy, Jardine isn't it, only got into this mess because he contracted leukaemia. And he could have brought some impressive character references to Court..." he began tentatively.

"Do you have some particular interest in this case, for I'd hate you to say something inadvertently that might compromise me," she immediately interrupted, with a sharpness in her voice that made the intended rebuke only too clear.

This was excruciatingly difficult, Hathington thought to himself, but he had no choice but to press on.

"No, no. No interest at all. Never met the boy, nor his family. Complete strangers to me. But apparently the father is a great servant to this country, much respected by the powers that be. Unfortunately, he and the lad became estranged, then the lad became very ill and got involved in whatever escapade brings him in front of you," he continued, looking directly at Helen Gaynor, whose expression was one of increasing alarm.

"You do seem to know rather a lot about my case. Are you trying to tell me something? Because if you are, it's probably better if we change the subject at once," she declared.

"Not trying to tell you anything. Just that I heard that if the boy wanted, he'd have had available very powerful character references. But he never told his father what had happened and now it's all too late. Father only learned very recently. Just character reference chat, that's all. Great shame, when father has done so much for the country. Respected at the highest level and he..."

"I have got your message," she interrupted, "and I really think it better if I hear no more, but I'd like to know where you got your information from, given that you profess to know nothing about this family."

"Just a character reference from the powers that be. The highest powers that be. Well, I'll be off, back to my murder," he said getting quickly to his feet and breathing a sigh of relief that the dirty deed was done. Now he could honestly tell Roger that he had done everything he could, in what had been extremely difficult circumstances. She had got the message loud and clear. He could only hope that she acted upon it. "Look forward to seeing you at lunchtime."

Mrs Justice Gaynor made no reply but fixed him with a steely glare as he withdrew from her chambers. All of the rumours about him did not do him justice. He was far worse.

When Hathington returned to his chambers his clerk had arrived with his robes and a message from Junior Counsel for the Defence that they had just received some important instructions from their client and would be most grateful if the Judge delayed sitting for half an hour, so that they could deal with the matters raised. Hathington was quite content to have the luxury of another half an hour to himself, so that he might fully recover from the strains of his recent encounter with Helen Gaynor. He could only hope that she imposed a very low sentence and that Roger would thereby consider the debt repaid.

In Court Number Two Mrs Justice Gaynor was preparing to pass sentence on Charles Jardine, still seething at Hathington's transparent performance. His much publicised connection with high places apparently had many ugly dimensions and it had been her bad luck to have drawn a case where a favour was obviously being called in. The stink of attempted corruption still lingered in her nostrils.

Detective Sergeant Ron Perry had been in his seat well before the Number Two Court proceedings began, ensuring that he heard everything that Paul Dickinson, Jardine's Counsel, said in mitigation. So far there had not been the slightest suggestion that Jardine had breathed a word about the missing fifteen hundred pounds, and all that remained was to watch the little creep pick up his six or seven years. Thereafter, he could wander over to Court Number One and oversee the process of Trevors getting his comeuppance. Everything seemed to be falling neatly into place as Mrs Justice Gaynor thanked Dickinson for his help and ordered Jardine to stand up in the dock. What a wreck he looked, thought Perry. He seemed to have deteriorated in the few days since Perry had last seen him in Manchester.

"Charles Jardine. I have to sentence you for conspiring to import about fifty thousand pounds' worth of cocaine into the United Kingdom. Last week I sentenced your co-accused Derek Mount to eight years' imprisonment and the appropriate sentence in your case would start at just below that level.

However, I do accept the points made on your behalf by Mr Dickinson, which distinguish your position from that of Mount and I detailed those in my remarks in Manchester. In particular, you are younger. You have no previous convictions whereas he has a number of extremely relevant convictions. You indicated in interview on the night of your arrest that you would plead guilty and you have done so. You have been wholly frank and I accept your remorse to be genuine. Your reward was to be modest.

Most importantly, I am convinced that your entry into the world of drugs was a result of your serious illness and, but for that condition I do not believe that you would have experimented with drugs at all, let alone become involved in smuggling them into the country. Above all else, it is that illness which has concerned me and has led me to order an up-to-date and comprehensive medical report upon you. I have today read that report and, within it, find compelling reasons to reduce your sentence even more than I originally had in mind. You remain very ill with leukaemia and the condition is not fully controlled. It is a debilitating illness and it is clear that you will be on strong medication for the entirety of your prison sentence, which will make the sentence exceedingly difficult for you to cope with. The long-term prognosis is completely uncertain. One hopes that you will survive, but you may not. In my judgement you are paying a terrible price for your crime. The Law is entitled to be merciful, even to a drug smuggler. I do not believe that there is any real risk that you will ever reoffend. As an act of judicial mercy I am restricting the sentence to one of three years' imprisonment. You will serve half of that sentence, less the six months that you have been in custody on remand. This means that you will be released on licence in less than twelve months time. You have received exceptional leniency and, because Mount received so much longer, I have deliberately explained in detail the reasons for that distinction, so that it can be seen that doing justice in mercy to you, does not mean that Mount has suffered any injustice. Take him down."

Detective Sergeant Perry was furious. Three years for smuggling cocaine. It was a disgraceful sentence. Why do they let a Family Division Judge loose in the Criminal Courts? Mount picked up the tariff sentence, whereas the university boy with the privileged background strolls away with a sentence that means he'll be out in no time. What an absolute bloody disgrace. Jardine was not a name he would easily forget, he thought to himself as he left Court Two, heading for the Trevors trial in the adjacent Court. Within a very few minutes he would come to realise just how accurate that observation would turn out to be.

* * *

Haskitt had taken up his position in Court One well before ten thirty only to be informed by the Court Clerk that the Defence had requested a half-hour delay, which the Judge had allowed them. It was no surprise to Haskitt that this had been done without the courtesy of any communication to him from Cadogan beforehand. Deciding to remain in Court until the delayed start of the trial and thereby reducing the chances of any inadvertent contact with his opponent, he was still in his seat when Dickie Lampard came bursting through the double doors in a state of high excitement, brandishing a bright blue A4-size piece of paper.

"Bertrand. You'd better read this little lot before we kick off. Just been given it by the Defence. Take a look," he declared breathlessly as he thrust the blue paper into his Leader's hands.

Haskitt read the document with care and then read it for a second time. He did not like what he had read one little bit. This was exactly the kind of dirty material that Cadogan was an expert in exploiting.

"What do you know about this Perry, then, Dickie? Have you come across him before this case?" asked Haskitt in a tone which displayed his concern.

"Oh, yes. I've prosecuted and defended in cases involving 'Perry the Peril'. He's loathed. Wouldn't trust him as far as I could throw him," replied Lampard, looking around nervously as he checked that there was no one else in the Courtroom. "But no one has ever managed to nab him. I know for a fact that he's got no disciplinary record. Anyway, he doesn't give that much evidence against Trevors in this case does he?"

"Well, there's the incriminating reply on arrest which only he claims to hear and you remember what Cadogan said about the Voice ID Parade last time. I suspect that he'll be featuring there," answered Haskitt. "But we really could do without this couldn't we? It's going to make for serious aggravation somewhere along the line. We're going to have to check this out very thoroughly. How did you get hold of this in the first place?"

"Naomi Nicholas has just handed it to me. She gave me two copies, saying that they were disclosing this material and that Cadogan thought there was some skulduggery here. Those were her exact words – Cadogan thinks there's skulduggery here."

"Christ, Dickie. That's all we need. If there's some history between Perry and Trevors. If they've dredged up some background, then it could do our case enormous damage. We're going to have a word or two with this Detective Sergeant. Start setting it up…"

"Morning Haskitt," came the interruption from behind, causing both Prosecution Barristers to turn their heads and behold the gigantic figure of Cadogan, standing there smiling at them. They had never heard him come into the Courtroom or creep up behind them. For such an enormous man, he still retained the ability to be light on his feet when the occasion demanded.

"Got my little billet-doux, I trust? Someone's been a naughty boy, haven't they?" chuckled Cadogan.

"You may rest assured that it'll be properly checked. Seems completely inadmissible to me, though. You'll never be able to call him," responded Haskitt nervously.

"Don't bank on it. Don't bank on it. And, remember that I am challenging the admissibility of the Voice Identification Parade. So don't open that to the jury. When we reach that point in Mrs Checkley's evidence, the jury can go out while we argue admissibility. Don't open it to the jury and then claim that you hadn't been told the Defence challenged admissibility," declared Cadogan. "You've heard me say it Lampard, so no tricks Haskitt, none of your tricks, your Junior is the witness."

"I don't pull tricks, Cadogan. That's your style, not mine. Like this Jardine business. That has a certain smell of you about it," responded Haskitt, safe in the knowledge that Cadogan could not physically threaten him there in the Courtroom.

"The main smell round here is the rank odour of you trying to funk this case. Very convenient little tumble off the chestnut steed. I do hope that Dr Hamer passed on My Lord's message of sympathy to diddums. I've waited a long time to settle my score with you, Haskitt. You're locked in this to the death."

At just that moment the Court Clerk appeared through the Judge's access door into Court and caught Cadogan's attention. "We're ready to begin, Mrs Morton, bring the Judge in, without any jury panel first, please," announced Cadogan. "A small preliminary point to clear up, then we can kick off," he continued as he made his way to his place at the far end of Counsel's row, leaving Haskitt swallowing hard and Lampard looking aghast at the hatred which Cadogan displayed towards Haskitt.

Within a couple of moments the whole arena came alive. Naomi Nicholas took her position behind Cadogan, with Roger Sylvester immediately behind her. The doors to the public area of the Court were opened and all of the seats were rapidly taken. The Press Benches were filled by the old hacks with their notebooks. The prison officers appeared in the dock, the ushers and other court officials filed in, Perry and Noble sat with David Nathan from the CPS, as they were permitted to be in Court while the jury was sworn. Then, with a rap on the door and an order from the Judge's Clerk for everyone to stand, the red gowned figure swept onto the dais and stood in front of his chair, emblazoned with the crest of the Crown in gold on its back, whilst his Clerk opened the Court.

"All persons having anything to do before My Lords the Queen's Justices, draw near and give your attendance."

The Judge bowed, studiously avoiding the eyes of both Naomi Nicholas and Ronan Cadogan, angling his body in the direction of the Prosecution, as he awaited the start of the proceedings, just as soon as Trevors appeared in the dock and was formally identified by the Court Clerk. However, as soon as this had been completed, Cadogan rose to address him.

"My Lord. We thank you for the time allowed. It was requested as a consequence of information being provided to us by the Defendant in conference this morning. I would wish Your Lordship to be handed a copy of this document and to read it," he announced, as he ostentatiously held up the electric blue piece of paper for the usher to take and deliver to the Judge.

"Before I read this, Mr Cadogan, I would like to be told if the Prosecution have been given a copy," enquired Hathington, already suspicious that Cadogan was up to something.

"I took the view that the Prosecution were not entitled to this information, My Lord. This may be, in certain circumstances, evidence that the Defence may choose to call, and we are not under any obligation to provide any information about proposed Defence evidence of this nature. However, the allegation involved is of such gravity, that I have concluded that full disclosure is the appropriate course and I have ensured that both Counsel for the Prosecution have copies of the document, which I would now invite Your Lordship to read. It is only one full page of typescript," he explained, resuming his seat whilst the Judge perused the contents of the blue piece of paper.

Naomi Nicholas had kept her head down until now, preparing herself again for the moment when she had to look at the odious hypocrite, sitting up there on the High Court Bench as a bastion of integrity and righteousness. Aware that his beady eyes would now be concentrating on the statement, she allowed herself to glance in his direction and viewed with disgust the ginger beard and the flawed complexion. As she stared at him, reading Jardine's damning indictment of Perry, she was surprised to observe that his face bore the same kind of shocked expression that it had worn on first espying her presence in his Courtroom on the last occasion. There was obviously something in Jardine's statement that was causing him great alarm and he was so absorbed in his reading that he was not able to control his expression, nor did he make any attempt to speak until, eventually, Cadogan rose again to make his proposals.

"I hope that Your Lordship has now read the statement," he began.

"Yes, I have," came the muted reply.

Hathington found himself struggling to speak and on the edge of a genuine anxiety attack. Not thirty minutes earlier, at the behest of a Government Minister, in an attempt to influence a judicial sentence, he had passed on information in support of a man who, in the light of this statement, may become a Defence witness in a murder trial over which he himself was presiding. And that witness would say that the key officer in the case was a thief. It didn't bear thinking about. Further, there was no way he could keep it quiet, for Helen Gaynor was bound to hear, or read in the newspaper, that Jardine was featuring in his trial. Somehow, he had to head Cadogan off and, so as to gain some thinking time, he had to ensure that Jardine's name was not mentioned in public, certainly at this stage.

"I shall make an order, for the moment, Mr Cadogan, that the name of the maker of this statement is not revealed in these public proceedings. That order will remain open to review at a later stage," the Judge declared.

"As Your Lordship pleases. We can deal with that later. Our immediate objective is to request that Your Lordship directs the Prosecution to make enquiries into this matter. Your Lordship will appreciate that the witness is available for immediate interview, as he is on hand in this building, and that the other person referred to in Manchester can easily be located by the police and questioned. We would ask that all the answers given by these witnesses be disclosed to us forthwith and we shall thereafter be in a better position to know how much use to make of this information and when," explained Cadogan in an ominous tone.

"Mr Haskitt, do you have a view on any of this?" asked the Judge, hoping that Haskitt could somehow deal with the problem in such a way that the name Jardine was never mentioned in open Court.

"Yes, My Lord, the Crown have a very clear view. Although we were only handed the statement just before the Court sat, we immediately concluded that this witness cannot be called for the Defence for procedural and evidential reasons which we can argue at the appropriate stage in the trial. However, we are fully prepared to make such enquiries as we can and disclose the results to the Defence, although we anticipate that there will be no material to support the claims made by this witness, this convicted drug smuggler," answered Haskitt, thereby lifting the Judge's hopes that there might be a way to suppress this information, the public revelation of which could spell personal disaster for him.

"Quite so, Mr Haskitt. You instruct the police to instigate their enquiries in the appropriate directions whilst we embark upon the trial."

"I am not anxious to delay matters further, My Lord, but we would ask Your Lordship to allow us a little while to discuss this development with the officers in this case and to arrange for other officers, who have nothing to do with this case, to conduct the interviews suggested"

"Yes. You may have half an hour to make those arrangements. Then we shall proceed with the trial. You can inform the Defence of the results by the end of the day, but there is no reason to delay the start of the trial. As you rightly say, there would appear to be good reason why this witness cannot be called in any event," announced Hathington, giving Haskitt every possible encouragement that he could, to go down the line of keeping Jardine out of it. Staring directly at Haskitt as he spoke, so as to reinforce the message, he got up and left the Court.

Picking up his piece of blue paper Haskitt headed for a conference room, directing Lampard to collect David Nathan, Perry and Noble and bring them along immediately.

Ten minutes later, the five men were huddled together in one of the small conference rooms, where the blue pieces of paper were passed around Nathan, Perry and Noble, who duly read and digested the content. Perry was in a dark grey suit which had turned shiny with wear, a faded green shirt and floral patterned tie. Haskitt noticed with distaste that his hair looked more unwashed than ever, his fingernails were dirty and, despite his outward appearance of calm on reading the document, he was sweating profusely.

"Well?" demanded Haskitt in Perry's direction. "What's the story here?"

"No story, sir. It was an ordinary arrest of a fool of a kid and another dealer. A straightforward case where they both had to plead guilty as the evidence was overwhelming. Jardine's case was adjourned for sentence because he was ill and the Judge wanted an up-to-date medical report and she gave him three years this morning. In fact the sentence was a disgrace 'cos he should have got six or seven. Five at the very least. That's all there is to it. I did nothing wrong," replied Perry, his voice rising with self-righteous indignation as he protested his innocence.

"But what about this missing fifteen hundred quid?" barked Haskitt.

"There never was any missing fifteen hundred quid. No money went in my back pocket. It's garbage," snapped Perry aggressively.

"Why's he say it, then?" enquired Haskitt forcefully.

"These little shits will say anything. Listen, the first thing you need to do is look at his taped interview after arrest. All of the papers'll be here in this building and his lawyers'll still be here, so I suggest you get the transcript now and you'll see that I asked him how much he got paid for the run. I specifically remember asking the question in the interview. You read his fucking answer, Mr Haskitt, then perhaps your tone will be slightly different. I don't mean to be rude, sir, but this is crap and you appear to be taking it seriously. The kid's a drug smuggler. His word's worth shit," Perry insisted angrily.

"Right, we'll do that now. Get his lawyers. Get a senior officer from another station, Mr Noble, who knows nothing about this case. Get him down in the cells with Jardine's lawyers and check him out. In particular, read the interview, find the section that Sergeant Perry refers to and hit him with it. Have it all tape-recorded. Do an identical operation at Strangeways with Mount. Now. This morning. Sergeant Perry, you said that was the first thing to do. What else?" commanded Haskitt, warming to his task as he saw the prospect of making Cadogan look very stupid, so long as Perry kept his cool.

"The man behind this allegation will be Trevors. Somehow there must have been contact between Trevors and Jardine and we need to find out how. They've both been in the nick, but I thought that Jardine had been in Strangeways until this morning. We need to speak to the prisons where each of them has been. If you find a point of contact then you'll have your answers," asserted Perry.

"Good thinking Perry, put it in hand. You may even get the answer from the prison officers down in the cells at the moment. Anyone else got anything to say?" enquired Haskitt.

"Nothing at all," replied David Nathan.

"Just one matter," interjected Lampard. "Do you have a particular reason to really rub it in for Trevors? Is there some history somewhere, because if there is we need to know, it could prove to be very important?"

"No history. Nothing. I knew that he'd been a target criminal on a Division I worked on some time ago but I'd never been involved in any enquiry concerning him and I'd never set eyes on him before I pulled him in for this murder. As for Jardine, I'd never even heard of him until the drugs case when I received a tip-off from a snout that there was a student bringing drugs in at Manchester. So I put the feelers out, identified the face and locked him up. There's no history and no pinching the notes. Nothing."

"You need to understand, Sergeant," continued Lampard, "that it's very important that we know everything. Correct, Bertrand?"

"Correct," nodded Haskitt.

"There's nothing more to know," Perry assured them.

"Then I'd like to get cracking with this immediately," announced Noble, speaking for the first time. "How about you gentlemen starting the case in Court. I'll have a quick word with Perry in here and then we'll put the wheels in motion. We'll have everything for you by the end of the day."

Noble and Perry shuffled back their chairs to make room for the exit of the lawyers and, as the door closed behind them, Noble leaned across the table and stared straight into Perry's eyes.

"I've watched you for quite a while now, Perry, and I don't much like what I've seen," he began.

"So you're saying that you'd take the word of a convicted crackhead over mine, are you Sir?"

"That's what we're about to find out. You think you're above the rules. If it's true..."

"Well, it's not true, Governor," Perry interrupted. "Trevors is behind this, mark my words."

"So you say. But I dread to think what else you may have been up to in his case. You'd better hope we can sit on this Jardine business, I can tell you. I just hope that this isn't the case that brings you down, 'cos I see no reason for Jardine to come up with this little lot, no reason at all."

"I tell you, it'll be Trevors. I don't know what he's got on Jardine. Money, favours, threats, whatever. Let me loose on it and I'll find out. They've met. They're in cahoots," Perry continued.

"Let's get on with it then," said Noble. "But you stay out of it. Right out of it. I'll get Bill Clayton from Bradford CID. Very senior. Very quick and very reliable. You'll know where you stand soon enough"

"I've nothing to be worried about and I'm getting pissed off with the flak that's coming my way. I'm a quality copper. Tough but straight."

"Let's hope the jury thinks so," replied Noble with a sigh. "They're the ones that you've got to convince."

* * *

The jury panel filed slowly into Court. The players were all in place.

"Stand up, Gary Peter Trevors," declared the Clerk of the Court. "The names you are about to hear are the names of the jurors who are to try you. If you object to them or any of them, you should do so as they come to the book to be sworn and before they are sworn and your objection shall be heard.

"Members of the jury in waiting, will you please answer to your names as they are called and step into the jury box on my left, in the order in which you are called."

"Tracy Havard"
    27. Blonde. Thick make-up. Telephone sales assistant. Lives with male partner, factory worker. Rented flat. Never voted.

"Saffad Aziz"
    21. Female. Asian. Sari. Spectacles. Single. Waiting to start business course at local college. Lives above newsagents' shop owned by parents. Never voted.

"Daniel Fitzgerald"
    60. Irish. Left school at 15. Labourer for twenty-five years. Now claims Disability Benefit (various chest conditions, heavy smoker, heavy drinker). Divorced. Lives alone in council-owned high rise. Only voted twice, both times Labour.

"Darren Perkins"
    23. Single. Grade 1 haircut. Tattoo of small bird on left side of neck. Unemployed. Never worked since leaving school at 16. Lives at home with mother. Father unknown. Two children by different mothers. Makes no financial contribution. Voted once, Labour.

"Ann Goodhall"
    58. Office cleaner. Married. Three grown-up children. Husband, van driver. Always votes Conservative.

"Richard Spiers"
    44. Divorced. No children. Computer technician. Teetotal. Votes Liberal-Democrat.

"Christine Mills"
    31. Married. Housewife. Husband, Managing Director of Design Company. One child, 7. Own house on mortgage. Voted once. Conservative.

"Dennis Aulton"
    39. Married. One grown-up child. Milkman, but made redundant last year. Doesn't expect to work again. Always votes Labour.

"Lee Buffey"
    18. Lives in lodgings. Mother's whereabouts unknown. Father

serving 2 year prison sentence in Spain for assault. Excluded from school in last year. Passed no exams. Never worked. Lives on Benefits. Has asked to repeat oath as dictated by Clerk, says dsylexic. Never voted.

"Leroy Beckford"
20. West Indian. Single. Unemployed. Lives alone in rented flat. Earrings both ears. Anti-police (wrongly arrested twice). Never voted.

"Jane Wheeler"
28. Single. Schoolteacher. Lives with partner, female. Buying house together on mortgage. Very short hair. Butch. Will affirm, won't take oath on bible. Votes Green.

"Roger Frobisher"
38. Married. Two children, 11 and 9. Electrical engineer. Wife, computer recruitment consultant. Owns detached house on mortgage. Votes Conservative.

After the jury had been sworn, the Clerk of the Court put the Defendant in their charge, reading out the words of each charge. Then, after months of preparation and manoeuvrings, the decks were at last cleared and the hostilities could commence.

"Yes, Mr Haskitt," the Judge announced grandly, "we are ready for you to open the case to the jury. Let us begin."

In graphic and florid terms Haskitt embarked upon his opening to the jury, providing every last detail of the injuries to the Checkleys, dwelling on the gruesome photographs of the disfiguring wounds to the wife and the fatal stab wounds to her husband. He spoke of the stealth of the intruder, the extent of the planning, the viciousness of the attacks and reminded the jury, ad nauseam, that they were trying a dangerous and ruthless killer. Their duty, having properly reviewed the evidence, would be to convict this Defendant. No other verdict would realistically be left available to them. The Prosecution would present a wealth of evidence against Trevors but his objective at this early stage, he explained, would be merely to highlight some of the reasons why it was so clear that the police had got the right man.

Skilfully, he sought to transport the jury to Trevor's squalid flat as he gathered together his burglar's paraphernalia.

"Members of the jury, you may picture this man preparing for the operation. Obtaining his thin rubber gloves, his ballet shoes, his balaclava-type mask. Determined to leave nothing to chance he lengthened the mask, so that no part of his skin or hair would be visible, even if someone tried to pull the mask up or off. His victim would not even know whether he was white or black. But he hadn't bargained for the remarkable resistance of Sarah Checkley. The trace of blood on the inside of that material, and we know it is the inside from the pattern of the stitching, is of a DNA profile which matches his."

Eventually, as the hands of the large Courtroom clock approached one o'clock the Judge caught Haskitt's eye, conveying the judicial signal that it was time for lunch.

"My Lord," responded Haskitt obligingly, "I am approaching the end of my opening and I observe that it is almost one o'clock. Would that be a convenient moment to adjourn for lunch?"

"Yes, Mr Haskitt, it would," replied Hathington. "Members of the jury, we shall now adjourn for refreshment. I must direct you that, during this adjournment and at all times that we are apart, you must not discuss this case with anyone outside your own number. You must not talk about it to your family, your friends, or anyone. You have sworn to try the case upon the evidence, not upon the opinions of your family or friends who have not heard the evidence. It is your verdict, uninfluenced by outside sources who have not heard the evidence, that the Court requires. Please bear that in mind throughout the duration of the case. We shall resume at 2.15."

"Court rise!" shouted the Clerk, and Mr Justice Hathington, grabbing his white gloves from the bench, rose and headed for his chambers, the limousine, the Lodgings and Helen Gaynor.

Before Hathington even had the chance to remove his wig, the telephone on the desk in his chambers rang out shrilly and, knowing exactly who it would be on the line, he asked his clerk to withdraw whilst he dealt with a personal matter.

"Sir Michael Hathington here," he began.

"Michael, just a quick call to point out that the outcome is viewed as very satisfactory," declared the Ministerial voice. "Very satisfactory indeed."

"I don't yet know the outcome," said Hathington.

"Three years."

"Three years. I see. Well, it's raised a serious problem. Potentially very serious," came the worried reply. "This boy, on whose behalf I passed on a character reference, may now become a witness for the Defence in the murder trial over which I am presiding."

"Then, why didn't you mention that when I spoke to you earlier?" demanded Denstone, unable to disguise the anger in his tone. "That would have made it impossible."

"Because I didn't know then, for goodness sake. It's only just happened," snapped Hathington. "Anyway, so far, the name and the circumstances have not been mentioned in open Court and I've managed to put a temporary embargo on the name. But that may not last. If the name does come out it could be extremely awkward. Gaynor's the only area of risk. She'd know that I'd presided over a trial where I'd communicated material to her, favouring a Defence witness in my trial. My impartiality would be blown out of the water. And the evidence that the boy could give is highly newsworthy, allegations of a crooked police officer."

"Well, you'd better sit on that name and ensure that the boy doesn't give evidence, hadn't you?" declared Denstone. "Keep me posted. If it does go pear-shaped and Gaynor chooses to say anything, then she could only speak to the Lord Chancellor's Department. So long as you give me a few hours notice I should be able to handle that. But your job is to see it doesn't reach that stage, I'm sure you understand."

"I'll do what I can," answered Hathington disconsolately.

"You will remember, won't you, that under no circumstances can my name or the Department ever be mentioned in any of this, whatever happens. These phone calls have never taken place. They are routed in such a way that they are quite untraceable. We have never spoken on this matter, never," Denstone ordered.

"I understand the way it works. Always have."

"Right. I've every confidence that you'll handle things at your end just fine. Look forward to seeing you and Laura for dinner when you're back in London. Bye."

The phone went dead and Michael Hathington prepared himself for the limousine trip to the Lodgings and the prospect of an acutely embarrassing lunch with Helen Gaynor. However, when he climbed into the Daimler, Mrs Justice Gaynor was conspicuous by her absence. Apparently, an apple and a carrot in her chambers were infinitely preferable to sitting opposite her fellow Judge for an hour and a quarter, pretending that everything was hunky-dory. As he picked disinterestedly at the miserable ham salad that the Lodgings' chef had served up as an excuse for lunch, the haughty butler entered the dining room with a letter that had arrived that morning and discreetly placed it alongside the Judge's plate, postmarked London and endorsed as 'Personal'.

Hathington swiftly slit the white envelope open with the silver bread knife and scanned the few lines, plainly written in a female hand, whilst the butler hovered in the background. A fleeting smile of satisfaction appeared on the Judge's face as he turned to the butler and curtly declared that he would be dining out tonight and the chef was to be informed accordingly.

* * *

As Haskitt concluded his opening, an atmosphere of intense anticipation pervaded the whole courtroom. Naomi Nicholas was filled with a sense of great sorrow, as the lonely figure of Sarah Checkley walked slowly towards the isolation of the witness box. Dressed in a severe, black suit with her blonde hair scraped back and held in a neat French pleat, she looked as if she was marching to her own execution. Her back was ramrod straight and her eyes stared straight ahead, never wandering in the direction of the dock. From beginning to end she never looked at the face of the man who she knew had murdered her husband, cut open her own body and ruined her life. She gave her evidence as if the murderer himself did not exist, as if he was a dead man who had done unpardonable wrong and was now being erased, eliminated from the world and publicly disposed of. Her evidence was his burial in limestone.

Her voice was strong, her conviction was absolute as she recounted every last gruesome detail. Haskitt was left with little to ask for, at a slow and deliberate pace, in her own way, she literally transported the jury back to that dreadful scene and, in clinical detail, described the evil perpetrated by the monster in the dock. Never saying anything that directly proved he was the killer, she told the jury, by her tone, by her looks, by the expression in her eyes, by the movements of her body, that the man in the dock was the murderer of her husband.

Trevors stared intently at her, his dead, soulless eyes never wavering from her face. As the sense of outrage in the courtroom grew, so various jurors turned to look at him, imagining the ballet shoes being pulled upon his size 9 or 10 feet, the woollen balaclava upon his head, the knife viciously ripping open the flesh of this dignified lady in black and taking the life of her husband.

Cadogan watched her like a hawk. Whenever he could, he stole looks at the jury and surveyed the deadly impact that this witness was having upon them. With every word she spoke, every toss of her attractive head, their thirst for revenge on her behalf was growing. If she could give them just one firm piece of evidence to tie this murder to Trevors, then the chances were that they would convict him. But, despite the horror of it all, the only direct link she was capable of providing was the subsequent identification by voice. That is what he had to try and exclude from the jury's hearing and, as she approached that stage in her evidence, Cadogan rose to inform the Judge that a matter of Law must now be argued in the absence of the jury.

His argument was fluent and had been prepared over many hours. The evidence of the Voice Identification Parade was inadmissible, he declared emphatically, and must be excluded from the jury's considerations. He explained to the Judge that no expert evidence was to be called by the Prosecution to lay the ground which might enable the jury to understand how similar different voices may sound to someone from a different locality if they shared the same dialect. Two Irishmen may sound very similar to a Londoner and yet, to a Dubliner, they would be as different as chalk from cheese. He submitted that a criminal of the sophistication of the one who had committed this murder may easily have put on a false voice and a false accent which, by chance alone, had happened to coincide with one of the men on the parade attended by Mrs Checkley. The Prosecution, he contended, were not calling a linguist or an expert in dialects, to explain to a lay jury how these matters may affect the safety of any purported identification by voice. No attempt at all was being made, he claimed, to show a jury how acoustics may affect the sound of a voice in one setting and yet make it sound similar in another setting.

Thereafter he turned to the Law. He defied his opponent to produce one precedent of a Voice Identification Parade being allowed to go before a jury in English Law without some expert foundation dealing with the possibilities of disguise, distortion by the mask and other technical effects. He asserted that voice identification evidence generally posed far more dangers than eye witness evidence of visual identification and, as the cases showed, there had been numerous examples of injustices on eye witness identification. In this case, he continued, the spoken words relied upon had been very few. Moreover, they had been delivered in circumstances of extreme stress, when the chances for error must be at their highest, and the purported identification at the parade was also in stressful conditions. He concluded that the Prosecution, without calling any expert evidence on the subject, were inviting the Judge to break new ground, make new Law on the hoof, lay himself open to severe censure by the Court of Appeal and to expose a man to the risk of conviction for murder, on material which lay within uncharted territory.

Haskitt's response was equally well rehearsed. This was a witness of quality, he submitted to the Judge. This was not an impetuous, reckless woman struggling to remember these events. Mrs Checkley had fluent, detailed recall. She was consistent, careful, calm and balanced. All of these virtues were relevant to the Judge's appraisal of her reliability and her capacity to remember the nuances of the killer's voice, the sounds of the vowels, the pitch of delivery. The parade itself had been conducted in strictly controlled conditions with the consent of the Defendant and his solicitor. Juries did not need experts to tell them that sometimes voices of the same dialect might sound similar to a foreigner. A sensible jury could make all proper allowances for such eventuality. The test for this jury was, judging the quality of this particular witness, whether or not they believed she had the capacity for accurate recognition.

Mr Justice Hathington had remained completely silent from beginning to end of these arguments, noting virtually every word as each point was urged upon him. His objective, if at all possible, was to allow the Crown to lay the evidence of the Voice Identification Parade before the jury. He was quite prepared to strain every metaphorical muscle to achieve this. However, he had to act within the constraints of legal precedent otherwise, in the event of a conviction, Cadogan would undoubtedly be dragging him through the Court of Appeal and, with the dreaded Jardine factor still looming ominously in the background, the last thing he wanted was to provide the Defence with a guaranteed Ground of Appeal. Haskitt must provide him with a proper basis in Law for the admission of this category of evidence.

Naomi Nicholas watched Hathington grapple with the problem and relished his obvious discomfort. Whilst she had no idea that the added dimension of Hathington's conscience on the Jardine question was contributing significantly to his dilemma, she nonetheless recognised that this was a serious evidential problem of extremely significant proportions. It was a tough decision for any Judge, let alone one who had no real experience of Criminal Law. Did Hathington have the guts to admit a highly unusual type of parade and defy Cadogan? She very much doubted it. As Jack had pointed out, most bullies were cowards at heart and she had seen nothing to suggest that Hathington would prove to be the exception. Eventually, as the arguments wore on through the afternoon, Hathington spoke, and the message in the question he threw at Haskitt, confirmed Naomi in her views.

"Mr Haskitt," interposed the Judge, "your argument is sound and persuasive on the facts. I am clearly of the view that the jury would be entitled, if they see fit, to assess Mrs Checkley as a witness of high quality. However, it is the principle of Law that is causing me some concern. Have you been able to identify a criminal case where the precedent has been established to admit evidence of a Voice Identification Parade, unsupported by any linguistics expert, in such specific circumstances as we have here?"

"My Lord, it is not incumbent upon me to do so. If Your Lordship concludes that the parade was properly and fairly conducted and that the witness is capable of belief, then it is for the jury to assess the value of the parade as a question of fact, rather than for Your Lordship to do so as a question of Law."

"Whether that is right or not, Mr Haskitt, I would be grateful if you could deal with my actual question. Have you found a precedent or not? If there was one in similar circumstances it might ease my task."

"I would argue, My Lord, that the absence or existence of exact precedent does not necessarily provide the definitive answer to this question. The resolution of this issue lies within your Lordship's discretion and …"

"Then I take it that the answer to my question is 'no'," interrupted the Judge with more than a hint of irritation in his voice.

"I accept that," conceded Haskitt ungraciously, "but I submit that absence of precedent is not fatal to the admissibility of this evidence…"

"Yes, thank you very much, Mr Haskitt," interposed the Judge. "It is now twenty past four and too late to resume with the jury this afternoon. I shall give this problem the most careful consideration overnight and deliver my judgement at ten fifteen tomorrow morning. The jury will return at ten thirty. Kindly close the Court formally."

Haskitt slumped back in his seat and, so as to avoid any contact with Cadogan, waiting for several minutes after the adjournment of the Court, before gathering his papers and heading for the small conference room previously commandeered by Mr Nathan. Dickie Lampard and Nathan were already in place when Haskitt came in, still gowned but minus his wig. His lank hair was stuck to his forehead with the sweat generated by his desperate argument to Hathington and his distrustful eyes were blinking nervously behind the rimless glasses.

"We're likely to lose the parade evidence," he grunted as he lowered his stick-like body on to one of the vacant plastic chairs. "This case needed a Judge who knew the ropes, not some mercenary from the Commercial Division. One of the old breed who had the nouse to massage the rules."

Neither Lampard nor Nathan was prepared to interrupt this lament by Leading Counsel. They knew that Cadogan had almost certainly out-argued Haskitt and there was no purpose in pretending to the contrary, so they sat in silence, as Haskitt continued to blame Hathington until he was interrupted by the arrival of Noble and Perry with the results of the Jardine enquiries.

Perry looked like the cat who had stolen the cream as Noble recounted the details.

"Number one," Noble began. "Jardine and Trevors shared a cell over the weekend in Armley Gaol. They were together continuously from the Friday night to the Monday morning. Jardine wrote out his allegations on paper provided by Trevors. Said it came about because he saw Perry's name on Trevor's case papers, which were on the table in the cell and they got to talking."

"Just like I was saying to you, Mr Haskitt. It's crap. Exactly what I…" exclaimed Perry, before Noble simply ignored him and continued.

"Number two. Derek Mount won't speak to no one. We can't make him. He's in the custody of HMP. Unless we suspect him of a further offence we can't arrest him and interview him, so we're dependent on his consent. He told the screws that he doesn't want to know."

"Finally, whilst Jardine insisted to Superintendent Clayton, the officer we put in charge of this enquiry, that what he'd said was true and that there was originally a pay-off of three thousand pounds, it is the fact that in his taped interview under caution he said and I quote:

"Question from Mr Perry. Booked in as an exhibit is the fifteen hundred pounds that I recovered from you on arrest. Does that represent your total pay-off?

Answer from Jardine. Yes. End of quote."

"In short, it was all bullshit, Mr Haskitt," interjected Perry. They can't make any of it stick. They are shit and they talk shit. Just let them try it on me in the witness box with any of this stuff and I'll stick it right up that Cadogan's arse. I'm ready for him," he threatened, quite unable to contain himself any longer.

"Yes, that'll do, Perry, thank you," declared Noble. "Any further enquiries we can make on this overnight, sir?"

"No. Let's hope that's enough for us to deal with it, if Cadogan decides to run this particular hare. I almost hope he does, now that you've done your homework. Well done. No doubt you have all of this in writing, Mr Noble. I'd ask you to give a copy to Mr Nathan and he'll serve it upon the Defence and the Judge," directed Haskitt. "It's time to get back to my accommodation and prepare for tomorrow. I'll bid you all good afternoon."

"Not one word of bloody apology," grumbled Perry after the departure of the lawyers. "He believed the bastard. I know he did."

"He wasn't the only one either, Perry," grunted Noble. "The only difference is that I still do."

CHAPTER 19

Haskitt was close to despair, for he believed that if the Judge excluded the Voice Identification Parade evidence, then there was a real possibility that a murderer would walk and, even worse, Cadogan would have achieved a humiliating victory of epic proportions. For much of the night Haskitt lay awake, tossing and turning, incessantly rehearsing the argument as to why the evidence was admissible, whilst realising throughout, that only the most robust and experienced judgement from Hathington could save him and, from what he could see, this inadequate Judge was running scared.

At a quarter past six in the morning he eventually abandoned all attempts to extract any more sleep from the endless night and threw back the starched bedclothes, feeling like death. Knowing that Cadogan would be staying in the city's only 5 Star Hotel he had chosen to find safe accommodation a few miles north on the road to Harrogate. Tucked away on the edge of a small village near to one of the great old Estates of Yorkshire lay the Chair with Three Legs, a hostelry which currently boasted a chef of international reputation. The identity of the chef was a closely guarded secret because his term of service at the Chair with Three Legs was an act of self-imposed exile, designed to provide escape from the wrath of a minor Prince in Riyadh in whose Royal Palace he had been working as the Master Chef. An indiscreet dalliance with the Prince's youngest daughter had led to an attempt to skewer him on one of his own boning knives and he had fled the Kingdom in fear of his life. The attraction of a small hostelry on the edges of the Yorkshire countryside had provided the refuge he sought and, working under an assumed name, he had been lying low for the best part of a year whilst his supreme culinary skills had transformed the pub into a celebrated venue amongst the gourmets of the North. Acting on a recommendation, Haskitt had booked himself into one of the four residential bedrooms for the duration of the trial. However, he had returned there last night in a state of such deep depression, that he had foregone dinner and ordered a cold plate to be delivered to his room. Now, as he pulled on a black, thick, polo-necked jumper and a pair of corduroy trousers, the half-eaten chicken salad stared forlornly at him from the plate sitting on the dressing table in the early morning light. A short walk in the bracing air before breakfast might help revive him and prepare him for the ordeal of the day that lay ahead.

Slipping down the carpeted stairs and out through the main doorway on to the car park there was no sign of life at all. The windows on his Volvo Estate, and the black Mercedes saloon parked alongside it, were rendered opaque by the layers of thick ice that the long night had brought and his breath froze on the morning air as he briskly made his way towards the narrow lane and the village beyond.

After fifteen minutes of hard walking, the dull ache at the back of his head had slowly started to recede and he retraced his steps back towards the pub to take a hot bath, before sampling the promised full English breakfast which might lift his spirits. As he neared the car park he espied the day's first signs of human life. A fellow guest was emerging from a side entrance of the pub and heading towards the black Mercedes. Haskitt observed the man, incongruously dapper at that early hour in a dark, pin-striped suit, placing a small overnight Gucci bag in the boot, before battling to scrape the hardened ice from the car's windscreen with a sharp-edged plastic tool. Even from a distance, Haskitt noticed something familiar about the figure, his quick movements and the shape of the head. So engrossed was the Mercedes owner in his task, that he neither heard nor saw Haskitt's approach and the two men were virtually on top of one another before the man looked up and, in obvious horror, stared into the unshaven, cadaverous face of Leading Counsel for the Crown. There was a silence of several seconds before either man regained sufficient composure to speak.

"Good morning to you, Judge," spluttered a bemused Haskitt, knowing full well that a High Court Judge trying a case on circuit was required to reside in the Lodgings and could have no legitimate business skulking out of a country pub at a quarter to seven in the morning. Every movement that Mr Justice Hathington was now making exuded acute discomfort and Haskitt's nose visibly twitched as he smelt scandal in the Yorkshire air.

"What the hell are you doing here, Haskitt?" blustered Hathington, characteristically deciding that attack was the best means of defence.

"I'm staying at this pub, Judge. I've a room here for the duration of our trial. Is there some problem with the accommodation at the Lodgings that brings you out here?" retorted Haskitt.

Hathington's eyes darted around the car park as he ensured that no one else was about and then took a step closer towards Haskitt.

"Listen closely, Haskitt," he barked, abandoning all pretence that his presence in these circumstances could have any innocent explanation. "You know that there's no problem at the Lodgings. My own personal arrangements are none of your bloody business. If I want to take dinner out with a bottle of wine and avoid driving back at night, then that's my choice. If you put it around that you have seen me, then your name will not be well received in the corridors of power. Do we understand one another?"

"There's no need to be quite so aggressive about it, Judge, if you don't mind me saying. It's hardly my fault that I've bumped into you in compromising circumstances," Haskitt responded directly into the angry, bearded face of the Judge, realising from the ferocity of Hathington's overreaction that some dark secret must lie behind the Judge's rendezvous at the pub. Knowing what he did about Hathington, there was bound to be a woman tucked away inside that cosy pub. It mattered not whether it was a tart or a Duchess. Hathington could simply not afford for anyone to know. Slipping away from the Lodgings at night during a murder trial to screw some woman behind his wife's back would ruin him, whatever connections he might have in high places.

"Compromising? Compromising? Your choice of word is extremely unfortunate. I would remind you that you're talking to one of Her Majesty's Justices. It's necessary that we behave as if this meeting has never taken place. You haven't seen me. I haven't seen you. I shall require your word upon it now, this instant." Hathington spat out the orders with such intensity that Haskitt now knew for sure that the Judge was completely cornered and that a heavy price could be exacted for his silence. Such opportunities were few and far between and Haskitt wasted no time in spelling out his demands.

"If you say so, Judge. I'll make no mention of this meeting. You have my word on that," he agreed, speaking in soft and conciliatory tones, observing Hathington beginning to relax at this response. "Of course," he then added, with an edge to his voice that made the Judge suddenly stiffen in horror, "I'm looking forward to a successful morning in Court."

"Are you offering me terms, Haskitt? I trust not. I do hope that I've misread your meaning. It would be a very serious mistake, wouldn't it? Seeking to influence judicial decisions?" declared Hathington with a discernible hint of menace in his voice.

"Quite so, quite so," agreed Haskitt with a smile. "It was just a polite changing of the subject. Your secret is absolutely safe with me. After all, the whole profession would suffer if the papers got hold of this and splashed it across the front page. You can count on my discretion and we can both get on with the trial, listening to the evidence of the Voice Identification and all of that."

"The papers got hold of what, Haskitt?" barked Hathington.

"You know Judge, got hold of the wrong end of the stick. Now, I must be off, if you'll excuse me. Time for breakfast and a pleasant chat with the other guests. I'll bid you good morning and see you later in Court."

Without waiting for any reply Haskitt turned on his heel and hurried away towards the pub entrance and the breakfast room. It was essential that he established who it was that had made Hathington run such an enormous risk. As he pushed open the heavy oak door he looked back quickly over his shoulder. Predictably, the Judge was sitting in the driver's seat of the Mercedes, the door standing half open, and he was frantically pressing the buttons on a mobile phone. Doubtless, the lady was being warned to remain in her room until after Haskitt had left for Court. Had she already come downstairs? As soon as he was through the door, Haskitt ran down the flagstoned hall towards the small breakfast room at the side of the main bar. At the exact second that his hand turned the brass knob and he entered the room, he heard the high-pitched warbling of a mobile phone ringing within. Only one table was occupied. Its occupant was a coarsely attractive lady with a low-cut blouse, heavily made up, but still showing the signs underneath the foundation cream of having expended a good deal of energy during the night. As she fumbled to press the answer button on her phone she turned to observe who it was that had entered the room. Her recognition of Haskitt and her connecting to the voice on the phone were simultaneous. "But I'm already downstairs, it's too late, I'm afraid," she blurted out spontaneously to the caller as a look of utter disbelief appeared on her face.

Haskitt smiled politely at her before discreetly withdrawing from the room, allowing the delectable but flustered Della Montanari to continue her urgent call in privacy. "He's seen me, Michael. He just came in," were the last words he heard her uttering, as he closed the door quietly behind him.

On reflection, he would take a relaxing, hot bath before breakfast and picture the Honourable Mr Justice Hathington surreptitiously stealing in through a back door of the Lodgings, hurriedly rewriting his judgement on the admissibility of some crucial evidence and then going down for breakfast with Mrs Justice Gaynor, as if he had spent a peaceful night upstairs. That invitation to the Glanville's dinner party must have been preordained he thought to himself, as he slipped his long, white, hairless body into the piping hot bath water.

Hathington's judgement had driven Cadogan into a cold fury. He had completely ignored the arguments about the Law, declaring that, even without expert linguistics evidence, there was a direct analogy between an Identification Parade held to assess physical appearance and one to assess the sound of a distinctive voice. So long as the jury were directed by the Judge, as he repeatedly assured everyone that they would be, that they must approach the evidence with great care, then justice demanded that this evidence be admitted. As the Judge put down his pen at the conclusion of his judgement on this issue, justice was the last thing on his mind. Justice had not demanded that the evidence be admitted. It had been Haskitt's blackmail that had made the demand that the evidence be admitted and, as far as Hathington was concerned, blackmail carried far more weight than any notion of justice.

Upon the return of the jury to Court, Mrs Checkley had embarked upon her chilling narrative of the parade and her absolute certainty when Number 5 in the parade had spoken. It had seemed devastating, but the time had now come for Cadogan to show these provincial hacks and this ill-chosen Commercial Judge, how the job was done at the top end of the Criminal market.

Cadogan:
> From the hospital to the police station where the Identification Parade was held has been measured at 3.8 miles. Who drove you on that journey?

Checkley:
> Detective Sergeant Perry. He collected me at about ten o'clock.

Cadogan:
> And the drive would take about ten to fifteen minutes? Would you agree?

Checkley:
> About that long I would imagine.

Cadogan:
> Mr Sylvester, the Defendant's solicitor, noted your time of arrival at the Station as 10.41 a.m. Why had it taken you about 41 minutes to cover 3.8 miles?

Checkley:
> Mr Perry must have arrived late.

Cadogan:

How late?

Checkley:

Five minutes, maybe ten. I really don't know.

Cadogan:

Let us assume the longer. Ten minutes late. Why had it taken 31 minutes to cover such a short distance?

Checkley:

Perhaps your Mr Sylvester's watch was fast.

Cadogan:

No. A few minutes after your arrival the Inspector asked you to sign the Parade Form. That is noted as 10.47a.m. The times confirm that your journey took in excess of half an hour. Why?

Checkley:

You'd better ask Mr Perry about the traffic conditions. That was a very traumatic morning for me. I can't be expected to deal with every detail of the car journey.

Sarah Checkley's hands were gripping the narrow shelf inside the witness box so tightly that her fingers were beginning to ache whilst Cadogan, in the space of half a dozen questions, had immediately identified and exposed the weakness in her account, making it increasingly difficult for her to remain calm.

Cadogan:

En route did you and Mr Perry stop and conduct any kind of discussion, about the parade?

Checkley:

I believe that Mr Perry stopped the car at one point because he was concerned at my state of health and wished to confirm that I was fit to continue. I'm not sure, but I think that may have happened. As a matter of fact, I don't feel at all well in this Courtroom. Your questions sound as though I am the criminal not the victim.

Cadogan:

You were undoubtedly the victim, Mrs Checkley. My questions are designed to investigate whether you are the only victim in this Courtroom, or whether my client is also a victim. Can't you help us as to what was said when Mr Perry stopped the car?

Mr Justice Hathington:

Mrs Checkley. You said a moment ago that you were not feeling well. I wonder whether a short break might be appropriate?

Checkley:

I would welcome a break, My Lord. I'm still weak and this is a great strain for me.

Mr Justice Hathington:

Of course. Kindly go with the usher and she will arrange for you to have a cup of tea. Members of the jury, perhaps you would also retire while we give the witness time to recover. I'm sure that we all understand that this is an ordeal for her.

Cadogan quietly resumed his seat as the witness was led away and the jury filed out of the side door to their room. His instinct seldom let him down. Perry had found a way to tip her off. His sort was as predictable as rain on a Bank Holiday. The skill now lay in communicating to the jury that this is what had happened, without ever actually suggesting it. If he spelled it out, then Haskitt would be granted leave to cross-examine Trevors on his previous convictions when Trevors went into the witness box. However, Cadogan had walked this tightrope too many times before to fall off, particularly when the only characters tugging at him were of the calibre of Hathington and Haskitt.

"I didn't wish to interrupt my learned friend," Haskitt announced, "but I really do wonder where this line of questioning is going. Now that the jury is not present, Your Lordship may wish to establish with Mr Cadogan the precise relevance of these questions. Is it to be suggested that there was some impropriety between the witness and the officer concerning the authenticity of the parade? If so, then my learned friend should be warned that the consequences of such suggestion will likely be the admission of his client's previous convictions when I come to cross-examine the Defendant."

"Yes, Mr Haskitt. You have touched upon the very matter that was exercising my mind. What do you say, Mr Cadogan?" asked the Judge.

"I say that the state of mind of the witness at the time of the parade is highly relevant. Was she in a state of such anxiety in the car that the officer had to stop to calm her down? Was she so agitated that her reliability may have been affected? May the officer inadvertently have said something to her, attempting perhaps to soothe her nerves, which influenced her in some way? There are numerous possibilities. They are relevant. They are legitimate. My learned friend has no basis to object."

"Yes. Very well, Mr Cadogan. Thank you. No doubt you will ensure that certain lines are not crossed in the way that you conduct such enquiry," observed the Judge. "We'll resume in ten minutes."

Sarah Checkley was seated in the corner of the grubby witness waiting room in a state of extreme anger. This man Cadogan seemed to have worked out exactly how Perry operated. His questions had already made it sound like she and Perry had spent half an hour cooking up a plan, whereby she would be secretly pointed in Trevors' direction and, in truth, that is precisely what had happened.

Every question that Cadogan had asked made her feel that he had been there in the car with them. And it was all completely unnecessary, for she had known that voice in an instant. She would have recognised it out of a thousand voices, but that manipulator Perry had to bend the rules and compromise her. She had already lied on her oath and she knew that, by the time Cadogan had finished with her, there would have to be numerous further lies. Finishing off the insipid cup of tea that had been provided, she got up and prepared to return to Court. Compromised or not, she would fight to the end. Nothing would stop her. The owner of that voice would never see the light of day again if she had anything to do with it. Cadogan might better her on intellect but, when it came to determination, she would show him. The usher guided her back into the Court and she readied herself for combat as the massive figure of the Defence QC rose to his feet to continue his onslaught. His first question showed that, despite her state of health, he still had no time for the niceties.

Cadogan:
Well, Mrs Checkley, what did you discuss whilst you were stationary?

Checkley:
I imagine that Mr Perry just tried to put me at my ease. It was my first day out of hospital. I was weak and this parade was bound to be an ordeal.

Cadogan:
What did he say to put you at your ease?

Checkley:
I don't remember. He probably asked how I was feeling. No more than that.

Cadogan:
Other than stopping for what, on your description, can only have

been for a moment's conversation, do you offer any other material for the jury to consider as to the inordinate length of this car journey?

Checkley:

No. I don't. Nothing else happened.

Cadogan:

Why did you stop at man Number 5, and not at least listen to the other five men on the parade?

Checkley:

I knew it was his voice as soon as he spoke. I shall never forget it.

Cadogan:

How many voices that you heard in that room that morning, other than Number 5, had a north-eastern accent?

Checkley:

I believe that Number 5 was the only one.

Cadogan:

Precisely. So is the position that, as soon as a man spoke with a north-eastern accent, you declared it was the intruder?

Checkley:

Only because...well... it's difficult to explain...

In the dock Trevors was imperceptibly nodding with approval as he listened to the ruthless QC decimating the Crown's key witness, savaging her with his disbelieving tone just as cruelly as Trevors had savaged her with his knife.

Cadogan:

You can give your reasons after you have answered the question. As soon as a man spoke with a north-eastern accent, did you declare him to be the intruder?

Checkley:

Yes. Because it was him.

Cadogan:

Without even troubling to hear if any of men 6 to 10 had a similar accent?

Checkley:

I didn't need to hear them.

Cadogan:

Need? Rather than 'need' do you really mean that you didn't 'want' to hear any more?

Checkley:

No. I don't mean that.

Cadogan:

How do you know that the voice used by the assailant on the night was not a disguised voice?

Checkley:

I don't.

Cadogan:

Are you qualified in any field which entitles you to claim an expertise in dialect or voice identification?

Checkley:

Of course not.

Cadogan:

Did you feel at ease in the car with Mr Perry?

Checkley:

No, I... I felt nothing in the car. If I was ill at ease, it was because of the circumstances, not on account of anything that Mr Perry suggested.

Cadogan:

Suggested. Why do you use the word 'suggested'? What exactly did Perry suggest?

Before she had even completed the answer Sarah Checkley was kicking herself for choosing the word "suggested", but Cadogan's questions were relentless, giving her no time for thought and, although he was several feet away from her, he leaned forward so that his huge head seemed to dominate the intervening space. Predictably, he had seized on the word "suggested" and was obviously going to exploit her slip of the tongue as he sought to press home the attack. There was an interminable pause while she tried to force her mental processes to resist him and Cadogan allowed the deadly silence to continue for so long that eventually the Judge had to come to her aid.

Mr Justice Hathington:

Mr Cadogan, what exactly are you suggesting? You understand the boundaries within which you must operate, don't you?

Cadogan:

I am suggesting nothing, My Lord. I am asking questions. The witness introduced the word 'suggested'. Within the constraints upon me, I am entitled to probe as to why she should select such a word.

Checkley:

It was a mistake. The word was a mistake. Perry suggested nothing. Nothing. He suggested nothing, I tell you. I refuse to be compromised.

Cadogan:

'Compromised'? Whose word is 'compromised', Mrs Checkley? Who has compromised whom please?

Checkley:

[Silence]

Cadogan:

Will you anwer?

Checkley:

[Silence] [Tears]

Cadogan:

Why did you tell the Court that you refuse to be compromised, Madam? What lay behind your choice of word?

Checkley:

I meant compromised by you and your questions. I haven't been compromised by anyone else.

Cadogan:

So you say, madam. I positively suggest to you that, for whatever reason, you are in error when you assert that man Number 5 on that parade was the man in your house on that fateful night. You have misidentified the person and the voice, simply reacting to the first north-eastern accent.

Checkley:

That was the voice. I am not in doubt.

There was an eerie silence as Sarah Checkley was led out of the Courtroom. The whole complexion of her evidence had been changed by the cross-examination. Whilst suggesting precisely nothing, Cadogan had suggested everything. To the end, she had never once looked at the dock. Had she done so at this moment she would have observed a satisfied smile playing around the corners of Trevors' thin mouth, whilst his cunning ensured that his face was angled away from the eyes of the jury. His brief had done the business all right. Cadogan was the Man. He couldn't wait for them to bring on that bent bastard, Perry.

* * *

Much of the afternoon was taken up with the gruesome evidence of the Crown Pathologist. Haskitt had relentlessly compelled him to pick over every inch of every wound in the case, referring to the goriest of the photographs that he could find. The gushing of the blood, the angles of entry of the murder weapon, the rupturing of blood vessels, the mechanics of death, no detail was left unexplored as the jury reeled from the deluge of aortas, jugulars, windpipes and arteries that Haskitt encouraged the pathologist to throw at them. Cadogan asked no questions.

Squeezed in at the end of the day came the doctor who had examined Trevors and found some marks of injury to the back of the neck. By the time that Cadogan had finished with him, he had been forced to concede that trying to put an age on Trevors' injury was impossible and it may well have been sustained before or after the date of the murder. Moreover, he was obliged to agree, it could have been caused by a piece of masonry falling off a skip and striking Trevors, just as Trevors had asserted to the police. There was nothing in the type of injury to contradict Trevors' explanation of it, nor its timing.

CHAPTER 20

At the close of the Court's business for the day Naomi Nicholas had asked Cadogan if he required her to do any particular preparation or research overnight but, unsurprisingly, her enquiry had been patronisingly rebuffed. In fact, she was delighted with the refusal, because Leeds United were playing the second leg of a major European match against Bayern Munich under the lights at Elland Road that night. A first leg without a goal meant that there was everything to play for. Jack was commentating and would find her a spot in the Directors' Box, to be followed by dinner together after the match. Two soccer teams of similar quality, pitched in combat against each other, would be a refreshing relief from the one-sided massacre she had witnessed in the Courtroom that afternoon.

There were forty thousand spectators in the crowd that night. Naomi wore her Versace mohair, full-length overcoat which exactly matched the blue in the Leeds United strip. Her Russian white fur hat also matched part of the team colours and, as Jack had arranged for her to be escorted to her seat by one of the French glamour boys of the modern game, she caused such a stir as she entered the Directors' Box that she felt like a Hollywood film star. The heads turned and the wolves whistled, making her laugh out loud as her escort, currently Aston Villa's leading goalscorer, acknowledged the cheers. As he had scorched the winning goal past his own country's illustrious goalkeeper at Villa Park last Saturday, thereby denying Leeds' most fearsome opponents even a point, the local crowd gave him a warm welcome.

When the home team ran out of the tunnel into the simmering cauldron, a familiar thrill of excitement ran down Naomi's spine. The shadows of the players, cast by the harsh arc lights, darted across the green playing surface as the athletic, lithe figures created their own geometric magic. After the fierce opening exchanges had subsided, a dazzling, mesmeric run down the left wing by the blonde Bayern fullback was followed by a pinpoint cross, which was smashed into the roof of the Leeds' net by the Germans' giant, square-shouldered striker and an eerie silence descended across the whole ground. With away goals counting double in the event of a draw, United would now have to score at least twice to win the tie. Predictably, the Germans immediately moved into their well-rehearsed mass defence mode, swamping the midfield and denying the home team any space. Half time was only two minutes away when the mercurial Leeds forward imported from Trinidad slipped his marker for the first time, raced straight down the middle at breathtaking speed, deftly rounded the last defender leaving only the advancing goalkeeper to beat. Dipping the left shoulder he feinted to the left, veered right and unleashed a searing shot which crashed into the German goal in the angle between the right post and the crossbar, billowing the net like a force ten gale. Elland Road erupted into a cacophony of sound which continued unabated until the referee blew his whistle for the break.

Aston Villa's Frenchman had been hurried away for a BBC radio interview and so Naomi found herself alone in the corner of the Directors' Bar, sipping the glass of white wine that the Frenchman had deftly lifted from the passing waitress's tray, before the radio reporter had whisked him away. Jack's commentary box for the cable company was in a gantry high up on the opposite side of the ground and he would be far too busy to escape for the fifteen minutes of half-time. The bar was very crowded and thick with smoke, much of it seemingly coming from cigars smoked by visiting dignitaries and wealthy businessmen from Munich. Finishing her wine, Naomi got up from her seat and began to ease her way towards the door, so as to return to the stadium for the second half and escape from the heavy, smoky atmosphere. As she glanced to her left just before passing through the door she was amazed to catch a glimpse of a familiar but unwelcome figure. The giant Cadogan was leaning against the wall, whisky glass in hand, deep in conversation with a portly, Germanic figure, dressed in an extremely expensive, Bavarian green overcoat. The wearer of the coat however was not presently paying too much attention to Cadogan for he was transfixed, staring directly at Naomi as she made her way through the door. Naomi was only too accustomed to the kind of look he was giving her and she hurried away before Cadogan might follow the gaze of his German friend and see her. She had had enough of him for one day and she most certainly did not want to be introduced to his companion. Delighted to be back in the fresh air, she resumed her seat and waited for the game to resume.

For the first twenty minutes of the second half play swung wildly from one end to the other. Leeds were playing at a frenetic pace and the Germans were holding them and then launching counter-attacks spearheaded by their dangerous striker, whose aerial strength was causing the Leeds back four all kinds of problems. Then, right on the half hour, there was a scramble on the edge of the Bayern penalty area, which culminated in Leeds' most recent signing from Liverpool suddenly emerging with the ball at his feet and the German defence still in a tangle. Bringing his left foot back like a piece of hammer artillery, he unleashed a shot which, whilst it was plainly flying wide, had enormous pace on it. Unfortunately for Bayern, one of their midfield men, who was standing just inside their penalty area, had instinctively turned his back to the fierce shot and was quite unable to avoid contact with the ball, which struck him on the right hip, taking the most wicked of deflections, before soaring high into the top of the Bayern goal, completely wrong-footing their goalkeeper, who was left to pick the ball disconsolately out of the back of the net.

Such a cruel blow seemed to convince the Germans that this was never going to be their night. Compressing their defence even tighter, they desperately looked for the elusive break, which would enable them to send a long ball up to their striker, but the break never came. Leeds danced forward, teasing and baiting, picking up a myriad of free kicks for frustrated, ill-timed attempts by Bayern to dispossess them. Every German tackle was booed and every Leeds surge forward was applauded, the cheering acquiring a meaner and crueller edge, as the minutes ticked away and the sense of anticipated victory turned cheering into ugly crowing.

Naomi recognised the territorial instincts that these games evoked, but the baying of the mass crowds, whether it was in victory or in defeat, always disconcerted her. Hordes of Englishmen, armed with their cudgels, would have made the same primitive sounds in centuries past, when they took to the streets in the days of riots, marauding, and peasant unrest. Despite this display of the baser spirit, excitement and fervour still engrossed her as, in the dying seconds of the game, the scorer of Leeds' first goal was released on the right, picking up the ball in full flow from a magnificent pass by the right back, before sending a low, skidding cross directly into the path of his teammate, who was advancing straight up the central channel. Without checking his speed or altering his line by even an inch, the Leeds forward blasted the ball into the bottom left corner of the net, leaving the diving Bayern goalkeeper grasping at air and his team out for the count. As the crowd erupted, Naomi found herself on her feet, screaming and cheering in elation at the beauty of the geometry and the ruthlessness of the kill.

Afterwards, in the heady atmosphere of the crowded bar, the gallant Frenchman deposited Naomi at a corner table with a double vodka and ice, to await Jack's appearance as soon as he had wrapped up the commentary. It was not long before the young wife of one of the United directors had determinedly enticed the Frenchman over to her table and Naomi had a minute to herself to reflect over the magnificent climax of the match. Her reverie was short lived however, for the hulking figure of Cadogan suddenly slipped on to the seat to her left, whilst his Germanic companion in the green coat moved in on the right flank.

"Quite a match, Naomi, out of the very top drawer, I would say," began Cadogan, with such an obviously forced tone of civility, that Naomi wondered what on earth had made him bother to come over and speak to her. Her puzzlement was immediately resolved in Cadogan's follow-up remark.

"I'd like to introduce a German friend of mine, Dieter Meyer from Munich. Dieter, this is Naomi Nicholas, my Junior in the murder trial I am currently conducting," continued Cadogan without pausing for breath.

All became clear as Naomi turned to look at the overfed, oversexed claret-faced Teuton to her right. Seizing her right hand in both of his chubby, manicured sausage-fingered hands, he brought his wet, pink lips down on to the back of her hand, making her skin creep.

"Delighted to meet you, Naomi, so delighted," he declared. "Ronan has been telling me how much he relies on you in his case," he added.

"Ronan has been telling you that, has he?" she queried, extracting her hand as rapidly as decorum allowed. "I find that something of a surprise. Is that what you have actually been saying, Ronan, or is there an element of poetic licence in your friend's remark?"

Cadogan made no attempt to reply as Meyer, without the slightest attempt at subtlety, moved into his hackneyed chat-up lines, pushing his bucolic face so closely into hers that she could smell the stale cigar smoke and whisky fumes on his breath.

"Ronan represented our company last year. Multimillion-pound litigation which, as you would expect, he won. So he is my guest tonight. As perhaps you would also be. We shall be dining in a private suite in my hotel with some of the Bayern directors and their ladies. Your addition to our party will be most welcome. I am sure you will enjoy yourself," he pronounced, almost oozing oil as he spoke and allowing her no time to decline.

"You'll be the most decorative addition, my dear, and you can tell me all about your case. I'm so interested in these criminal cases and your English lawyers in their white wigs. I would love to see you in your wig, Naomi. Perhaps you will show me?" he ventured, leering into her eyes.

Hemmed in on each side, immediate physical escape was impossible. Cadogan had made the introduction, no doubt at this German creep's instigation, and, having thrown her to the lions, was simply sitting back, enjoying his large whisky and letting Meyer play his hand. It was plainly a matter of complete indifference to Cadogan whether the German successfully seduced her or not, and her feelings and reaction to being set up were seemingly an irrelevance. It was one of those situations where there was no middle course to be steered. Polite withdrawal was physically barred. Either she told both of these men to leave her table immediately, in words of one syllable, or she sat it out until Jack came down to the bar and rescued her. Sometimes it could take Jack as long as half an hour to get away if he was conducting any of the post-match interviews. It was always a matter of the producer grabbing whoever was available in the media scrum that invariably followed these major games. Naomi decided that her salvation was in her own hands.

"Mr Meyer," she interrupted loudly, as he persisted with his odious platitudes, now blatantly pressing the side of his thigh against her own.

"Kindly stop pressing your ham of a leg against my thigh and move your face away from mine so that I'm spared the smell of your latest cigar."

Smiling with a degree of satisfaction as the crudity of her words succeeded in shutting him up, she continued. "I've no interest in accompanying you and Mr Cadogan anywhere. This isn't a pick-up joint, even though Mr Cadogan seems prepared to act as an amateur pimp. My fiancé'll be down here shortly to meet me. I suggest you move before he shows up."

"You're a rude little tramp, aren't you, my dear. With a very big mouth…"

The sentence was never completed as the massive open hand of Jack Farnham appeared from nowhere, snaked across the table and grabbed Meyer's tie and shirt front. "I believe it's time for you to rejoin your friends," Jack declared, his face within six inches of the German's. "You've worn out your welcome."

It took the visitor but a second to weigh the odds, before beating a hasty and undignified retreat back to his compatriots at the bar, spluttering indignantly as he straightened his shirt and tie. Cadogan, quite unhurriedly, also began removing himself from his seat, an amused smile playing around his lips.

"Your boyfriend's got a quite a temper, hasn't he?" he remarked sufficiently loudly to ensure that Jack could hear. "Still, there's nothing like a bit of rough, is there, girl?" he added.

"Ignore it, Jack. Just leave it," she insisted as she saw Jack's fists instinctively clench and his right arm move backwards.

"Good advice, I think," offered Cadogan with a smile.

"Don't be late in the morning. We've a big day ahead of us. Tomorrow I can be nasty to Detective Sergeant Perry."

"Just be yourself," replied Naomi over her shoulder as she led Jack away. "Just be yourself. The human species doesn't come any nastier than that."

CHAPTER 21

Whilst Leeds United had been entertaining Bayern Munich, Detective Sergeant Ronald Perry had been entertained by Jenny Dodds in the private quarters of the Bull and Beetle in Chapeltown, a tired and run-down section on the edge of the inner city. When Perry was attending the local secondary modern school, Jennifer Pringle, as she then was, had always made herself available for the curiosity of any of the boys, regardless of their age, size or appearance, so long as there was something in it for her. In those days her demands were modest and it had usually been a clumsy episode of squeezing and groping in the park on the way home, in exchange for a cinema ticket or the latest record.

In adult life she had learned to market her wares on a more profitable basis and had landed herself two husbands, both considerably older then her, and who were more than prepared to pick up the tab for her lavish and reckless spending, in exchange for her considerable talents in the bedroom. The first husband had suffered a fatal heart attack after only two years of a very active marriage and the second, Jimmy Dodds, was currently serving three years for handling stolen goods. Whilst he was a guest of Her Majesty, Jenny had taken over as licensee of the Bull and Beetle, which had been in the hands of the Dodds family for as long as anyone could remember. Chapeltown may have declined, but the pub had flourished and provided several generations of Dodds with a plentiful supply of cash but Jimmy, faced with a combination of his own greed and a wife twenty years younger than himself, with an insatiable appetite for Mercedes cars and fur coats, had succumbed to the publican's disease of trading under the counter in goods of questionable origin, which had, after several warnings, led to a three-year sentence for storing one hundred colour televisions in his garage after their mysterious exit from an electrical warehouse in Barnsley.

After the sentence had been passed, Sergeant Perry had called in at the pub to ask if there was anything he could do to assist Jenny in holding the fort whilst her husband was locked up. Little favours like warning the uniformed boys to leave her alone when she was providing after hours drinks to privileged customers, and ensuring that the Customs and Excise did not pry into the source of her van loads of cross-Channel, duty-free

Benson and Hedges, had earned Perry the occasional night in her private quarters. Last night had not been very satisfying. Perry had sat in the corner of the tap room until closing time and had consumed the best part of a bottle of Bell's whisky before Jenny had dispatched the last of her staff and slid the lock across the heavy black front door. In his cups Perry had become morose and, although he would never admit it to himself, he was extremely nervous about giving evidence in Court the next day. Cadogan was obviously a ruthless bastard and had to be watched like a hawk. Being cross-examined in a high profile murder trial by a devious and clever QC was not an experience to be relished, even when you had nothing to hide. Perry had plenty to hide and, as the hour of confrontation grew closer, he needed a bellyful of Bell's and the plump, bodily charms of a Jenny Dodds to see him through. For her part, Jenny was quite prepared to lie on her back and think of the advantages to the Bull and Beetle of allowing Perry to pleasure himself within her, but last night his awkward groping, followed by his drunken snoring, had irritated even her and at three o'clock in the morning she shook him awake and sent him on his way, explaining that she, too, had a busy day ahead of her.

When Perry heard his name called by the usher at ten thirty the next morning to give his evidence, he was not feeling at his best. The taxi had not got him home until quarter to four and he had managed only a fitful hour or two's sleep. The electric shower in his flat had recently lost all of its power and he had stood shivering under a lukewarm trickle trying to brace himself for the imminent struggle. His head still ached, despite four Anadin, and his blue suit, the one he always wore for the witness box, looked tired and out of date. The collar on his check shirt refused to lie flat and was half a size too big, making his scrawny neck look even more bird-like, as he involuntarily craned his head this way and that as he spoke.

In answer to Haskitt's questions he had recited his account to the jury. The Judge had given him leave to look at his notebook in the witness box, so that the details of his assertions as to what had been said on Trevors' arrest were there in black and white for him to read out. The interviews were on tape and the jury were given a transcript of the record, except that all abusive references by Trevors to Perry being bent had been edited out. Even Cadogan had agreed to those omissions as the forensic price for their inclusion would be for the jury to be told of Trevors' previous convictions. By the time that Haskitt sat down, Perry's head was feeling noticeably better and he was ready to put the arrogant Defence QC firmly in his place. This was his patch and no London smart-arse was going to undermine that. Cadogan had other ideas.

Cadogan:

You have told the Court that the Defendant tried to jump out of the second floor window. How far did he get out?

Perry:

It was a swivel window. He'd managed to get one leg and one shoulder out and was about to ease his head through when my officers grabbed him.

Cadogan:

So but for your officers' intervention he would have escaped?

Perry:

Without a doubt, sir. He was flying the coop.

Cadogan:

Did you take statements from any persons in charge of the building?

Perry:

That would have been completely unnecessary, sir. A waste of police time.

Cadogan:

But, Mr Perry, if you'd bothered to check, you would have found that this window was controlled by a restricted swivel hinge. It only opened twelve inches and it would be quite impossible for a man of the Defendant's size to do as you have described.

Perry:

Who says that it only opened twelve inches? Your client?

Cadogan:

Yes. My client. And the caretaker of the building who has been there for two years. He's a retired police officer and he examined the window and will give evidence for the Defence to that effect. You cannot have seen what you claim.

Perry:

I saw what I saw. I can't answer for the desperate lengths your client may go to, sir. I can only describe what I saw him trying to do.

Cadogan:

How did Mr Trevors end up with a black eye and a cut to his cheek?

Perry:

No doubt he was injured in the struggle as he tried to escape. There was a melee, involving six officers trying to subdue a violent man

Cadogan:

You say that the Defendant was violent. Did you or any of your men receive any injury?

Perry:

Not that I'm aware of, sir. But I believe that it was necessary for one of my officers to strike the Defendant. To subdue him as he was violently resisting arrest.

Cadogan:

Violently resisting arrest in a way that left all the officers unmarked and the Defendant injured?

Perry:

It happens, sir.

Cadogan:

After the Defendant was handcuffed on his bed, is it your claim that he said to you and I quote your evidence verbatim, "Sooner or later you can expect to be sliced up as well"?

Perry:

That's exactly what he said. It's not my claim, as you put it. Those were his words. It was a chilling threat. I remember it very clearly. There'd been no release to the media as to how the Checkleys had received their injuries.

Naomi stopped taking notes, fascinated by the confrontation as, answer by answer, Perry was growing more irritable, more aggressive and more reckless whilst Cadogan probed and prodded, seeking to provoke the explosion that would show the jury exactly what kind of police officer Perry really was.

Cadogan:

In this small room with six officers present can you explain how it is that you are the only officer to claim that you heard any such remark?

Perry:

Easily. I was leaning over him on the bed. My face was very close to his. He whispered it for my ears only.

Cadogan:

I suggest to you that you did not hear what you claim. He said nothing.

Perry:

Then, your instructions are wrong, sir, just as one would expect.

Cadogan:

What do you mean by adding "just as one would expect"?

Perry:

I mean that your client has to deny that remark, doesn't he? If he admitted it, then his guilt is obvious.

Cadogan:

At the time of his arrest you were unaware of any injury to the Defendant's neck, you didn't know his shoe size and Mrs Checkley's purported Identification had not yet taken place? You needed evidence.

Perry:

We had plenty. The DNA. What more could we want?

Cadogan:

The DNA? A match probability of 1 in 600? How many people in the United Kingdom might that match?

Perry:

Not that many, sir.

Cadogan:

Statistically there could be 100,000 people in this country who would match. Do you not consider 100,000 to be many?

Perry:

[Silence]

Cadogan:

Do you agree that at the time you claim the Defendant made the threat that you attribute to him, the only admissible evidence that you had against him was that he might be one of about 100,000 people in the United Kingdom who could match the DNA?

Perry:

[Silence]

Cadogan:

Did you search the Defendant's flat?

Perry:

Of course.

Cadogan:

You found nothing that incriminated him, did you?

Perry:

He had ample time to dispose of anything incriminating. You're twisting the facts.

Cadogan:

Is the answer "no"?

Perry:

You know exactly what I mean. I don't have to play your games, sir.

I'm a respected and experienced police officer. Just because some London QC is sent up here to attack my evidence doesn't faze me. I can handle myself well enough, sir.

Cadogan had bided his time with the utmost care. The layout of the Court put him quite close to the witness box and, as Perry's stay in the witness box stretched out, the odour of the whisky he had consumed the night before began to exude from his pores and waft in Cadogan's direction. This man was on the edge. You don't drink like that the night before you are to give evidence in a murder trial without there being some reason. The show of temper in the last barked answer was just what he had been waiting for. Reaching slowly and deliberately for the electric blue sheet of paper, which had hitherto been under his notebook, Cadogan placed it conspicuously on top of his lectern and let Perry observe him reading it, seemingly preparing for the Jardine onslaught.

Cadogan:

You can handle yourself well enough, you say?

Perry:

I command respect from my men and I play by the rules. I don't have to put up with word games. Barristers representing guilty men may play games. I don't. And what's more, that piece of paper you are brandishing contains nothing but lies. Lies.

Cadogan:

How do you profess to know what is on my piece of paper, Detective Sergeant?

Perry:

Because, as you know, I've been shown a copy

Cadogan:

A copy?

Perry:

Yes, a copy of a ridiculous allegation that I stole £1,500 from a prisoner in a drugs case. It was a complete lie, trumped up by your client. You listen to the interview tapes and you'll hear the prisoner actually admitting on tape that I'd recorded the full amount on the Police Exhibits Register. It's a try-on by a guilty man.

Cadogan:

But I had no intention of raising that, Detective Sergeant. You have simply volunteered that. This piece of paper in my hand, a copy of which you claim to have read, simply contains my handwritten notes

reminding me of my instructions from my client on the Voice Identification Parade procedures, to which I was about to turn before your unsolicited outburst.

Perry:

You've tricked me into…

Cadogan:

[Interrupting]

I suggest that you withdraw that word immediately.

Haskitt:

My Lord, this is outrageous. I would ask Your Lordship to invite the jury to retire so that I can make certain submissions to Your Lordship

MrJustice Hathington:

I agree entirely, Mr Haskitt. Entirely. Members of the jury, a matter has arisen requiring my judgement rather than yours. Please go with the usher until you are sent for again. Detective Sergeant Perry, will you likewise retire for the moment.

The jury, who had been spellbound during the dramatic confrontation between Cadogan and Perry now withdrew, their faces wreathed in expressions of puzzlement. Perry's outburst about being accused of stealing £1,500 had startled them both in its content and in its intensity. There was something seemingly very suspicious about this police officer and they had little doubt that Cadogan was digging in very fertile ground.

"Yes, Mr Haskitt. The jury and the witness have left us. Please make your point," invited the Judge

"My Lord," began Haskitt. "By brandishing a piece of blue paper Mr Cadogan has tricked the witness into blurting out details of a false allegation against himself which, if it had been put directly to the witness by Defence Counsel, would inevitably have led to the introduction in evidence of the Defendant's previous conviction. It was simply a crude set-up, designed to provoke the witness into raising the allegation himself. A trick."

"I shall hear from Mr Cadogan in just a moment, Mr Haskitt but, on the assumption that he is unable to persuade me that you are wrong, what are you proposing that I do about it?" enquired the Judge.

"Our application is that Your Lordship either discharges this jury and we start all over again with a fresh jury, or the Prosecution are given leave to adduce evidence of the Defendant's previous convictions as part of the Prosecution case. This jury must not be allowed to continue in ignorance of the Defendant's criminal convictions, yet fully aware that serious allegations of dishonesty have been made against a police officer who is a very important witness in this case. A clear-cut choice. A retrial or the Defendant's convictions go in. One or the other. Nothing less."

"Thank you, Mr Haskitt, for your proposals," nodded the Judge approvingly. This transparent example of trickery by Cadogan had played right into Hathington's hands. The dangerous risk of being exposed for seeking to interfere in the sentence of Jardine, when Jardine himself was a potential witness for the Defence in Hathington's own Court, could now be eliminated. Haskitt's argument, if successful, would mean that this jury would be discharged and there would have to be a retrial. Hathington would then direct that some weeks should pass before the retrial commenced, so that the current publicity surrounding this trial could subside and therefore be fairer to the accused. By the time that the retrial was listed, Hathington would have finished his tour of duty at Leeds Crown Court and the trial would fall into the lap of the next High Court Judge on the rota, who would be unsullied by any contact with the Jardine case. Cadogan had blown it. Hathington had a way out. As these thoughts raced through the Judge's mind, Cadogan was rising slowly from his seat with an expression of supercilious amusement on his face.

"My Lord, I was cross-examining a senior and experienced police officer in an absolutely correct and proper manner. The officer made a number of offensive remarks, damaging to the Defence, which I ignored and which neither my learned friend, nor indeed Your Lordship, sought to prevent.

Eventually, when the witness blurted out something which the Prosecution did not like, my learned friend was on his feet protesting. Your Lordship is being invited to consider a retrial because, after numerous improprieties by the witness, which may have damaged the Defence, he eventually volunteered one which may damage the Prosecution. Moreover, throughout the entirety of these remarks, Your Lordship had remained silent.

All I had done was to look at a piece of blue paper containing my short notes on the topic to which I was then about to move. That is what happened. It is on the transcript. Indeed, I am handing in the very piece of blue paper to the Clerk of the Court, so that it can remain with the case papers. Thus, should Your Lordship see fit to discharge this jury then, in the event of any subsequent conviction, the Court of Appeal can see, as I invite Your Lordship to see now, that the piece of paper has my handwritten notes on that topic and no more.

I resist any application for a retrial. I submit that Your Lordship has no basis at all for ordering one. None. Indeed, I go further. Not only would such an order be unjustifiable in Law; not only would it be seen as Judicial intervention in favour of the Prosecution, in contrast to Judicial silence when the Defence were being improperly damaged; not only would it represent a massive waste of public money, but it would be an abuse of Article 6 of the European Convention on Human Rights which entitles this Defendant to a fair trial.

As to my learned friend's alternative proposal that, as part of the Prosecution case, the Defendant's previous convictions should be adduced, then Your Lordship is being invited to ignore and override all Statutes and all English Case Law over many centuries. It is a proposal which has no merit and borders on the absurd. The trial must continue."

Throughout Cadogan's response Mr Justice Hathington had felt the power of the argument overwhelming him. Everything that Cadogan said was true. Of course, the blue paper had been a trick, but no one could prove it. The officer had been getting increasingly out of control and there had been no attempted intervention by Haskitt or by himself. Perry's final outburst had been suicidal. Cadogan had not actually asked him a question, and there would be no doubt that the blue paper he had handed in would simply contain his handwritten notes. If ever the Court of Appeal looked at the transcript it would appear exactly as Cadogan had described. Unless Cadogan asked for a retrial the die was cast, and Cadogan was determined to continue because, in the eyes of this jury, Perry was now a discredited witness. Haskitt's alternative suggestion that the Defendant's previous convictions should be made part of the Prosecution case was a nonsense. Cadogan was right about that as well. In one Court session Cadogan had shafted Perry, Haskitt and the Judge himself. It was a nightmare. He had succumbed to Haskitt's 'Della Montanari blackmail' over the Voice Identification procedures, but this ruling could not possibly go in Haskitt's favour or he would be pilloried by the Court of Appeal and the whole case would be reviewed.

Whilst Hathington was struggling to come to terms with the inevitable continuation of the trial, Haskitt was back on his feet, advancing more and more hysterical arguments as he, too, saw that the Judge was cornered. Cadogan would never need to return to the Jardine allegation again. It had discredited Perry without a bullet even being fired.

Immediately after the Judge had announced his decision that the applications made by the Prosecution must be rejected, the usher quietly handed Haskitt a folded sheet of electric blue paper, which he

254

instinctively opened and read.

"*Normally, you would now be feeling as if you had been kicked savagely in the balls. In your case however, you do not have any. From your learned friend.*

PS Without respect."

As Haskitt furiously screwed the paper into a ball and thrust it deep into his trouser pocket lest anyone else should ever read it, he caught a glimpse of Cadogan out of the corner of his eye. The enormous shoulders were heaving with suppressed laughter. The bastard was laughing so hard that Haskitt could actually see tears running down his giant jowls.

Cadogan:
What time did you pick Mrs Checkley up from the hospital?
Perry:
In good time for the parade.
Cadogan:
Mrs Checkley has told the jury you collected her at about 10.00 a.m. Is she right?
Perry:
Probably.
Cadogan:
Did you stop en route for any reason unconnected with traffic or road signs?
Perry:
Not that I remember, sir.
Cadogan:
Did you stop for the purpose of speaking to Mrs Checkley?
Perry:
What are you implying, sir? If you spell out what you are suggesting I'll answer it.
Cadogan:
I'm implying nothing. I'm asking questions. Did you stop for the purpose of speaking to Mrs Checkley? Either you did or you didn't.
Perry:
I probably stopped to ask her if she was all right. She was very frail and not in good shape at all.
Cadogan:
How long were you stationary for the purposes of this conversation?
Perry:
Not long. Two or three minutes, perhaps.

Cadogan:

You didn't arrive at the police station until 10.41 a.m. It would be wrong to suppose that your conversation with Mrs Checkley was rather longer then you have described, would it?

Perry:

Yes.

Cadogan:

Then how did less than 4 miles take you nearly half an hour?

Perry:

I don't know. Traffic. Going slowly. All kinds of things can account for it.

Cadogan:

Is that your final answer on this topic?

Perry:

It is.

Cadogan:

Did you know the Inspector in charge of the parade, Inspector Raymond?

Perry:

I believe that our professional paths had crossed once or twice in the past.

Cadogan:

Did you have any discussion with Inspector Raymond about the impending parade involving Mr Trevors?

Perry:

None. I hadn't even spoken to Inspector Raymond in the six months previous to the parade.

There was a rustling of paper from beneath Cadogan's part of the bench as Perry delivered this answer and Haskitt's head shot round towards Cadogan ready to jump to his feet if some other piece of chicanery was about to be launched but this time, without pausing, Cadogan beckoned to an usher and placed a magazine in her hand which he directed be handed to the witness. Haskitt re-buried his long head in his notebook, awaiting the bad news whilst Perry, viewing the usher's approach with some agitation, ran his finger nervously round the inside of his shirt collar.

Cadogan:

We do happen to have a photograph, published in the Police

Federation Magazine, of several officers in evening dress at the same table at the Pudsey Branch Charity Dinner? Could you please be shown the magazine? It is open at the page containing several photographs of the event.

Perry:

Yes. I'm at the table in one of those photographs.

Cadogan:

Who is the man seated two chairs to your left?

Perry:

I believe that it may be Inspector Raymond. It's not a particularly clear photograph.

Cadogan:

When was this dinner?

Perry:

I really can't remember.

Cadogan:

Could you please look at the small print to the right of the last photograph of the event? You may be able to see a date printed there.

Perry:

Yes. There is a date. The date that the dinner was held is printed there.

Cadogan:

Is that date just the day before the date of the Voice Identification Parade?

Perry:

Yes. I'd forgotten that Raymond was there.

Cadogan:

By the time of that dinner did you know that the parade was due to be held the next morning, conducted by Inspector Raymond?

Perry:

I probably would have done, yes. But I can't remember speaking to him at all during that dinner.

Cadogan:

When you assured the Court, a few moments ago, that you hadn't spoken to him in the six months prior to the parade, had the Pudsey Dinner simply slipped your memory?

Perry:

Easily done, sir. There were hundreds of police officers at that dinner. I attend numerous such dinners, sir. That parade was all above board.

Cadogan:

> All above board? Of course. The fact that you sat watching the Inspector due to conduct that parade the next morning, stuffing down his meat and two veg and quaffed a few bottles of Chateau Pudsey together, had just temporarily escaped your memory. We can all understand that, I am sure. I have no more questions, thank you.

Inspector Raymond quickly and inevitably met a similar fate to Perry at the hands of Cadogan, as did the DNA evidence, which Cadogan rendered almost statistically impotent and, despise him though she did, Naomi recognised that she had witnessed a Master at work. Cadogan was running the whole show. Haskitt and Hathington were being outmanoeuvred at every conceivable turn and were terrified of him. The witnesses were but playthings, to be thrown up in the air, caught a few times and then thrown to the ground, smashing into a thousand pieces. With every passing session of the trial, Trevors was getting increasingly closer to acquittal.

"Your belligerent boyfriend will have to wait for his tea tonight, darling," announced Cadogan tartly at the end of the day's session. "We have to visit the customer. He'll be running out of the tunnel tomorrow. Best check he's not going to score any own goals."

The cells beneath the Court were at their worst at the end of the day. Nine hours of accumulated smells had gathered, ranging from the prison stink of numerous prisoners and their gaolers, to the lingering odours of the lunchtime bacon sandwiches. Being crammed in a cell with the three men, as the QC put the Defendant through his paces for tomorrow's excursion into the witness box, was a major assault on feminine senses. Naomi could smell that unique, rank stench that so often exuded from a guilty prisoner's pores, as the realisation struck him that his own turn to give evidence was imminent. Sitting in the dock, watching a skilled QC grind Prosecution witnesses into the dust was one thing. Going into the witness box and fielding the deliveries from the other side's QC was a very different matter.

Operating now without any notes, as the material was so well lodged in his brain, Cadogan took Trevors painstakingly through every topic that he intended to question him about and then alerted him to each line of attack that Haskitt was bound to pursue. Where the answers were clumsy or dangerous, the pitfalls were explained. Cadogan never actually broke the rules and directly told Trevors what the more sensible answer should be, but he prodded him and cajoled him to the point where the

Defendant's animal cunning suddenly saw the way out of the trap and the appropriate answer was filed away for tomorrow's performance. Prison officers in the corridor outside grew increasingly impatient, banging on the door and demanding that the conference end so that they could get their cargo back to the prison, but Cadogan simply told them that no one was moving until Trevors was word perfect. Two and a half hours later the exhausting process was over. Trevors was as ready as he was ever going to be. By now Naomi had a splitting headache, but Cadogan's strength and stamina had not seemed to flag by even one iota, despite the oppressive atmosphere of the cell and the tension of the situation. As they were finally leaving, Trevors offered a parting gesture.

"Nice one with the blue paper," he observed, the thin lips drawn back in a half-smile. "As neat as I've seen," he added approvingly.

"It was a misunderstanding on the witness's part. No more than that," came the sharp reply.

"Misunderstanding! My arse. You and I ain't that far apart in one sense are we, Mr Cadogan? Oh, you've got the class all right, but we've neither of us got a fucking moral to our names, have we?"

"Being offensive to me is rather stupid, isn't it?" replied Cadogan condescendingly, as he walked away.

"Offensive? Offensive? It's admiration I'm talking, mate. Sheer fucking admiration," shouted Trevors to the massive figure retreating along the corridor.

Despite her headache, Naomi smiled to herself as she followed the giant through the steel doors and back into the main Court building. Trevors had got one thing absolutely right about Cadogan and himself. They shared the same sense of morality. In Naomi's opinion it was the morality of the sewer rat.

CHAPTER 22

Back in the Judges' Lodgings at the end of the Court day, Hathington stretched out in the old-fashioned bath full of tepid water drawn by the housekeeper and reflected on the recent disasters that had befallen him. That stupid woman Della Montanari had left him perilously exposed to Haskitt's blatant threat of blackmail, although he was satisfied that the Voice Identification ruling in Haskitt's favour had more than paid off that score. However, his handling of Denstone's ill-timed calling-in of his debt, had so offended Helen Gaynor that she had absented herself from all meals at the Lodgings and had insisted on travelling in a separate car to and from Court, thereby avoiding any contact with him.

In the event, Cadogan's devious but successful stunt with the blue paper, meant that it was unnecessary for the Defence to try to call Jardine, so that should save him from further embarrassment on that front, although it had undoubtedly done substantial damage to Perry's credibility in the eyes of the jury.

Nonetheless, as if all that wasn't enough to cope with, the Defence Junior was yet another of the many skeletons presently emerging from his dark cupboard and he had caught her several times staring at him with undisguised contempt. The only consolation was that he very much doubted that she was broadcasting to her learned friends what had happened between them so long ago, as it was absolutely obvious that the bitter animosity that existed between Haskitt and Cadogan had eliminated any of the social exchanges between Counsel that usually occurred. Indeed, Cadogan seemed to be universally despised by lawyers, Court staff and Judges alike.

Tomorrow Trevors would go into the witness box. In a case of this importance, it was reasonable to expect that Haskitt would have been provided with some potent artillery to deploy during cross-examination and, given the extreme violence that lurked within Trevor's psyche, one might hope that the jury would get a true insight into the man and his guilt would become clear. The skilled cross-examination of a Defendant was invariably the critical stage of a criminal trial. The quality advocate could bring all of the evidence together and leave the Defendant with no hiding place.

Before that however, Hathington was faced with a tricky social evening to negotiate. It was customary for the visiting High Court Judges to hold the occasional dinner party at the Lodgings for various local dignitaries and tonight had been scheduled for such an event, which meant that he and Mrs Justice Gaynor would be obliged to act as co-hosts. Not easy at all, pondered Hathington, as he eventually extricated himself from the bath and stood admiring his naked form in the bathroom mirror.

Apart from the High Sheriff and his wife, the guest list also included Professor Nadine James from the Law Faculty at the University and her husband, Dr Brian James who had won eighteen caps playing at inside centre for the Ireland Rugby XV. Apparently, he was now greatly in demand on the after-dinner speech circuit, so hopefully he would brighten up tonight's proceedings.

Skilfully avoiding anything other than cursory contact with Helen Gaynor during the pre-dinner drinks, Hathington was much relieved to observe that the butler, sensitive to the friction between the two resident Judges, had placed them at opposite ends of the imposing, silver and crystal-laden table. Consequently, Hathington found that the evening was passing with comparative ease.

Contrary to expectations, Dr James had been completely overshadowed by his loquacious wife, who evidently saw a black-tie event in the company of a Dame and a Knight as the ideal forum in which to ventilate her frustration at the plethora of criminal justice legislation that this Government was continuously introducing. Seemingly, her husband had heard it all before and had sought relief in the excellent Nuits St George from the Lodgings' cellars, and by the time that the ladies withdrew and the port was circulating amongst the gentlemen, his tongue had loosened.

"This gruesome murder that you're trying at the moment, Sir Michael, am I right that Ronan Cadogan is leading for the Defence?" he enquired.

"Oh yes, Dr James, we've been subjected to his manoeuvrings for the best part of a week now. A baptism of fire for me in the Criminal Courts, but I think I have his measure," replied the Judge.

"Do I take it from that remark that he's proved to be a handful?" interposed the High Sheriff, who relished the tittle-tattle that these occasions invariably generated.

"He's a handful alright, High Sheriff," Hathington responded. Needs to be watched like a hawk. Astute, brutal, wily and extremely successful."

"And extremely unpopular wherever he goes," added Dr James in an acid tone, "he's a first class bastard, I can tell you."

"You sounded like you really meant that, now you'll have to elaborate," the High Sheriff prompted.

"We were both up at Trinity Dublin at the same time. Actually, he was a year ahead of me and already a force to be reckoned with in the University Debating Team when I arrived. Belligerent, aggressive but with a big reputation as a winner at whatever he did," Dr James began.

"I'd just made my debut in the 2nd XV and Cadogan was one of the established second row forwards. I could see immediately that he was never going to make it into the 1st XV. Too lumbering. Muscular and strong, but not fast enough, even for those days, when the pack was much less mobile than today's all-action supermen."

"If my memory serves me well, one of the Trinity second row forwards went on to play for the British Lions on that famous New Zealand Tour, so the competition must have been pretty fierce," interjected the High Sheriff.

"You're right, the unstoppable Declan, we called him 'The Bantry Buffalo', an inspirational figure," agreed the Doctor. "I played alongside him in the Irish Team and there was no way that Cadogan was going to displace him at University level. Anyway, we were playing Limerick, always a strong team and I'd been at school with their fly-half, Harry Keane. That day Harry ran rings round us. Small, light. Too light ever to make the big time, but he was like quicksilver. Couple of times he made an absolute monkey out of Cadogan. Then, selling Cadogan an outrageous dummy, he scored a try under the posts."

"I think I can see what's coming," said Hathington with a shake of the head.

"It was a shocker when it did come," continued Dr James. "A scrum broke up early, ball went out to Harry, Cadogan was a mile offside and flattened Harry, going down straight on top of him with his arms still around him in the tackle. On the floor, he put a bone-crunching bear hug on Harry that went on for so long that it took three of our players to break his grip. It was vicious. A trained assault. I know because I was one of the players trying to get him off. Harry, who was a tough little nut, was actually screaming in agony. The ball was nowhere to be seen. Cadogan was deliberately breaking his ribs. Six of them. Harry was stretchered off and Cadogan was sent off. That's how he was."

"Comes as little surprise to me," offered Hathington. "I can see it in the way he conducts himself in Court."

"That wasn't the end of it, though," Dr James added. "In those days, when we had a player sent off for foul play, we used to hold our own Players' Court after the match."

"A kangaroo Court?" asked the High Sheriff provocatively.

"In a way, I suppose it was, but the only opinions that good rugby players really respect are the opinions of other good players. If something really nasty had happened, this was our way of dealing with it. The skipper was always the Judge. The three most senior players, plus the skipper, made the ultimate decision. There was never a Prosecutor, just witnesses who spoke of what they'd seen. Cadogan of course, being supremely arrogant, chose to represent himself. Unfortunately, I was a witness as I'd seen the whole wretched incident. He accused me of lying because I'd been at the same school as Harry."

"Still uses the same tactics," laughed Hathington ironically.

"Obviously, he was found guilty. The sentence was that he wasn't eligible for selection for the next six games. Quite lenient really, because the verdict was that he'd deliberately set out to cause Harry really serious injury. Harry was in hospital for four days, in case a lung had been damaged, and Limerick lodged a formal complaint."

"How did Cadogan take it, then?" asked the High Sheriff, hanging on every word of this squalid account.

"If you ask me, I don't think he gave a damn about the six-match ban. But losing the argument. Being humiliated. By his own team. That sent him into a fury. Of course, it got round Trinity like wildfire and that added insult to injury. He never played rugby again. Concentrated on his wrestling at which, sad to relate, he was bloody good," concluded the doctor.

"So now we know why you call him a first-class bastard," Hathington said. "Trouble is, the first-class bastards often turn out to be the winners," he added.

"In the short term you may be correct, Judge," agreed Dr James. "But not necessarily in the long term. What goes around, comes around, you know."

"Perhaps so. Perhaps so," replied Hathington ruefully. "Let's hope that you're right," he concluded, with a transparent lack of sincerity. After all, he reflected to himself with alarm, the last person who could afford justice catching up with first-class bastards was Mr Justice Hathington, Bart, Knight of the Realm.

When the guests finally departed, the dreaded moment of being left alone with Helen Gaynor finally arrived. The butler had cleared away the last of the coffee cups and there was no means of escape without some direct contact. In the event, she walked straight towards him from the front door after bidding good night to the guests, cornering him at the bottom of the stairs and opening the exchange with a biting one-liner:

"I did speak to Marcus Buxton," she began abruptly.

Hathington visibly recoiled at the sound of the name. Buxton was the Lord Chancellor's hatchet man. Oily, treacherous, conniving and loathed by the Judiciary.

"Why did you speak to him, Helen?" Hathington asked nervously.

"I believe that you know exactly why. I didn't like your attempted interference into one of my sentences. I felt compromised. I decided that the Lord Chancellor's Department should be formally told that my sentence was lenient for a number of evidential reasons, none of which had anything to do with your ill-disguised message," she retorted.

"Did you mention my name to Buxton?"

"Of course," she replied.

"What did he say?"

"Not a great deal. I suspect that he knew something about it. He implied that the Attorney General was unlikely to ask for leave to refer my sentence of Jardine to the Court of Appeal as being excessively lenient and that was probably an end of it."

"Good. I fear that you did misunderstand me that morning," Hathington explained, breathing an inward sigh of relief at Buxton's apparent reaction. You had to hand it to Roger, he thought. Magnificent control.

"I hope that perhaps we can now put this unfortunate misunderstanding behind us and see this legal session out on rather better terms."

"I'm not a fool, so please don't treat me like one," was her immediate retort. "Nor is Marcus Buxton. The entry will have been made in your file. They'll be watching you. Indeed, I would imagine that they already are."

"And what precisely do you mean by that?" he demanded aggressively.

"Just this. Buxton thanked me for the call. He said perhaps I should make allowances. Maybe you'd spoken as you did because you were under great strain. Trying a very dangerous man for murder. A man the authorities believe to be responsible for at least two previous murders. No doubt, once he was convicted, the strain upon you would ease."

"He said all of that?" queried Hathington in disbelief.

"Oh, yes," she replied, now enjoying the spectacle of Hathington's undisguised alarm. "And he said one other thing I found quite interesting," she added provocatively, deliberately pausing to add to Hathington's distress.

"Well?" he declared angrily.

"It was the last remark he passed at the end of the call," she eventually added. "Let's hope that the villain doesn't slip through Mr Justice Hathington's fingers. Wouldn't make for a long judicial career, that's what he said."

"Am I really expected to believe Buxton said that?" retorted Hathington.

"It's entirely up to you what you believe and what you don't believe. I'm now going to bed. In two weeks' time I'm sitting in Liverpool so we shall have to endure each other until then. Thereafter, I shall ask the Presiding Judge to ensure that you and I never sit in the same Court again. Good night."

As Mrs Justice Gaynor marched briskly up the long flight of stairs, Hathington watched her departing, ramrod-straight back with a mixture of anger and fear, crudely reflecting to himself that the precious Lady brandished her integrity like a tart flaunted her cleavage. Normally he would never have tolerated a woman speaking to him in such contemptuous terms but he did not want her stirring Marcus Buxton up again. Buxton was far too dangerous.

Hopefully, Haskitt would do his stuff tomorrow and put Trevors to the sword. Now Trevors had to be convicted. Then Buxton's attention would wander elsewhere.

CHAPTER 23

Without so much as a single glance at his notes, Cadogan put Trevors through his paces, extracting every detail of his movements over the twenty-four hour period surrounding the Checkley murder. In his hard, north-eastern accent Trevors recounted to the jury his claims as to where he had been, what he had been doing and, in particular his interest in the programme on the Amazon Basin, which covered the exact time of the killing. Gaining in self-confidence as the morning progressed, he swore to the jury with a vehemence that even Naomi believed, that he had never threatened Perry with the alleged threat about "slicing Perry up as well". Whilst he was unable to control the feral, darting movements of his eyes, the rest of his performance was balanced and restrained, just as Cadogan had meticulously tutored him the evening before. Nevertheless, the dark wet patches that began to appear in the armpit region of the wretched, cheap suit that he insisted on wearing, gave some indication of the true extent of the strain he was under. Throughout the trial he had ensured that his shirt collar was high and covered the livid, unsightly scar on his lower right neck. Now that he was on public display and the focus of all attention, he could not stop himself occasionally pulling it up and involuntarily stretching his chin so as to keep the collar high. Despite these movements and the darting of the deep-set eyes and the thin, cruel mouth, by the time the QC reached his final questions in chief, Cadogan had succeeded in almost humanising the Defendant. This performance was not what the jury would have been expecting from their observations of the figure they had been watching in the dock over the last several days.

Cadogan:
    After the television programme had finished at midnight, what did you then do, Mr Trevors?
Trevors:
    Probably made a cuppa. That's my normal routine. Cup of tea. Checked everything was turned off. Then bed. I'd have been in bed by quarter past, sir.
Cadogan:
    Were you ever in Leeds that night?

Trevors:
Definitely not, sir. I hadn't been up to Leeds for at least a month.

Cadogan:
Mr Trevors, were you the man who broke into the Checkley house that night and attacked Mrs Checkley with a knife?

Trevors:
That wasn't me, sir. She's just picked me out 'cos of my accent.

Cadogan:
Did you kill Paul Checkley?

Trevors:
No. I didn't kill him.

Yet again, Cadogan had worked every edge. His timing was perfection, as the Court clock showed two minutes to one. There was insufficient time for Haskitt to begin his cross-examination, and so the jury would take their lunch with Trevors' final words of the morning still ringing in their ears. At two fifteen, mortal combat with Haskitt would begin and Trevors would be fighting for his life.

* * *

Haskitt:
When did you leave the North-East and move to Yorkshire?

Trevors:
When I was 18. My mother was killed in a factory accident. June 11 it was. My sixteenth birthday. Parents had separated when I was a bairn. My sister, well, my half-sister she is, looked after me for a couple of years, then I went South. Worked in Doncaster, Rotherham and so on, wherever there was work.

Haskitt:
Were you familiar with Leeds?

Trevors:
Yes.

Haskitt:
You would have known where the smart houses were? Where the rich people lived?

Trevors:
Is that a crime, then, sir? I knew the posh parts and I knew the not so posh parts.

Haskitt:

And you knew Alwoodley, didn't you? The very affluent suburb where the Checkleys lived.

Trevors:

I knew of Alwoodley. I don't deny that.

Haskitt:

Did you ever work in Leeds?

Trevors:

On and off. Bit of driving. Some bar work.

Haskitt:

Anything else?

Trevors:

Hard to remember. Oh yeah, had a job as a packer in a clothing factory for a few months.

Haskitt:

Just remembered that, have you? Or didn't you want the jury to know that you had worked in a clothing factory?

Trevors:

I'd forgotten.

Haskitt:

Of course, Mr Checkley owned clothing factories in Leeds, didn't he? That's where you'd heard his name. Well known. Important. Rich.

Trevors:

I'd never even heard of him before I was arrested.

Haskitt:

You made it your business to find out where he lived, didn't you? Ferreted around and discovered that he had a safe at home.

Trevors:

No.

Haskitt:

That is why you said to Mrs Checkley, "I know there's a safe in the house. Take me to it before I finish opening you up, you privileged bitch." Spoken in your north-eastern accent.

Trevors:

No. If that'd been me I'd have disguised my voice.

Haskitt:

You opened Mrs Checkley up from her navel to her breasts. You then put your blade straight between her legs. Your steel on her flesh. You didn't think for one minute that she'd be brave enough and cool enough to concentrate on every word you said and how you spoke?

Trevors:

You're just ignoring my answers. I'd never set eyes on the woman.

Haskitt:

In your eyes was she a woman of privilege?

Trevors:

I didn't know her.

Haskitt:

Rich. Beautiful home. Spoke nicely. Successful husband. A bitch, Mr Trevors, as you saw it?

Trevors:

A lady, I'm sure.

Haskitt:

But wrong about your voice?

Trevors:

She just went with the first north-eastern accent she heard. Never even bothered to listen to no others.

Haskitt:

And Detective Sergeant Perry is also wrong, is he, when he stated that you threatened him in these words: 'Sooner or later you can expect to be sliced up as well?'

Trevors:

Never said. Nor nothing like it. I was in bed. Naked. Six coppers just jumped on me, knocked me about. Cuffed me. I said nowt. Nowt.

Haskitt:

What size shoe do you wear?

Trevors:

9 or 10.

Haskitt:

The size within the range found by the scientists at the scene of the crime, imprinted in blood.

Trevors:

I'd wager you're about a 9 or 10, sir. Mr Checkley was about the same an' all.

Haskitt:

No. The evidence was that Mr Checkley was a size 8 and Mrs Checkley was only a size 5. The shoe print was 8 – 10, more likely the upper end of the range. Your shoe, I suggest.

Trevors:

Wrong.

Haskitt:

Can you sew?

Trevors:

No. It ain't too good for your street cred up in Gateshead.

Haskitt:

I suggest that you sewed an extra piece of cloth on to the back of your balaclava so there was no risk of the back of your head or neck being seen if there was any kind of struggle. You didn't want the victims to even be able to say whether you were white or black.

Trevors:

I had no balaclava. No cloth. Done no sewing. The police turned my flat over. They didn't find nothing.

Haskitt:

You'd had ample time to dispose of everything. The only thing you'd left at the scene was the piece of cloth that got pulled off your balaclava. That is your blood on that cloth isn't it?

Trevors:

Like Mr Cadogan put it. There's got to be a hundred thousand people out there who'd match that DNA blood.

Haskitt:

What work were you doing at the time of this offence?

Trevors:

Driving a skip lorry.

Haskitt:

What jobs had you done in the week immediately before your arrest?

Trevors:

Now you're asking. Too long ago to say but I told the coppers about the job where I caught a brick on me neck out on the Wakefield Road.

Haskitt:

Did you go to the doctor?

Trevors:

No. It's a hard job. Knocks is part of the deal. Don't normally give them a second thought.

Haskitt:

You couldn't risk seeking any medical attention because it might link you with Mrs Checkley's description of hitting the intruder with a golf club right on the spot where you were injured.

Trevors:

Untrue.

Haskitt:

Where do you say you were on the Tuesday night the Checkleys were attacked?

Trevors:

In my flat. Done a day's work, I reckon. Put me feet up. Watched TV. Normal night.

Haskitt:

Like numerous other nights?

Trevors;

Yeah.

Haskitt:

So how do you specifically remember that is what you did on that particular night?

Trevors:

'Cos the following week the coppers were crawling all over me accusing me of murder. I thought back. Remembered going to the match at Hillsborough on the Wednesday and being at home the night before.

Haskitt:

And at 11 p.m.?

Trevors:

Once I thought about the Tuesday I remembered I was watching TV.

Haskitt:

What programme?

Trevors:

The Amazon Basin. Lady reporter. Bit of a looker. Blonde. Showed the waterline on the trees. Fifteen, twenty feet up the trees. Floodwaters leaving their mark, that kind of stuff. All the damage to the wildlife.

Haskitt:

Something of a naturalist are you then, Mr Trevors, when you're not unloading your skips?

Trevors:

No, sir. It ain't that what I was interested in.

Haskitt:

What were you interested in, then?

Trevors:

The actual places. Peru, Brazil and so on.

Haskitt:

Why? Were you thinking of taking a degree in Geography?

Trevors:

No, no. But Maneus – that's Brazil like. It's right on the river. Amazing place. Iquitos, same thing, but further upstream. Into Peru.

Haskitt:

This is an artificial interest, isn't it? Designed to give yourself an alibi.

Trevors:

Not true. I watched 'cos I was interested. Simple as that.

Haskitt:

Of course. No doubt you were intending to visit these places for your summer holidays if Blackpool was sold out.

Trevors:

No, sir. I'd already been. That's the point, sir.

Haskitt:

You claim that you have been to Maneus, half way up the Amazon River?

Trevors:

Oh, yeah. I've been all right. And Iquitos.

Haskitt:

When?

Trevors:

Few years back, now. Done a year or so on the tankers. Merchant Navy. Peru, Brazil. And Venezuela like, but that weren't on this TV programme. Didn't the police tell you I'd done a turn in the Merchant, sir? That's why I was so interested in the programme, like. I'd been there. Seen it.

Whilst this answer stunned Haskitt into momentary silence there was an audible groan from Lampard, beavering away behind his Leader keeping a note of every question and answer. Cursing himself silently for not reading Trevors' police antecedents with sufficient care to spot that he'd once served in the Merchant Marine, he also blamed Haskitt for missing it and thereby allowing Trevors to score such a cheap point. On the other hand, Trevors looked so pleased with himself at the glibness of his answer it was just as likely to backfire on him in the eyes of a jury. Juries seldom liked slippery Defendants who smiled at their own answers in the witness box.

Haskitt:

You set up an alibi.

Trevors:

No, sir. Not true.

Haskitt:

You watched that video until you had all the details safely in your head and then destroyed all evidence of the video tape and the video player. As cunning as that.

Trevors:

What you say, sir, is wrong. The police, the Forensic, the Scenes of Crime lot, they was all in my flat for days. Never found nothing to back up what you say, 'cos there never was nothing to find.

Haskitt:

What clothing were you wearing on that Tuesday night?

Trevors:

I ain't got no idea. But I can tell you that the Forensic took every stitch I owned away with 'em. Must have checked the lot. They've still got it. My solicitor's been asking for it back for months. What they find on it? Nothing. 'Cos there never was nowt to find.

Haskitt:

Because the actual clothing you had worn that night had been spirited away. Burned I would venture.

Trevors:

You've got the wrong man, sir.

Showing little imagination in his cross-examination, Haskitt laboriously challenged every last detail of Trevors' account and, as the afternoon wore on, the attention of some of the jurors succumbed to the Prosecutor's tedium. Cadogan was lying back, slumped in his seat, only occasionally opening his eyes to inspect his watch, ensuring that the jury observed his gesture by puffing and blowing as Haskitt's dull tones continued unabated. Eventually, his voice suddenly changing to anger, he shouted his accusations at Trevors as he came to the end of his questioning.

Haskitt:

You broke into that house in Leeds. With your balaclava, your surgeon's rubber gloves, your soft shoes and your filleting knife, you viciously attacked Mrs Checkley and then murdered her husband.

Trevors:

This is all lies. What more can I say? Not me. I know how bad it all sounds when you just repeat what some bloke done to her. But the point is it wasn't me what done it.

Haskitt:

You showed the Checkleys no mercy.

Trevors:

I wasn't there.

Haskitt:

I put it to you, Mr Trevors, that you are a dangerous and ruthless killer without a shred of remorse or shame for what you have done.

Trevors:

Like I've said to you a thousand times. I've done nothing. None of this is anything to do with me. None of it.

Haskitt:

My Lord, that completes my cross-examination.

Mr Justice Hathington:

Very well, Mr Haskitt. Thank you. Do you have any questions in re-examination, Mr Cadogan?

Cadogan:

I do, My Lord, and I would like to ask them now before the Court adjourns until tomorrow, if Your Lordship would allow that.

Mr Justice Hathington:

Yes. You may complete your client's evidence this afternoon.

Cadogan:

Thank you, My Lord. Mr Trevors, did the police seize all the papers, bills and receipts in your flat?

Trevors:

Yes.

Cadogan:

Did they find anything to suggest that you owned a video recorder?

Trevors:

No. More than that. They even examined the bit on the back of the telly, the bit where a video connection lead would go. Looking to see if there was any scratch marks on the metal where a lead would go on and off, like. They found nowt.

Cadogan:

You referred to your trips to South America during your service in the Merchant Navy? Just tell the jury something about either Maneus or Iquitos which wasn't on the TV programme. So they can judge whether you really have been there or not, as Mr Haskitt seems to express doubt that you have.

Trevors:

I can tell you plenty. For a start, pigs. They've got pigs what run wild in the streets in Iquitos. Old marble steps down from the road to the river. From the days of the rubber boom. I've been there all right.

Cadogan:

Are you the man who broke into the Checkleys' house and committed these dreadful crimes?

Trevors:

No. I'm not guilty of these crimes. The police have got the wrong man.

Cadogan:

I have no further re-examination, My Lord. May the Defendant please leave the witness box?

Mr Justice Hathington:

In just one minute, yes. But there is a question I would like to ask him first. Mr Trevors, your evidence is that when you were arrested in your bedroom you deny saying to Detective Sergeant Perry that sooner or later he could be expected to be sliced up as well?

Trevors:

I never said that.

Mr Justice Hathington:

Well, what did you say?

Trevors:

Nowt.

Mr Justice Hathington:

But if you were lying asleep in bed and six policemen burst in, used force upon you as you claim, and then handcuffed you, why didn't you say something?

Trevors:

[Silence]

Mr Justice Hathington:

Why did you not say, for example, what am I being arrested for?

Trevors:

[Silence]

Mr Justice Hathington:

What am I to put in my notebook as your answer, please. So that I can remind the jury later?

Trevors:

Shock I s'pose. I didn't get time to think or say nothing.

Mr Justice Hathington:

I see. That is your full answer, is it? Very well, please return to the dock. We shall adjourn until tomorrow. Do you have any further Defence evidence to call tomorrow, Mr Cadogan?

Cadogan:

Just one witness. The caretaker of the Defendant's flats. He will deal with the extent to which the window could open. I imagine his evidence will last ten minutes, no longer.

Mr Justice Hathington:

Well, you heard that, members of the jury. The Defence case will close very early tomorrow. Thereafter, you will hear the final speeches of Mr Haskitt and Mr Cadogan and then I will sum the case up to you. I shall now ask my Clerk to close the Court formally.

Judge's Clerk:

All persons having anything further to do before My Lords the Queen's Justices may depart hence and give their attendance in this Court at 10.30 tomorrow morning. God save the Queen and My Lords the Queen's Justices.

* * *

In the car park alongside the Court Dickie Lampard was crossly inspecting the parking ticket, which he had found stuck to the windscreen of his old Range Rover when Naomi Nicholas loomed into view, heading for her own car which was in the adjacent row.

"Nice one, Dickie," she called out, observing his plight. "Didn't you have any change for the machine this morning?"

"I had plenty of change. I actually keep some in the car. But I was so bloody harassed this morning. Haskitt had me in such a spin to get here early, to go over any last minute ideas for his cross-examination of your client, that it went clean out of my head to buy a ticket. Now it'll cost me fifty quid," lamented Lampard.

"Are you admitting that some of those questions he asked were actually your idea?" she laughed, mischievously.

Lampard looked at her very carefully, advanced closer to her, hesitated and then spoke. "Naomi," he said earnestly, instinctively dropping his voice, "strictly between you and me, Scout's Honour, what did you think of Haskitt's performance today? I'd really like to know."

"I'm not answering that. You wouldn't be able to keep it to yourself now, would you?" she grinned.

"Probably not. Probably not. But I don't mind telling you that I'm seriously underwhelmed. Everytime your Leader gets to his feet old

Haskitt teeters on the edge of cardiac arrest. And today! He never laid a glove on your client, never even laid a glove on him," observed Lampard in a state of obvious dejection.

"Isn't that a bit of an overstatement?" she queried.

"Overstatement?" grunted Lampard increduously. *"You claim to have been half way up the Amazon, do you Mr Trevors? Oh, yes, Sir. Didn't the police tell you I'd done a turn in the Merchant?"* spat out Lampard sarcastically, mimicking Haskitt and Trevors as he spoke. "I tell you, I could have died. Like I said, the old fart never laid a glove on him."

"Well, it isn't exactly a bed of roses being led by Tyrannosaurus Rex," she offered by way of consolation. "He's an extremely unpleasant man, I can tell you. Anyway, no work for us to do this evening, Dickie. Our part is done. Just the leaders' speeches left and the arrogant bastard hasn't even bothered to ask me if I've got any ideas. So, I'm not even going to think about work tonight, I'm going home to persuade Jack to take me out to dinner. I suggest you do the same. Take your wife out and forget about Haskitt until tomorrow."

"Good advice. My wife must have had a bellyful of my moaning about the old Master of the Hounds. I'll do just as you say. Good night."

As Naomi was driving along the ring road, slowly picking her way through the interminable rush-hour traffic, one of Lampard's phrases kept playing on her mind. "Never even laid a glove on him," he had ruefully observed. "Never even laid a glove on him." The devil of it was, that Dickie was right. Trevors might actually walk.

Seeing her return home without any case papers to study for the following day, Jack had required little persuading to pick up the telephone and book their favourite corner table at Valentino's. The proprietor's son, Roberto, was now on the books at Bradford City and pushing for a first-team place in the midfield. Bradford's latest manager had played alongside Jack for two seasons at Port Vale and Jack had played his part in securing Roberto a trial at the Club, so there was never any trouble in getting a table. After the usual warm welcome, handshakes and kisses for the 'beautiful Signorina', Naomi and Jack were soon tucking into the Chef's special which was 'filetto casanova' that night, accompanied by a modest bottle of the house Valpolicella.

"How has that insensitive thug behaved towards you since the Elland Road incident?" enquired Jack cautiously.

"Behaved as if it never happened. Never mentioned it. Mind you, he virtually ignores me anyway. I've been an irrelevance to him since the trial began," she replied unhappily. "Truth is, this is the worst case I've ever been involved in. The Judge is a disgrace who makes my skin crawl. He's not only a hypocritical lecher but a craven coward as well. And Cadogan is an out and out bastard. What's more, Haskitt has been running scared of him over some massive bust-up they had a few years back. He's so terrified of the Irish bully boy that he hasn't done his job properly."

"How do you mean?" asked Jack

"Well, he's been out-manoeuvred at every turn, but today he cross-examined our client and, to quote Dickie Lampard, he didn't even lay a glove on him," Naomi explained. "Trevors is as vicious a killer as I've ever come across. I've no doubt he's killed before and, after Haskitt's performance today, it's even money that he'll walk. If he walks, he'll kill again."

"Come on. The jury may see through him. It's Trevors they've been really watching, not the barristers. The evidence decides the case, not the barristers."

"Don't you believe it. Sure, if there's some devastating piece of evidence in a case, then that will decide it. But, if the evidence is only so-so, like it is here, then the barristers become the key factor. Nine times out of ten it is the better barrister that will win," she declared emphatically.

"Well, it's hardly Haskitt's fault that there wasn't a devastating piece of evidence against Trevors, is it? You can't blame him for that," Jack insisted.

"But that's the whole bloody point," she sighed. "There was such a piece of evidence. Cadogan spotted it in the Solicitor's old files, but Haskitt has completely missed it."

"Go on then, explain," demanded Jack urgently, leaning across the table towards her.

"I shouldn't," she replied, shaking her head sadly. "I've said too much already. He is my client, after all."

"Your client? Free to kill again? Like you often say, there's no morality in your game, is there? Cadogan wins the intellectual game by bullying his way home. Haskitt blows it because he hasn't got the balls to fight back. And the whole farce is presided over by a Judge with a history of attempted rape. Instead of being sent down he's ended up with a knighthood and a seat on the Bench. The public are well served, aren't they? And I always believed in British Justice," proclaimed Jack with disgust. "And then you tell me that there's a piece of dynamite that could put Trevors behind bars for life and that weakling Haskitt has missed it. It's a bloody scandal. An outrage. "

"I've defended prisoners who I knew were guilty and they've been acquitted," she responded. "You have to do your job as best you can and learn to live with the consequences."

"And have any of those guilty prisoners that you've successfully defended been killers who you know will strike again?" asked Jack defiantly.

"No. The answer to that question is no," she conceded with an uneasy shake of her head. "This is the worst example I've ever known."

"So what exactly did Haskitt miss?" Jack demanded again.

"Ten years ago Trevors burgled a house and was disturbed by the occupant. He got eighteen months. A pitiful sentence but he pleaded guilty. Very unusual for him. He never pleads guilty, as he proudly announced to us when we first met him," she began.

"So?" prompted Jack

"So, when you've done the job as long as I have, and a villain who never pleads guilty, suddenly does plead guilty and gets a derisory sentence, then there's only one explanation," she declared.

"Information," interrupted Jack.

"Precisely. He grassed to the police on some other rogue about some other crime. The fact that he's provided useful information gets put in a little sealed envelope by the copper who did the deal with the Defendant. The envelope is handed privately to the Judge. Nothing's said in Court. Only the Defendant and Counsel know anything about it. The Defendant knows from the pathetic sentence that the Judge has done the business. Reducing the sentence on the basis of the secret in the envelope. The public never know the reason and nor does the villain who got grassed up. It's the system protecting the informant. Nauseating stuff, I'm afraid."

"How does any of this have any bearing on the Checkley murder?"

"As Trevors only got eighteen months, the full details of the offence are only kept in the police records for a few years. They keep a record of the fact of the conviction and the sentence, but not the full details. It's all very imprecise. If it was a long sentence, four years and up, then their record keeping is more precise and more detailed."

"And?"

"And the details of this particular burglary included the fact that Trevors wore ballet shoes when he committed it. And he wore a balaclava when he committed it. But it's the ballet shoes that clinch it. Similar fact evidence. If an act of criminal conduct is striking in its similarity, then it becomes admissible even if it discloses to the jury that a Defendant has offended in the past. How many burglars have you ever heard of who wore ballet shoes, Jack?" she asked.

Jack put down his knife and fork and stared incredulously across the table at Naomi. Neither of them spoke for a long time. Her question needed no answer. Their glasses were refilled by the attentive waiter and Jack still sat silently, reflecting on the enormity of the injustice that was likely to follow. Eventually he spoke.

"You said that Cadogan spotted this in the Solicitor's old files. How?"

"Roger Sylvester is an extremely efficient solicitor from the old school. He retains every brief. He's represented Trevors numerous times over the years. He put copies of all the old briefs in our murder brief. You've seen the size of my brief in this case. It fills my locker in the robing room. In fact I could hardly get it all in there tonight. Cadogan's been through every single piece of paper and spotted it."

"Well, it's hardly Haskitt's fault that your solicitor keeps better records than the police or the CPS, is it?"

"Yes and no. Trevors is a top grade criminal, but he's also a lucky criminal. The ballet shoes burglary was in a totally different part of the country and the links between Police Divisions down there and up here in Yorkshire aren't very close. But Haskitt knew from the police records that Trevors had relevant previous offences, including house burglaries, some of which were at night. Just like the Checkley burglary. He could have asked Sergeant Perry to contact all the relevant Police Divisions. Perry would do anything to get Trevors locked up. They could have identified the officers involved in that case and one of them was bound to have remembered the ballet shoes. Even ten years ago. It's so unusual. Haskitt's had months to prepare this case. He's a QC. The top of the pile. He's paid a lot of money to think through all the angles. He failed."

"I see what you're saying," acknowledged Jack. "And if this jury knew about the ballet shoes then …"

"Then Trevors would have been dead and buried," Naomi interrupted. Not even the mighty Cadogan could have dealt with that. Trevors would be convicted and sentenced to life imprisonment. Instead, he may be strolling down Boar Lane tomorrow night, courtesy of Haskitt and Cadogan."

"And when the dust settles, some other innocent person is going to be skewered on his filleting knife," added Jack, just as the waiter arrived with the dessert menu.

"It doesn't bear thinking about does it?" said Naomi, shaking her head in dismay and pushing her chair back from the table. "Excuse me for a moment. Just an espresso for me. I'm off to the ladies' room."

"Make that two espressos, Marco. And I think I'll have some tiramisu as well, please," Jack announced, watching Naomi depart in the direction of the cloakrooms at the far end of the restaurant.

As soon as she disappeared from view, Jack's hand dived swiftly into his inside jacket pocket and pulled out his mobile phone. Of course it was disloyal and breached a confidence, but Naomi was as horrified as he was at the prospect of this killer going free. Whereas she was not able to act because of her professional position, he was. This could save lives. Handled discreetly, no one need ever know who was the source of the information.

Dialling 141 first, so as to remain untraceable, he punched in the number of Leeds Central Police Station. When the telephonist answered he was quick and very much to the point.

"You have a Sergeant Perry working on the Checkley murder trial. Track him down now. Tell him I have some information for him. Crucial information. I'll phone again between midnight and one o'clock. Make sure he's there to take the call. Have you got that?"

As the female voice at the other end pressed for his name, he saw Naomi emerging from the cloakroom area and heading back towards the table.

"No names. Just tell him 'ballet shoes'. Tell him what I have to say about ballet shoes will nail his man." He rang off.

"Who was on the phone?" asked Naomi, resuming her seat, just as the waiter arrived with the coffee and Jack's dessert.

"The paper," Jack lied uneasily. "There's a big transfer deal brewing. They want me to come into the office and chase a few contacts by phone. Want me on the spot in case it's a race for the morning edition. I'll drop you home first when we've finished here. May be a late night."

"Who's after whom?" she enquired with interest.

"Your French escort at the Bayern match. Seems his presence at Elland Road may not have been a coincidence," replied Jack, now really hating himself for the glibness of his own deceit. Still, he reflected uncomfortably, sometimes the end justifies the means.

CHAPTER 24

Slipping into the Courthouse at seven o'clock in the morning through the canteen staff entrance was the best strategy that Perry could devise. He needed to discover in which burglary Trevors had worn the ballet shoes as the caller didn't know and there was insufficient time to trace all of the numerous burglary convictions recorded against Trevors and every officer involved with each enquiry. Seeking a key from a member of the Security Staff during the night would have run the risk of alerting someone to his activity. This way was far safer. Once into the building there would be no one about and experience told him that no barrister would enter the robing room much before nine o'clock. He would have as long as he needed to gain entry to Naomi Nicholas's locker, rifle her papers, copy anything that was needed and re-secure the lock before she was even out of her warm bed. Picking locks was a science in which Perry was well versed. Fourth locker on the left as you went in. That is what the mystery caller had said. Assuring the male voice that his anonymity would be protected was an easy and an empty promise. You didn't need to be a genius to work out who the caller had to be. Not only was it obviously someone very close to the woman but, despite the amateurish attempts to disguise the voice, even Perry had a passing interest in the goings-on of the Premier Division.

The lock on the old wooden locker surrendered to Perry's skill in less than a minute and, despite the voluminous size of the brief within, Perry's task was not particularly demanding. Ninety percent of the paperwork was produced by the Prosecution. The nugget of gold would be found within the actual instructions prepared by the Defence Solicitors, which was printed on a completely different type of paper in both texture and shade of white to that used by the CPS. Stacking the heavy pile of papers on a nearby chair, Perry quickly realised that his task was eased still further by the neat little tabs that Naomi Nicholas had put on each section of her brief. Green tabs for the Prosecution Witness Statements; yellow tabs for the Unused Material; red tabs for the interviews of the Defendant; purple tabs for the Proof of Evidence of the Defendant and, there it was, a blue tab for the Defence Solicitor's "Instructions to Counsel". Scanning through the early pages which dealt with the history of the proceedings, Perry soon struck gold.

"Counsel will observe that Instructing Solicitors have included within this murder brief, all previous briefs when they have represented the Defendant over a period of many years. These have been bundled together and filed as Enclosure 'H' in three box files delivered to Counsel herewith..."

Already sweating profusely, Perry scuttled eagerly back to the locker, his darting eyes quickly spotting several box files on the bottom shelf, which he swiftly extracted, placing them on one of the large tables littered with wigs, gowns, collars and the everyday clutter of the robing room. The first box file contained briefs going back to when Trevors was a juvenile. The second box was crammed with old briefs. It took ten frantic minutes to locate the prize. Tied up in faded red ribbon the treasured brief lay towards the bottom of the pile. Perry was in a state of intense animation. Why hadn't that buffoon Haskitt sent him off in this direction months ago, instead of this furtive, desperate chase at the eleventh hour? Almost salivating, Perry untied the tape, opened up the brief and stood transfixed as he read through the first page:

"Regina v Gary Peter Trevors"
In The Crown Court sitting at Cambridge.

Counsel is instructed to appear at the above Court to represent our client (aged 21) on a charge of burglary. The victim was a 47- year- old woman, Christine Blundell, who lived alone in a semi-detached house on the outskirts of the town. At approximately two o'clock in the morning she was in bed when she was disturbed by the sounds of the floorboards creaking on her landing. Despite being very frightened, she jumped out of bed, opened the bedroom door and put on the landing light in time to see a man in a balaclava, dark jumper, jeans and soft, black shoes retreating down her stairs. As soon as she shouted he ran. Miss Blundell remembered that his running made no noise, even on her bare flagstones in the hall. She believes that the burglar wore ballet shoes.

Our client was arrested the following night at an address in Ely where he was in bed with one Sheila Noakes. He made no comment upon arrest, as is always the case with this particular client, but, underneath the bed the police recovered a pair of ballet shoes, a balaclava and a black jumper.

At the police station the Defendant denied any involvement

in the crime, asserting that the items recovered from under the bed must belong to Noakes, despite the fact that the shoes were plainly a man's size and actually fitted the Defendant. The Defendant was thereafter remanded in custody.

To Instructing Solicitor's surprise (and, we suspect, following a visit by the police to the Defendant in prison of which we were not made aware) the Defendant has indicated in writing that he intends to plead guilty to this offence of burglary. This is the first occasion that the Defendant has ever pleaded guilty to anything and therefore our Mr Sylvester has discussed this plea with the Defendant with the utmost care and obtained his written instructions that the guilty plea is entirely voluntary and not the result of any inducement or oppression. A copy of that document is enclosed herewith in Counsel's brief.

Counsel is therefore instructed to attend at Cambridge Crown Court and to offer the following mitigation on behalf of…"

"Bingo" declared Perry aloud. "Cambridge. Got the bastard."

Satisfied that there was no real risk of anyone coming into the locker room in the next few minutes, he grabbed the two relevant pages and scurried upstairs, running along the still-deserted corridor until he reached the photocopier in the police room. Five minutes later, with copies safely nestling in his inside jacket pocket, he was back downstairs tucking everything neatly back into Naomi Nicholas's locker and re-securing the door so that there was no sign of any interference. Back in the police room, as his hand reached for the phone to contact Cambridge, he was laughing. "Wait 'til the jury hear this little lot," he said to himself. " They won't be out five minutes."

* * *

Haskitt:

My Lord, before the jury are brought into Court I have an application that the Prosecution be allowed to call certain additional evidence. Similar fact evidence. The use by this Defendant of unusual and very similar paraphenalia in a previous offence.

Mr Justice Hathington:

Similar fact evidence? Should not such evidence have been adduced as part of the Prosecution case, not at the end of the Defence case.

Haskitt:

Normally, my Lord, that is the position. However, somewhat unusually, the full implications of the evidence to which I am referring, have only become available to the Prosecution this morning...

There was a spluttering from Cadogan, akin to the rumbling of a volcano about to erupt, as he immediately realised that, at the eleventh hour Haskitt must have at last got wind of the old ballet shoes burglary. Jumping to his feet he furiously cut across the words of his loathed opponent.

Cadogan:

I haven't the slightest idea what my learned friend is referring to. He hasn't even had the courtesy to inform me of this application. It's not within my experience to encounter Prosecuting Counsel behaving in this unworthy manner.

Mr Justice Hathington:

Please sit down, Mr Cadogan. What is the nature of this evidence, Mr Haskitt?

Haskitt:

Ten years ago, this Defendant pleaded guilty to a nighttime burglary of an occupied dwelling house when he wore a balaclava and ballet shoes. A feature of striking, indeed stunning, similarity to the present offence. It is potent evidence of similar fact. I wish to call the police officer from Cambridge who was in charge of that case ten years ago and who, as we speak, is being driven to this Court under motor cycle escort so that he will be here within the hour.

Mr Justice Hathington:

This is plainly very important evidence and its relevance speaks for itself. I will now listen to anything that you have to say, Mr Cadogan.

Cadogan:

I am outraged. This is an attempt by the Prosecution to ambush us. It's quite scandalous that such an application should only be made after the Prosecution has long since closed its case. My learned friend seeks to ambush us, sidestepping the rules of procedure, evidence and fairness...

Quickly appreciating that the Judge had obviously already decided to allow the jury to hear about the Cambridge burglary, Haskitt moved rapidly from a state of nervous embarrassment to a tone of indignation that he should be under any criticism at all.

Haskitt:

I resent those ill-tempered personal remarks, My Lord. This Defendant pleaded guilty to that burglary, thereby acknowledging his use of a balaclava and ballet shoes. My learned friend may not like the evidence, hence his personal attack on me, but his objection based on the late timing in fact makes no difference at all.

Mr Justice Hathington:

Mr Cadogan, if this argument had been raised prior to the close of the Prosecution case, then any argument to exclude would have failed, wouldn't it?

Cadogan:

I don't accept for one moment that the admission of the evidence was inevitable. I would have advised my Instructing Solicitor to locate the lady householder, if she is still alive. I would have had to take detailed instructions off my client on the circumstances of that burglary and his plea of guilty.

Mr Justice Hathington:

If I am satisfied that this evidence is relevant and was always admissible, what difference does it make whether it was called during the Prosecution case or called now?

Cadogan:

A big difference. The Prosecution are trying to pull a rabbit out of a hat. They are breaching the procedural rules and abandoning all pretence at fairness. The difference is that the Defence will have been cheated.

Mr Justice Hathington:

But are the public not cheated if the jury is denied this potentially important evidence?

Cadogan:

My answer remains the same. I respectfully submit that Your Lordship should be asking my learned friend how he missed this evidence in the first place. And what has happened now, to prompt him to make this application.

Mr Justice Hathington:

Well, Mr Haskitt? I believe we are entitled to that information. Did you miss it, or is there some other reason? How do you come to be making the application now? Has there been some intervening act overnight?

Haskitt:

[Silence]

Mr Justice Hathington:

Would it assist if I allowed you a few minutes to consider your response, Mr Haskitt?

Haskitt:

It would, My Lord.

Mr Justice Hathington:

Then I shall rise until you are ready. I shall not make any final ruling until I am given the answers to those questions. However, it may assist Counsel if I indicate that I see this evidence as very important. It will require powerful reason to make me exclude it. Usher, please tell the jury that there is a delay for administrative reasons. We will send for them as soon as these matters have been resolved."

Before the Judge was even half way out of his seat, Naomi Nicholas was bolting through the rear doors of the Court and running towards the robing room where her mobile phone was nestling inside her wig tin. Pressing the speed dial key for Jack's mobile she was almost sobbing in distress. Surely Jack could not have done this to her? It must have been just a coincidence that her revelations to him last night over dinner were on this very topic. Jack would never breach her confidences. Never. His answering service clicked into operation after four rings. He wasn't answering his phone. He always had his phone on, except when he was commentating. Where was he? Leaving no message, she dialled home. Answering machine. No sign of Jack. Inhaling deeply, she forced herself into a state of apparent composure. Must keep calm. Fortunately, there was no one about in the robing room. Knees felt weak. Needed a few more minutes alone to regain control. Caught a glimpse of herself in the full-length mirror at the side of the battered, wooden lockers. She was deathly white. It was an awful moment. Her looks had never before let her down but, in that instant, she suddenly felt old and her own reflection was of a person she scarcely recognised. Staring out from that cruel mirror was the face of a woman who had been betrayed and the sight terrified her.

She hated them all. Trevors. Cadogan. Hathington. Jack had been the Rock. Honourable. Straight. Decent. If he was truly responsible then his name would be added to the list. Think it through. What were the other possible explanations? Haskitt had had months to set these enquiries in train, and would not have done so at the last minute of his own accord. He could be eliminated. Lampard wouldn't have had the nous to pursue it. Perry was a possibility. She had seen him pacing around the building, with a face like thunder, ever since his own disastrous excursion into the witness box. Perhaps he had checked through the relevant convictions, made a few calls and come up with the goods. Any comfort gleaned from this line of reasoning was suddenly dashed, as the picture of Jack last night, on his phone in Valentino's, when she returned from the ladies', rushed back into her mind. It had to be Jack.

A clear head was vital. The emotional dimension would have to wait until after the Judge had made his ruling. Her primary duty was to her client. However much she despised Trevors the reality was that, on the present state of the case, there was about a fifty per cent chance that he would be acquitted. If the similar fact evidence went in, then conviction was an absolute certainty. Every fibre of her being wanted him to be convicted, yet her professional obligation was to do everything within her power, within the rules, to secure his acquittal, even though he would doubtless kill again. In telling Jack of the similar fact evidence she had breached her duty of confidentiality to her client. If her disclosures to Jack ever reached the ears of the Bar Council she would be disbarred. Her breach would lead to the conviction of her own client in circumstances where he possibly stood on the brink of acquittal. Consequently, she had to move heaven and earth in the next few minutes to ensure that the similar fact evidence was not admitted by the Judge. Thereafter, she would have to face up to Jack's treachery. The immediate, critical objective was to help Cadogan win the admissibility argument.

Putting on a touch of make-up, and straightening her back, she set off back towards Court. Roger Sylvester and Cadogan were sitting in one of the alcoves on the side of the main Hall, deep in conversation. Marching resolutely up to them, she unceremoniously interrupted their discussions, spelling out her objections in the strongest terms that she could muster.

"This is quite intolerable," she began. "We mustn't allow Haskitt to win this argument. If he claims that it's additional evidence, then the answer is that it's too late. If he contends that it's evidence in rebuttal, then it has to have arisen in circumstances which the Prosecution could not have foreseen. The Prosecution have had the means to research the Cambridge offence for months. The fact that they haven't seen fit to chase up the details until now doesn't entitle them to claim that this is new evidence."

"Please sit down. Miss Nicholas," said Sylvester, sliding along the hard wooden bench to make room for her. "The points you make are just what Mr Cadogan and I were discussing," he continued.

Cadogan was observing her state of animation with close interest. "You seem to have got yourself very excited over this," he declared. "Is there anything more you want to tell us? You haven't let a careless word slip in any particular direction, have you?"

"I shall ignore that offensive remark," she replied as her cheeks reddened, cursing him silently for the accuracy of his guess. "But you're right about one thing. I'm very angry at Haskitt's attempt to get this evidence in at this stage of the trial. It's monstrous. The Judge wants to let it in and I don't trust him to make the honest intellectual ruling in our favour, unless the argument completely overwhelms him."

But the evidence is admissible, isn't it?" Cadogan responded calmly.

"Yes. It would have been at the right time. But it isn't now, that's the whole point," she said.

"If I may say so, Mr Cadogan, I share Miss Nicholas's anger over this," Sylvester interjected. "The Prosecution and the police were negligent in missing this. Our firm is meticulous in its record keeping, and its preparation. If we'd been negligent and missed out some important information from your brief, the Judge wouldn't be bending over backwards, ignoring the rules, to get us off the hook."

"You're quite right, Mr Sylvester," agreed Cadogan. "And I think if it is left to the Judge, then he will bend the rules and will admit the evidence. But, you know, there is often more than one way to skin a cat."

"And just how are we going to find another way to skin a cat in the few minutes that we have?" enquired Naomi, with more than a touch of desperation in her voice.

"Firstly by a process of elimination. Then by going on the attack," came the immediate reply from Cadogan. "This information about the ballet shoes is no longer on the police files. Up until the end of yesterday they knew nothing about it. So something must have happened, overnight, that provided them with that information and prompted them this morning to locate the Cambridge Officer who handled that case," Cadogan reasoned.

"And how does any of that enable us to go on the attack?" Sylvester asked in puzzlement.

"It takes us to your very perceptive observation of a moment ago, Mr Sylvester," Cadogan answered enigmatically.

"You've lost me, sir, I'm afraid," retorted the solicitor.

"Your firm's meticulous record keeping. Where, in the City of Leeds, in the last twenty-four hours, would you find, in black and white, the information about the ballet shoes that Haskitt now wants to adduce?"

"In our briefs," snapped Naomi in an instant.

"Exactly," smiled Cadogan. "And I know where my brief was. By my side. In my suite at the hotel and I never went out last night. Dined in my room. So where were your papers, Mr Sylvester?"

"That's easy," the solicitor replied. "Locked in the boot of my car which was locked in my garage, forty miles from here."

Both men simultaneously stared at Naomi.

"Well?" demanded Cadogan.

"In my locker downstairs in the robing room," she admitted in embarrassment. "There was no work left to be done. The locker was locked. I had the key."

"I've seen those old lockers down there," Cadogan grunted. "It would take a good thief, or a bent copper, about twenty seconds to pick the lock. And we all know that there's a bent copper in this case, don't we. He set up the Voice Identification Parade, no doubt corrupting both Mrs Checkley and Inspector Raymond in the process. He verballed Trevors. And last night, or early this morning, he went through your papers. You can count on it."

"But we can't prove it," Naomi said.

"Actually, we probably could. He won't have worn gloves to go hurriedly through piles of papers. His prints will be on your paperwork, particularly the page dealing with the Cambridge burglary. And a locksmith might be able to identify evidence of recent interference with your lock. But we haven't got the time for either of those enquiries. We'll be back in Court in a few minutes. So, as I said before, we go on the attack. We know that happened. We tell Haskitt that we know. He will tell Perry. In fact, if possible, we tell them both at the same time. The Judge wants to know how and in what circumstances Haskitt came into possession of this information overnight. If they think that we can tell the Judge, and prove, that Perry broke into Defence Counsel's locker overnight, then they will withdraw their application to adduce this evidence."

"It's a massive bluff," breathed Naomi.

"Bluffing is an essential part of the barrister's craft, Naomi. Don't tell me you hadn't realised that by now. The most unsavoury aspect of this particular bluff is that I'll have to speak directly to Haskitt again. Never mind, it won't take long. Come on, let's find him," said Cadogan getting up from his seat and preparing for battle.

For just one fleeting second Naomi was glad that she had him on her side.

* * *

The temperature in the CPS Conference Room was rising by the minute. Haskitt's well-worn wig lay on the table, where he had abruptly tossed it a moment ago as Perry had, yet again, evaded the question of how he had come by the ballet shoes information overnight. Lampard and Nathan sat nervously at opposite corners of the table, equally worried at the realisation that they had failed to instigate the proper enquiries, while Detective Chief Inspector Ernie Noble simply stared at Perry, his eyes never wavering, fighting to retain his self-control.

"Chief Inspector," repeated Haskitt, pacing angrily around the room, "can you please get it into your Detective Sergeant's head that we're at crisis point. The Judge will let this evidence in for sure, once we satisfy him that we came into possession of it through a legitimate source. If it becomes necessary for me to say publicly, that I may have been at minor fault in not seeking the information earlier, then I'll say it. All I need is some indication of how he came by the information overnight."

"He knows that well enough, Mr Haskitt," answered Noble, still staring at Perry who sat alone, in the far corner of the room, exuding defiance. "It's not as if he has to tell us the whole story, is it?"

"No," Haskitt agreed. "Just an indication. Then, once that evidence goes in, Trevors is destroyed."

"All right, all right," snapped Perry in exasperation. "It's no big deal. Last night Leeds Central received a phone call. Male voice. Asking for me by name, saying he'd call back in an hour. I came in. Well after midnight I got the call. Refused to give any name. Just said that ten years ago Trevors had done a burglary with ballet shoes. That's all there was to it. I'm entitled to keep my sources private, you know that, Chief Inspector. Anyway, that's the top and bottom of it."

"So what did you do?" Haskitt demanded.

"I checked out his burglary convictions. Found one near Cambridge. Phoned Cambridge CID, sir. First thing this morning. Before eight, I'd say. They phoned me back within twenty minutes. Piece of cake, they said. Gary Peter Trevors. Got eighteen months for burglary, ten years ago. Identified the Officer in charge as John Laidlaw. Now a Traffic Sergeant. He'd been a DC when he did Trevors. They said Laidlaw had been given my mobile number and he'd call before nine. As soon as he called, I asked him what he could remember about the case and you know what he did, sir?"

"No," replied Haskitt impatiently.

291

"He laughed. He laughed, Mr Haskitt. 'Called the villain Rudolph when we nicked him,' he said. 'Remember it like yesterday. Rudolph.' I asked him, why Rudolph? Know what he said, sir?"

"Rudolph Nureyev," answered Haskitt, "the greatest ballet dancer of them all."

"Exactly. You've got it in one. The ballet dancer. So now Laidlaw's on his way up the motorway. I've told you what you need to know. You tell the Judge. One anonymous call, bit of checking, followed by that conversation with Laidlaw. I don't see anything wrong with that, sir, do you?" barked Perry.

"Then, why didn't you volunteer this to us immediately?" Haskitt asked.

"Because he hasn't told you the whole story, has he, Mr Haskitt?" interjected Noble. "But you've got enough, haven't you, to answer the Judge's questions, deal with the crisis and get the evidence in. You can leave Perry to me."

"What have you missed out, Perry? What have you missed out that might damage our case or might damage any of us professionally?" persisted Haskitt furiously.

"You've got your answers, Mr Haskitt. You're now sitting on information which will convict a dangerous murderer. I don't tell you how to do your job, so I'd be grateful if you let me do mine," Perry replied gruffly. "The fact is that the gaffer's wrong. I have told you the whole story. There's nothing else to tell. Nothing at all."

"Did you recognise the voice in the anonymous phone call?" Haskitt demanded.

"Absolutely not. Could have been anyone. Complete stranger," came the immediate reply.

"Did you do anything else, other than receive that call and then make your enquiries with other Divisions including Cambridge this morning?"

"I did nothing else, sir. Nothing else. It's all kosher. Laidlaw will be here…"

The sentence remained unfinished as the door to the room suddenly burst open and the enormous bulk of Ronan Cadogan stood towering in the doorway, his face set in an expression of such menace that Haskitt instinctively took a pace backwards, whilst Dickie Lampard shrank even further into his corner.

"I'll say my piece while you're all together," announced Cadogan, entering the room, followed by Naomi Nicholas and Roger Sylvester. "Close the door please, Mr Sylvester. What I have to say is not yet for public consumption."

Cadogan's threatening presence dominated the whole room. Haskitt stood with his back to the far wall, his hands subconsciously gripping pieces of his silk gown so tightly that his knuckles turned white. Perry had jumped abruptly out of his seat mid-sentence and his whole face was now covered in a sheen of sweat. Noble, Lampard and Nathan remained seated, their gaze transfixed on the ferocious face of Cadogan, who stood in the centre of the room, flanked by Naomi Nicholas and their solicitor.

"At 4.30 yesterday afternoon none of you knew anything about the ballet shoes in the old Cambridge burglary," Cadogan began. "You'd all missed the boat. By 10.30 this morning you knew all about it."

"So what?" declared Haskitt, trying desperately to undermine Cadogan's dominance and authority. "Information reaches the police in numerous ways. It's the content that matters."

"Not quite, Haskitt. If a police officer had obtained that information by dishonestly raiding the Defence brief and accessing privileged material, then different considerations apply," replied Cadogan.

"What the hell are you talking about?" shouted Perry in a fury. "It's bound to be my name you're trying to blacken. That's been your tack from Day One. You're just desperate."

"Stop your shouting and listen. At some time overnight, you, Perry, have raided Miss Nicholas's locker. You've scoured her papers, found the ballet shoe information and then put everything back in her locker," announced Cadogan, slowly and quietly.

"I demand that you be reported..." exploded Perry.

"Sit down and shut up, Perry. Your prints will be found on the relevant page of Miss Nicholas's brief and a locksmith will, if necessary, be making a statement that the lock has been recently interfered with. Do you want me to tell Mr Sylvester to start those enquiries, Perry? It's your call."

Complete silence pervaded the room. Perry slumped back into his seat. None of them would dare to call his bluff. It was Haskitt who eventually broke the silence.

"What exactly are you proposing, Cadogan? Understand, I'm not accepting what you allege, but I will listen to any proposals," he declared, struggling to mask his terror at this revelation.

"I'm proposing that Perry has attempted to pervert the course of justice. Breaking and entering into Miss Nicholas's locker and rifling privileged material. I'm proposing that, unless you immediately withdraw your application to adduce this evidence then you, Haskitt, will be aiding and abetting the attempted perversion. I'm hoping that you don't withdraw it because nothing would give me greater pleasure than to see you disbarred and then locked up. But I'm giving you the option because of my duty to my client. I think, if you withdraw your application and this case continues, then Trevors has a fifty-fifty chance of being acquitted and I'll take those odds. But if you want to go the other route, then call my bluff. Those are my proposals. No fudges. Withdraw your application or go to hell. The pair of you. It's hard to decide which of you is the bigger shit. See you in Court."

Turning on his heel, Cadogan strode out of the room, leaving the Prosecution team hung, drawn and quartered.

* * *

Haskitt:
> Thank you for allowing us time to discuss this matter, My Lord. We are very grateful

Mr Justice Hathington:
> Not at all, Mr Haskitt. Are you now in a position to provide the information that I required so that the evidence can be properly adduced?

Haskitt:
> My Lord, after very careful consideration, the Prosecution have decided not to pursue this application further. We're no longer seeking to adduce the evidence.

Mr Justice Hathington:
> What? You're choosing to abandon potent, incriminating evidence which, half an hour ago, you were adamant was admissible?

Haskitt:
> Yes, My Lord. I am unable to satisfy myself that we have truly identified the means whereby the Prosecution learned of this material. I believe that it would take a considerable time to make all the appropriate enquiries and I have therefore resolved not to proceed with the application.

MrJustice Hathington:
> No, Mr Haskitt. Not good enough, I'm afraid. I have the duty of seeing that justice is done to all sides, including the public. You don't abandon evidence of this importance because of time constraints. You may have as much time as you need to make your enquiries. I'm quite prepared to adjourn the case until tomorrow, which will give you ample time. I do not accept the withdrawal of your application.

Haskitt:

My Lord, with great respect, I must inform Your Lordship that my decision is final.

Mr Justice Hathington:

You mean that you're capitulating?

Haskitt:

I would not choose that word, My Lord. This decision has been made in consultation at the highest level. Mr Nathan of the CPS, Detective Chief Inspector Noble, my Junior, Sergeant Perry and I have discussed this matter with great care. It is our considered, unanimous and final decision that our application is herewith irrevocably withdrawn.

Mr Justice Hathington:

I refuse to accept that decision. This evidence may well represent the difference between conviction and acquittal. I'm completely satisfied that Mr Cadogan can cross-examine the Cambridge police officer just as effectively now as he could have done if the officer had been called during the Prosecution case. Any suggestion by Mr Cadogan that he might have called the Cambridge householder, Miss Blundell, I treat as fanciful. You may have such time as you need to complete your enquiries, Mr Haskitt. This evidence is not going to be allowed to disappear for some obscure, unidentified reason.

Haskitt:

With great respect, My Lord, the eventual decision in circumstances such as these, lies with the Crown and not with the Judge. On behalf of the Crown I withdraw the application. Unequivocally and finally.

Mr Justice Hathington:

You realise that the Judge can report Counsel to the appropriate Disciplinary Body, do you not?

Haskitt:

I do.

Mr Justice Hathington:

You have considered the Code of Conduct, have you?

Haskitt:

I have.

Mr Justice Hathington:

I don't suppose that there is anything that you wish to say, Mr Cadogan?

Cadogan:

No, My Lord.

Mr Justice Hathington:

Mr Haskitt, you have made your decision with which I fundamentally disagree. I am most disturbed at the circumstances in which you have withdrawn your application but, as you say, I cannot make you change your mind. I shall consider any further disciplinary matters after the trial has ended. We shall resume with the jury in fifteen minutes. Until then I shall retire to my room so that my anger at your capitulation can subside.

* * *

In his final speech to the jury Haskitt pulled out all the stops. If, somehow, now against all the odds, he could wring a conviction out of the havoc that Cadogan had left in his wake, then Hathington would back off in his disciplinary threats and he would, at a terrible price, have laid the ghost of Cadogan to rest. Whatever the damage done to the Prosecution during the trial, the jury had still seen and heard Trevors whose guilt oozed from every pore, whatever the actual state of the evidence. Hammering away for all he was worth at the DNA, Mrs Checkley's voice identification, the tell-tale injury to the Defendant's neck, the size of the shoe print and the details of some of Trevors' answers in cross examination, he pressed for a conviction for all he was worth, frequently reminding the jury that they represented the public and the safety of their fellow citizens lay in their hands.

As expected, Cadogan's response was sheer magnificence. Weaving his spell, he sought to decimate the Prosecution case, focusing his attack on Perry about whom he spoke with undisguised contempt. The power of his oratory was reminiscent of the old, great advocates from another time, whose mastery could transport a jury on a magical voyage to inevitable acquittal. For nearly two hours he never faltered, his strength never ebbed, his commitment never wavered. With reason, with craft and with raw power he seduced the jury away from Haskitt's arguments and fought for the freedom of his client. It was a tour de force.

By the end of the afternoon Mr Justice Hathington was nearly halfway through his summing-up. Still seething at Haskitt's apparent capitulation, the Judge utilised all the weight of authority that his position afforded, to nudge the jury along the path towards conviction. He would not have been the first Judge in the history of the English Criminal Courts to see himself as an extra player for the Prosecution but, of course, that was only a part of his motivation. Ever since Helen Gaynor had reported those words of Marcus Buxton to him in the hallway of the Lodgings, they had haunted him. "Let's hope that the villain doesn't slip through Hathington's fingers. Wouldn't make for a long judicial career." Within those ominous words lay the selfish motive that drove Hathington into his partisanship. Paying lip service to the Defence case and hardly mentioning Cadogan or his arguments at all, he pushed relentlessly for conviction. Tomorrow, he promised the jury, it would be their turn.

When Naomi arrived home there was no sign of Jack. His car was not on the drive and his mobile phone was still switched off. On the kitchen table, however, there was a brief note. "Had to go down to London unexpectedly. Work. Back tomorrow evening. Love, Jack." By then, thought Naomi, when she finally confronted him with her allegations, the trial would likely be over. Perhaps it was better that the showdown with Jack happened when she knew the result. Following a quick cup of tea and a boring cheese sandwich made with yesterday's bread, she took a bath and then collapsed into bed. It had been one of the most horrendous days that she had ever experienced. Her relationship with Jack was probably ruined and the bitter twists and turns within the trial had left her emotionally exhausted. Trevors, Haskitt, Perry and Cadogan were, in their own particular ways, as loathsome as each other. But as sleep slowly came, it was nevertheless the figure of Cadogan that she saw, standing in that CPS Conference Room like an unarmed and outnumbered warrior, facing down the enemy with steel-eyed bravado. Despite herself, she was filled with admiration at his sheer guts. Furthermore, by preventing Haskitt from adducing the Cambridge evidence, he had saved her from the anguish of being responsible, via Jack, for the introduction of the piece of evidence into the trial which would have ensured her client's conviction, and she was not sure that she would have been able to handle that, let alone the destruction of her own career if, as she feared, her loose words to Jack had been the source of the information.

* * *

"Jury bailiff, do you promise that you will keep this jury in some private and convenient place. You shall not suffer anyone to speak to them nor shall you speak to them yourself, unless it be to ask them if they are agreed upon their verdict, so help you God," recited the Clerk of the Court at the conclusion of the Judge's summing-up. "My Lord, the jury are retiring at 11.23."

* * *

The twelve figures took their places around the large square table and embarked upon their task, firstly electing Roger Frobisher, the rather self-important electrical engineer as their foreman, on the basis that he was the only volunteer for the job and then the discussions began in earnest. Sandwiches were ordered and delivered. A message was relayed to the jury that no verdict would be taken by the Judge between 1.00 and 2.15 over lunch. The atmosphere grew heavy and heated as the discussions passed into late afternoon. At 3.45 the Judge sent for the jury and they filed solemnly back into Court.

The Courtroom was packed. The press galleries were crammed. Barristers from other Courts had come in to listen. The public gallery was full to capacity. The jury filed into their places, all looking down. The door in the dock swung open and Trevors was brought in, deathly white, with two male prison officers on each side.

"Will the foreman please rise," the Clerk declared.

Roger Frobisher rose to his feet. This was his moment.

"Mr Foreman, will you please answer my first question either 'yes' or 'no'. Have the jury reached a verdict on any Count in the Indictment on which you are all agreed?"

"No, My Lord," came Frobisher's clear response.

"My Lord, the jury retired at 11.23 and returned at 3.47. They have been in retirement for 4 hours and 24 minutes."

"Thank you, Madam Clerk," responded the Judge. Mr Foreman, please be seated. Members of the jury, the stage has now been reached where I am empowered to accept a verdict from you, which is not the verdict of you all. I shall ask you to retire again and strive to reach unanimous verdicts. If, however, this is truly not possible, then I can accept a verdict upon which at least ten of you are agreed. Now, please retire again. If unanimity is beyond you, then verdicts with which at least ten of you agree are acceptable."

As the jury withdrew, the enormity of their impending decision weighed heavily upon everybody. Naomi just hoped that they made their decision that afternoon, as she did not relish yet another tense day of this wretched trial, particularly as Jack's note indicated that he would be home tonight. It would make such a difference if this trial were to be over before having to cope with that dreaded confrontation. She needed a clear head but, by quarter to five, it had become painfully obvious that the jury were not going to reach verdicts tonight and, at just before five o'clock, a message was sent by the jury that they were tired, had no prospect of arriving at any verdicts that day and wished to go home. Accordingly, the Judge reconvened the Court in an atmosphere of reduced tension, everybody realising that no verdicts were about to be delivered. With the customary warnings to the jury about not discussing the case overnight and not being influenced by any of the media publicity that the case was attracting, the Judge adjourned the hearing until ten o'clock the next morning. Naomi would have to face Jack with the outcome of the trial still unknown.

* * *

Although the house was in total darkness, Jack's car was parked on the drive so, unless he had gone out for a run, in which case he would normally have left at least the hall light on, the chances were that he was at home. In letting herself in through the front door Naomi was deliberately noisy, rattling her keys in the lock and banging the door loudly behind her, but she provoked no welcoming or enquiring call from elsewhere in the house. Although the television was on in the sitting room, tuned to Sky News, downstairs was otherwise deserted and, with increasing apprehension, she ascended the stairs and checked each of the bedrooms, without finding any sign of Jack's presence. Whilst in the back bedroom she looked through the window that overlooked the rather untidy, two-tier garden.

Adjacent to the path which led across a patchy lawn on the first tier, Jack had positioned a large, wooden bench which he had bought from the old Rugby Club when it had to close down its ground at the end of last season. It bore an inscription dedicated to one of its former members, whose son Jack had known long ago, and he had been determined to acquire it. Naomi had put on all of the downstairs lights while she was searching the house and, through the light cast out into the garden, she could now see Jack sitting on his bench, shoulders slumped and head bowed forward. There could be no doubt that he was aware of her return home, but he was making no attempt to enter the house and face her. With a heavy heart she slowly descended the stairs and went into the kitchen and, pouring herself a generous glass of red wine from an opened bottle, she sat disconsolately at the large oak table that they had bought together. The enormity of what Jack had done still provoked intense anger in her but, as she had stared at him from the bedroom window, the anger had given way to deep sadness and a feeling of impending loss, for she doubted that the relationship could ever survive his treachery.

Halfway through her second glass of wine the back door opened and Jack came hesitantly into the room, avoiding her eyes and shuffling towards a chair on the opposite side of the table, his hands shaking from the cold outside, as he reached for the bottle and poured himself a glass of wine. Naomi remained completely silent, looking away and fighting to retain control as she felt her bottom lip quivering and her heart pounding.

Eventually he spoke.

"I know you can never forgive me," he began nervously. "Whatever I've done wrong in my life, I've never been dishonourable before. Now I have been and I shall never forgive myself."

"Spare me the self-pity," Naomi snapped cruelly. "Just tell me why you did it. I assume that you realised that you could have ended my entire career."

"You told me the murderer was going to walk and that it was because Haskitt had missed the ballet shoes evidence. I thought about the victim's wife, I suppose that was my mistake. I remembered how I'd have felt if that drunk driver who killed Christine hadn't been convicted. Trevors was far worse. He'd killed deliberately. Killed her husband, while she watched, and now he was going to be free. How could she live with that? Allowing myself to think like that was my mistake," Jack explained with his head in his hands.

"But you knew the rules. I represent criminals. I'm told things in confidence which, if I breach the confidence, can cost them the case and cost me my job. I spoke freely to you because I loved you and trusted you. You betrayed me," she declared, fighting back the tears, but determined to continue. "If that evidence had been allowed to go to the jury then Trevors would undoubtedly be convicted. I would always believe that my breach of confidence was the reason for the conviction. My own conscience would never have permitted me to continue the job and, if anyone ever found out that I was responsible for the leaked information, I'd have been thrown out of the profession anyway," she shouted at him.

"I knew that you'd work out it was me. That's why I didn't come home yesterday. I realised it would be all over," he replied, shaking his head.

"You mean you lied about going to London, just like you lied in the restaurant about some breaking transfer news," she barked back at him.

"Yes. All right. I lied," he agreed. "There can be no proper excuse. At least the ballet shoes evidence didn't go in, did it?"

"No, it didn't," she answered, looking directly at him. "How did you find that out?"

"Yesterday morning. After I had thought it through properly and realised the full extent of how it could hurt you, I got a call through to the officer who I'd given the information to, and asked what had happened. He said something about it all backfiring and not being used. I did it all without him knowing who I was, so there's no connection to you, I muffled my voice," he quickly added.

"Perry, of course?" she responded bitterly.

"Yes," he acknowledged.

"And you didn't think that cunning bastard would still recognise your voice and put two and two together?" she enquired angrily. "Not that it matters anymore, because you're right, the evidence didn't go in. And do you want to know why it didn't?" she snapped, before continuing without waiting for his answer. "Because of Cadogan. Cadogan worked it all out. But he had no proof. Even without any proof, he went and fought them. And it was Cadogan who saved my skin and my career in the process."

"He was fighting his case, not fighting for you. He had no means of knowing that I was the source of the information and that therefore you were involved in the leak," replied Jack defensively.

"Cadogan was fighting full stop. Not for me. Not for his client. Just fighting. That's what he does. He's a warrior. He fights to the death. If I was disbarred, he wouldn't give it a second thought. He just wants to win. But he's no fool. Don't tell me that he couldn't work out the source of the leak."

"Well, he took an instant dislike to me anyway," Jack observed. "And after the Elland Road incident he'll be delighted that I'm getting my comeuppance."

"I doubt that he gives a damn. He never mentioned your name yesterday. He just sat down, worked out Perry was in the thick of it, marched into the CPS Room and terrified the living daylights out of them. Any effect any of this might have on you or me is a complete irrelevance to him. But I still can't believe what you did, Jack. How you could be so deceitful? You were the most straightforward and honest man that I'd ever met. Now you've ruined everything," Naomi declared as the tears streamed down her cheeks.

Jack looked away as the anguish he felt threatened to become unbearable. Every fibre of his being demanded that he get up, walk across to her, put his arms around her and protect her from this pain. But he was responsible for that pain. For those few minutes in Valentino's, he had allowed the prospect of a murderer going free and the lifetime of distress that Sarah Checkley would thereby suffer, to outweigh the sanctity of his relationship with Naomi. Now he must pay the price. Sadly, he lifted himself from his chair and, without looking at Naomi, headed slowly towards the front door. Despite himself, in the kitchen doorway, he turned back and spoke.

"The irony is that it was all for nothing. I've destroyed our relationship, but, if Trevors is acquitted, then Cadogan will still have destroyed Mrs Checkley. If Haskitt had done his job properly, then the ballet shoes evidence would have gone in without any of this mess. Everyone's a loser except for Trevors and Cadogan. And I'm the villain of the piece. Where's the justice in any of this, Naomi?"

Through her tears Naomi looked up at him as he stood forlornly in the doorway. If only she could find a way to forgive him. Now approaching her mid-thirties, it was most unlikely that she would ever find a man like Jack again. Their relationship had been the best thing that had ever happened to her and she had never doubted that he loved her. Surely, she could find it in her heart to forgive and seek to repair the damage? But, instead of forgiveness and conciliation, she heard herself speak out in hard and biting terms.

"That's your problem. You think it's all about justice. If you want justice then keep away from a Court of Law. That's the last place you'll find any justice. What this is about is trust. Trust between a man and a woman. And loyalty. You've failed me on trust and loyalty and failed yourself. Goodbye, Jack."

"I'm going. I'll come for my things in a few days when you're out. You're right, I have failed you. And I've been disloyal, which is unworthy and dishonourable. But this is the only time in my life I've ever behaved like that and my motive was to see a murderer punished," he replied. Then, hesitating long and hard before he spoke again, he hit back. "And, one last word, you shouldn't forget that once, you too breached a trust between a man and woman. And your motive then was a selfish motive. Mine was not."

Looking at him in horror, Naomi exploded. "How dare you bring that up? I was desperate for money to finish my exams. I told you that no one suffered as a result. Dov's deal went through. He made his millions."

"Your integrity suffered, Naomi. You did what you had to do. But it was every bit as disloyal as what I've done and I venture to suggest that my motive was less ugly. We can all commit the sin, can't we?" he replied quietly. "I'm not justifying what I did, I'm asking you to remember that we can all have our moments of weakness, even Naomi Nicholas."

Naomi remembered old Miss Wickham and her words all those years ago. "There will come a time in most people's lives, dear," she had said, "when they have to take a big chance. If they don't they may regret it for ever." Jack had seen the chance to see that a vicious murderer was convicted. She had seen the chance to earn twenty thousand pounds by deceit. The problem was that Jack was right. His motive was far less ugly than hers. His calm voice interrupted her silent reflections.

"Goodbye, Naomi. I did love you and I still do. I never expect to meet a woman again and feel as I do about you. I'm so sorry for what I did. I reminded you of your own transgression so that, in time, you might be less hard on me. If ever you think that you may be able to give me another chance, then I hope that you'll get in touch. I'd never let you down again for as long as I live," he said slowly and deliberately, before turning on his heel and gently closing the door behind him.

Naomi's head sank on to the cold surface of the table as she sobbed with an intensity that racked her whole body. Jack had gone. Maintaining his composure to the end, he had gone. How could she ever hope to go on without him? He had become everything.

CHAPTER 25

When Naomi arrived at Court the next morning she had to fight her way through the media circus which had camped outside the building, before eventually reaching the Security Check Point, where a long queue had formed. Billy Gray, an old faithful of the janitorial staff, was operating one of the screens and, spotting her at the back of the queue, he called her forward and ushered her through.

"Thank you, Billy," she said kindly. "I'd have been there all morning."

"Anytime, Miss Nicholas, anytime," the amiable Billy replied. "Are you feeling all right today? You look a bit peaky, if you don't mind me saying," he offered.

"Just a cold coming on. See you later," she lied as she moved away towards the robing room. The truth was that she looked just awful, despite the unusually heavy layers of make-up she had applied before leaving home. A night almost totally without sleep, and tears that had reddened her face and eyes beyond cosmetic redemption, told their own story. She had cried for Jack with sobs as bitter and desperate as anything she could remember in adult life. When this case was over she needed some time to herself in which she would have to wrestle with the question of whether she could make that telephone call and try to forgive. There was no point in even trying to understand how she felt until the mental and physical exhaustion of the trial were well and truly behind her. A fresh assault with the foundation creams and eye drops in the robing room made little difference and, as soon as the Judge had sent the jury out again at ten o'clock sharp, she hid herself away in a tiny conference room at the far end of the building, with an old Dick Francis paperback, which she had fortuitously found abandoned on the public seating in the corridor. The Court tannoy system would alert her to the jury's return, but by lunchtime she had read over half of the book and still there was no sign of a verdict. Her stomach was empty as she had been unable to manage any breakfast and, feeling slightly queasy, she ventured out of her hiding place and bought herself a coffee and a bar of chocolate in the cafeteria, carefully avoiding being drawn into conversation with any of the various familiar faces that she saw. Since the Judge had sent the jury out again this morning, she had not set eyes on the other Counsel in the case and had no desire to do so. Withdrawing again into her room of sanctuary, she sat and waited. Heaven forbid that the jury could not agree and a retrial had to take place.

At some stage she must have drifted off into a half-sleep for, when she was awakened by the door opening, the book lay on the floor at her feet and it was getting dark outside.

"The tannoy's packed up, Naomi," the anxious voice of Dickie Lampard breathed as he came into the room. "The Judge's Clerk has given me the task of rounding everybody up. The Jury's ready. They've got a verdict. I couldn't find you. Looked everywhere. Come on, girl, let's get it over and done with."

"What time is it then?" she asked, dragging herself to her feet and feeling nauseous as the moment of truth approached. Verdict time was always horrendous, but this was worse than ever before. Apart from the emotional storm she was trying to weather because of Jack, this was a case that she was desperate to lose. Trevors had to be convicted.

"It's after five. Judge just left them to stew and it seems they've finally hammered it out. I say, is everything OK, you look awful. Are you ill?" Lampard asked with obvious concern.

"I'm not feeling too clever, I have to admit. Had a bad night. But, like you say, let's get it over and done with," she answered as he held the door open for her.

"Marching to the execution, eh?" Lampard laughed as he escorted her to the short flight of stairs which led down to their courtroom.

"Yes, but whose bloody execution?" she enigmatically responded as they came to the doors of the courtroom around which a large throng of people had gathered, trying to gain entry. The ushers and police were holding them back, shouting repeatedly that the public gallery was full and that there was no room for anyone else.

Eventually a path was cleared for the two Junior Counsel and they pushed their way into the well of the Court. Yesterday there had not been a spare seat but today, it seemed to Naomi, there were even more people crammed into every nook and cranny. Many of the press were standing at the sides of the doors and between the seats, the aisles were full of uniformed police and the public gallery was like a football crowd. Haskitt and Cadogan were in place. Every seat on the solicitors' and Counsels' rows was occupied and there was some awkward sliding and shifting as room was found for Naomi and Lampard, at their respective ends of the row.

As Naomi squeezed on to her seat the Clerk called for silence and the hubbub subsided. The Judge's door opened and the red-robed Mr Justice

Hathington walked sombrely into Court, his face also displaying the extent to which many lives were about to be affected by the imminent verdict.

Placing his white gloves on the desk before him, the Judge nodded in the direction of one of the jury bailiffs, heralding the long-awaited return of the jury. The twelve jurors walked into a wall of overpowering silence and gruesome expectation. Their faces were drawn and two of the ladies, Saffad Aziz and Christine Mills, had plainly been crying, whilst at least two of the men wore expressions of thunder. All twelve of them seemed shocked by the bloodlust atmosphere of the arena into which they had just come. This was a crowd which had come to witness death.

The sound of the gaoler's keys and the lock turning, announced that Trevors had been brought up from the bowels of the building and was about to be led into the dock. The same four burly prison officers were in attendance. Two of them emerged first. Then Trevors, pale and now sweating with naked fear. Then the final pair of officers. All eyes stared at the white face, looking straight ahead, standing defiantly in the centre of the dock, hemmed in on all sides by brawn and uniform. Less than fifty years ago he would have been destined to swing from the gallows, reflected some of the older Court staff who had slipped in for the verdict.

The Clerk of the Court began the ritual.

"My Lord, the jury retired yesterday morning at 11.23 and returned at 3.47 for the majority direction, retiring again until 5.01. Today, they retired at 10 o'clock, returning at 5.27. They have been in retirement therefore, for a total of 13 hours and 5 minutes.

Mr Foreman will you please rise."

Roger Frobisher stood tall, clutching a piece of paper firmly in his unsteady hands, staring straight ahead as he prepared to deliver the jury's verdicts.

"Mr Foreman. Please confine yourself to answering only 'yes' or 'no' to my first question.

Members of the jury, on Count 1 of the indictment, have at least ten of you agreed upon your verdict?"

"Yes," answered Frobisher, in as strong a voice as he could muster.

"Members of the jury, on the Count of Murder, do you find the Defendant guilty or not guilty of murder?"

"Not Guilty, My Lord."

There was an audible intake of breath followed by a desperate wailing sound from a corner of the police benches where Sarah Checkley sat, dressed in black, surrounded by a group of uniformed police officers. The sound she made was primeval and sent shudders down Naomi's backbone. Still wailing, and in a state of uncontrolled hysteria, Mrs Checkley was hurried out of the court by two policewomen. Outbursts of raucous cursing erupted from the public gallery and, as police officers moved closer to those responsible, Mr Justice Hathington's voice, amplified by his microphone, boomed out above the shouting.

"There will be silence. There will be silence. Unless there is immediate silence the whole Courtroom will be cleared. Silence."

His intervention brought quiet to the proceedings and he then continued.

"The remaining two verdicts will be delivered in complete silence. Anyone who shouts out will be arrested. I want that clearly understood. If anyone feels that they will be unable to control themselves, that person must leave now."

"Yes, Madam Clerk, continue please," he stated, observing that no one had made any move to withdraw.

"Mr Foreman, please confine yourself to answering only 'yes' or 'no' to the next question. Members of the jury, on Count 2 of the indictment, have at least ten of you agreed upon your verdict?"

"Yes, My Lord," replied Frobisher, his voice now shaking after the ferocity of the public reaction to his announcement of the first verdict.

"Members of the jury, on the Count of Aggravated Burglary, do you find the Defendant guilty or not guilty?"

"Not Guilty, My Lord."

"Mr Foreman, please confine yourself to answering only 'yes' or 'no' to my next question. Members of the jury, on Count 3 of the indictment, have at least ten of you agreed upon your verdict?"

"Yes."

"Members of the jury, on the Count of Wounding with Intent, do you find the Defendant guilty or not guilty?"

"Not Guilty, My Lord."

"So, in respect of each of Counts 1, 2 and 3 at least ten of you have found the Defendant not guilty, is that correct?"

"Yes."

"Thank you, Mr Foreman, please sit down."

Cadogan rose solemnly to his feet and delivered the final thrust of his rapier. "My Lord, I ask that the Defendant be discharged and that there be a Defendant's Costs Order."

"Yes," spat Hathington, his face now ashen. "I shall withdraw."

As the Judge flounced out of Court, without even acknowledging the jury, pandemonium broke out. Reporters and broadcasters ran for the doors. The jury were ushered quickly away through their side door and, wisely, the four prison officers bundled Trevors back through the door in the dock towards the cells, mumbling that it would be safer to let him out the cells door, once the crowds had dispersed.

As the Court emptied, Haskitt and Lampard slipped away without a word to anyone. Naomi Nicholas turned to Roger Sylvester and whispered, "I actually feel sick. Physically sick."

"So do I Miss Nicholas. You're not alone," came the mournful reply Cadogan stood up and gave them their orders.

"Short farewell conference with the client, then I'm getting the 6.35. See you in the cells in five minutes."

* * *

The group of four, consisting of the Defendant and his legal team, was gathered in the corridor between the cells and the rear exit door used by the prison vehicles. The prison officers had washed their hands of Trevors and were just waiting to open the exit door as soon as they got the all clear that there wasn't a lynching mob in waiting. In the space of ten minutes, Trevors had been transformed from one of the most dangerous men in England into a free man who was about to set off for a pie and a pint.

Naomi Nicholas and Roger Sylvester stared at the floor, saying nothing and averting their eyes from the offensive look of triumph that covered Trevors' face as he crowed about his victory.

"Told you not to worry about me in the box, Mr Cadogan. Told you I knew how to do the business. A set-up from beginning to..." Trevors boasted before he was interrupted by Cadogan.

"Just shut up, will you. I've only got three things to say to you. One, you've had the luck of the devil. You can never be that lucky again. Two, don't leave here for at least another fifteen minutes when the crowds will have started to disperse. Three, when you are in trouble again, as I've no doubt you will be, don't ask for me. I wouldn't wish to represent you again. Goodbye."

"Hang on," protested Trevors. "You can't talk to me like that, now. It's all changed. We're equals now. Innocent men. I'm innocent. I want my compensation. I want Sylvester telling the TV outside that I'm innocent and demand compensation. And what do you mean, you wouldn't represent me again. Why you saying that?"

"Because I never represent guilty men twice," replied Cadogan. "Come on, Naomi, I'll walk out with you. Mr Sylvester, you'd better prepare your statement with Trevors for the TV. They'll want something. I'll leave that up to you and your client. Good day."

Ronan Cadogan and his Junior walked in silence up the stairs towards the private room, secured for him by Arthur, where he had changed during the trial. At the top of the stairs, their ways finally parted.

"Goodbye, Ronan," she said, breaking the silence. "I hope that our paths never cross again. But, I'll always remember you for your performance in the CPS Room when you faced them down over the ballet shoes. Not even I can deny that you were magnificent. Beyond that, I've found you quite loathsome."

"Have you finished with him, then?" laughed Cadogan cruelly, completely ignoring her remarks.

"What the hell are you talking about? Why should I finish with him?" she shouted in temper.

"Naomi, Naomi. Come on. Despise me as much as you like. I really don't give a fig, my dear. But don't underestimate me. Do you think I can't see what happened?" he retorted condescendingly.

"One day you'll pay for all of this. Your contempt for everybody except yourself. What goes around, comes around," she barked back at him.

"What goes around, comes around. That's what I suspect you've just found out with your precious Jack," he shouted to her as he wandered away.

Yet again he had got the last word, thought Naomi to herself, and yet again, without fully realising the nerve he had touched, the bastard was absolutely right. It was only as he strolled nonchalantly down the corridor and out of her life that the full irony of what had happened struck her. The loathsome bully had accurately identified exactly what had passed between her and Jack. If ever it had got out that she had leaked confidential, privileged material during the case to her lover which had led to its introduction into the trial, then there could be no doubt that the Bar Council would have thrown her out of the profession.

In his demolition of Haskitt in the CPS room, the detestable Cadogan had actually saver her career.

* * *

Two large, white outside broadcast vans were parked directly outside the main entrance gates to the Courthouse, each with its space-age satellite dish fixed to the roof, pointing to the heavens, poised to beam out images and signals to the world beyond. Powerful portable lights had already been set up and were picking out the frenzied movement of the reporters and technicians, as the final act was being played out.

Whilst Roger Sylvester had already been seized by the pushy BBC News front man, Alistair Simmons, and was unenthusiastically preparing to make a statement on the steps of the Court, Lisa Bond of Sky News had managed to corner Detective Chief Inspector Noble in the middle of the cobblestoned forecourt as he sought to slip by unnoticed.

"Can we have the police view on the verdict, Chief Inspector?" demanded the blonde, hard-faced female interviewer, thrusting the microphone directly into Noble's face as he tried to walk away.

"We all have to accept the verdict of a jury," declared Noble sourly.

"This was a terrible murder. Can you tell us what the police have said to Mrs Checkley?" asked Bond with deliberate insensitivity.

"We can only offer her our continuing sympathy and support and counselling if she wants it," replied the Chief Inspector, seeking to retreat from the fray. "Our thoughts are with her and her daughter. Now, I must ask you to excuse me."

"Will you be keeping the enquiry open, Mr Noble? Will you still be looking for the killer?" the reporter continued, deliberately ignoring Noble's attempted withdrawal.

"That's a matter to be discussed over the next few days, when we've had a chance to consider the full implications of the verdict," answered Noble as diplomatically as he could.

"I would suggest that the public have a right to know now whether you are just writing the case off, or whether you are still actively seeking the killer. Will you not tell the people what the position is?" Bond persisted aggressively.

"Speaking for myself," Noble reluctantly responded, "I should be surprised if we were to look elsewhere. I don't believe that we'll be looking for anybody else. That is all I'm prepared to say at the moment. Now, if you'll excuse me. Thank you very much."

With obvious delight, the interviewer turned directly to the camera which was transmitting the material live.

"There you have it, then. Detective Chief Inspector Noble has revealed, exclusively to Sky News, that the police have little intention of continuing to look for the killer of Paul Checkley. Make of that what you will. Lisa Bond, Sky News, Leeds Crown Court."

Meanwhile, the BBC's man had failed to persuade Sylvester to bring Trevors out of the building and in front of the cameras.

"You get a short, prepared statement, read out by me. No follow-up questions. No Trevors in view. Take it or leave it," he had told Simmons curtly.

"It'll have to do for now then, Mr Sylvester," he conceded with a resigned shrug of his shoulders. "Suppose he's already agreeing to an exclusive with one of the tabloids. Anyway, we're about to be cued in. You follow immediately after my intro," he continued as the controller counted down from five to one, pointed at the lead camera, called for silence and Simmons fluently rolled into action.

"In a stunning ending, to what has proved to be a sensational trial at Leeds Crown Court, the jury of seven men and five women, after a retirement of more than thirteen hours, have just acquitted Gary Trevors on all three counts, including the murder of Leeds businessman Paul Checkley, who was brutally stabbed to death in his own home in front of his wife, who was also seriously wounded. Mr Trevors is presently declining to comment, but his solicitor Roger Sylvester is about to make a statement on behalf of his client. Mr Sylvester."

Reading loudly and nervously from his prepared script, Roger Sylvester forced himself to deliver the hypocritical, weasel words of his ruthless client.

"Mr Trevors is greatly relieved that this terrible ordeal is over. Of course, he offers his sympathy to Mrs Checkley in her dreadful loss but, as the jury have decided, that was nothing to do with him and he has been in custody for many months, awaiting trial for a crime which he did not commit. He will be looking to the police and the authorities for substantial compensation for putting an innocent man through this agony. He has no more to say at this time. Thank you."

"There you have it," cut in Simmons immediately, "a call for compensation by Gary Trevors as he tastes freedom tonight. For Sarah Checkley and for the police, a devastating blow. For the Yorkshire public, the certain knowledge that, one way or the other, a vicious murderer is still out there, somewhere. Alistair Simmons. BBC News. Leeds."

Fourteen million viewers watched the news broadcast. One of them was the sad, lonely figure of Jack Farnham. Alone in his flat, unshaven and with an almost empty bottle of whisky on the coffee table in front of him, he had not ventured beyond his front door all day, in the forlorn hope that his phone might ring and he would hear again that beautiful, clear voice which had become such an important part of his life.

CHAPTER 26

Three months were taken in coming to the decision and a further five months were dedicated to meticulous plotting and planning. There could be no mistakes here. No risk of a life sentence. You had to learn from experience and produce the faultless performance. All the little details that had been picked up. Understanding the new scientific techniques that the police had available to them. Identifying the kind of garments that did not shed any fibres. Everything had to be black. Better headgear and not home-made, so that there was no chance of stitches coming undone on this occasion. The prey had to be painstakingly stalked. The victim's routine carefully observed. Always keeping out of sight but watching, waiting, planning. The right day of the week had to be chosen and precise timing was vital. A foolproof bogus alibi was essential although, as it happened, that had proved one of the easier aspects of the operation.

A day trip to London had been necessary to identify the supplier of ballet shoes. Just noted the address, as the purchase would be made through the post; payment by postal order; false name down at one of the DHSS lodging houses and nip in there immediately after the postman called; door was always open; none of the residents were up at seven fifteen in the morning.

Whilst down in the capital, a short diversion to a culinary stall in the fish market had produced an exquisite weapon. A double-edged filleting knife with razor sharp edges and a white curved handle that fitted snugly into the hand. Ten inch blade. Once the surgeon's gloves were acquired, the grip felt just perfect. Learned how to use the World Wide Web. Internet cafes. No names. Studied the sites on pathology and anatomy. Knew exactly the right spot. Now just one thrust should be enough. One second, two. Like quicksilver it would be. But the planning was everything. Patience, application, desire. The prize had to be worthwhile.

Eventually, a particular Thursday night was selected. The prey always walked from the Club to Glanville Street. At the far end of Castleford Lane the houses stopped, there was a hundred yard stretch, that was bordered by waste ground on each side, and there was no street lighting. Just beyond the chosen location, the lane joined Glanville Street which, within half a mile, passed under the motorway. A few small industrial units were situated on the left hand side of Glanville Street. The area was always deserted at night and the getaway vehicle could be safely parked near to one of those units. Had acquired false car registration plates from Watford. Cost eighteen pounds, no records kept, cash. After the strike, it would need a fast dash on foot to the vehicle, maximum three minutes. Under the motorway, link up with the dual carriageway as far as the next junction, straight on to the motorway itself and heading north. Maximum five minutes. Disposal of clothing, weapon and false plates en route home added eight minutes, leaving a thirty-minute drive home. The whole operation, from the strike to the front door, was forty-six minutes. Carried out two dummy runs on the preceding Thursdays. Never saw a soul. Forty-eight minutes and forty-four minutes respectively. On the night the adrenalin rush would make it even faster. Everything was ready.

Pitch black night. Heavy cloud, no moon. Four or five degrees above freezing. In position behind the oak tree. Invisible. Full length balaclava down. Black, lightweight training suit, tight on body and legs. Ballet shoes. Gloves on, knife out, right hand held inside top to prevent any risk of glint from the blade. Ten o'clock. Approaching footsteps. Forty yards away. Right on time. Heart pounding. Stay cool. Long, deep silent breaths. Control the heartbeat. Adrenalin pumping hard. Twenty yards. Eyes staring intensely through balaclava slits. No blinking. Tightening in stomach and bowels. Five yards. The footsteps loud now. Can hear the prey breathing. No doubts. No second thoughts. Prey now just passing. Count to three. Emerge from behind tree and approach swiftly from behind. Completely silent approach as the ballet shoes come into their own. Right up behind. Then prey senses my presence. Begins to turn. Strike. Strike. Swing the arm hard and fast at lower neck level. Straight into the jugular. Thrust so hard blade went clean through and out the other side. Prey tries to grab me. Blade still in neck. Got to get it out. Twist. Prey grunting and trying to scream but just gurgling, as blood spurts out . A fountain of blood. Blade free. Swing arm round and thrust into centre chest. Straight through ventricles of heart, push for the aorta. Can smell him. Can feel him. His strength ebbing away. Falling. Dying. Hands running down my body as falls. Even more blood than anticipated. No words. Death. Ecstasy. Run. Run. Run. Stay cool. Survive. Run faster. Feet silent on the pavement. Silent in their ballet shoes. Those beautiful, black, size five ballet shoes.

* * *

At noon the following day Superintendent Ellway alighted from the rear of the Jaguar at the front door of Blossomfields, Alwoodley in Leeds. Telling his driver that he did not expect to be long, he rang the bell and awaited a response. The door opened and the attractive, demure figure of Sarah Checkley appeared, dressed in a sky blue silk blouse, designer jeans and white, Dior sandals.

"Mrs Checkley?" enquired the Superintendent politely.

"That is correct," she replied with a smile.

"My Inspector telephoned you this morning and you kindly agreed to see me. Superintendent Derek Ellway is the name," he announced.

"Come in, Superintendent. Come in, please. Can I arrange a cup of tea for you, or a coffee?" she offered.

"No Madam, really not. If I can just step inside. Won't take a minute."

As he entered the hall, she closed the door behind him and they both moved a few paces further inside. Although he did not realise it, the Superintendent came to a halt in the exact place that Paul Checkley had met his death.

"Mrs Checkley, as you were informed on the telephone by my Inspector, a man by the name of Gary Peter Trevors was killed in a knife attack last night in a small town about forty miles from here. Given that this man was acquitted of murdering your husband, I am sure that you understand that it was necessary for us to establish your whereabouts at the relevant time," the Superintendent carefully explained.

"Of course, I understand," came the relaxed reply. "I was asked if I could account for my whereabouts at about ten o'clock last night."

"Yes. Trevors was found at ten past ten by a man walking his dog. He called 999 on his mobile phone and a paramedic crew and a doctor were there by ten fifteen. The medical evidence is that the sites and severity of his wounds would have led to almost instantaneous death, and he could only have been dead for a few minutes. So, give or take five minutes either way, the time of the fatal attack can be put at around ten," Superintendent Ellway related.

"I follow," nodded Sarah Checkley. "And I was able to explain to your Inspector that I was here at home all evening with my daughter, although she went to bed shortly after eight."

"Quite correct, madam. A note was made, by the Inspector, of the details you provided. Apparently, you then had a visitor at about nine fifteen. Is that correct?" enquired the officer.

"Between nine fifteen and nine thirty," came the reply. "He came by arrangement and the time we'd fixed was nine fifteen, but he may have been a few minutes late. He stayed at least an hour. I've no doubt about that. He had to explain to me all the findings of the Criminal Injuries Compensation Board. I'm to get some financial compensation, it seems. There were masses of pieces of paper and he went through them with me most carefully. He certainly didn't leave until at least ten fifteen, although I suspect it was nearer half past."

"Yes, Mrs Checkley. His account is that he left your house at ten twenty five. He is confident of that because he looked at his car clock as he went down your drive," the Superintendent confirmed. "We're quite happy with all of that. You won't be hearing further from us, but, in the circumstances, it was felt appropriate that I should come and speak to you personally. Thank you for your time."

Moving towards the front door to let him out, Mrs Checkley smiled directly at him. "Goodbye Superintendent. I do appreciate an officer of your rank taking the trouble to come and see me. I was lucky, wasn't I, that I was with a policeman at the relevant time. Saved me a lot of questions, I imagine."

"Probably so, madam," replied Superintendent Ellery as his driver opened the passenger door for him. "It was helpful that Detective Sergeant Perry chose last night to visit you. Funny how these things work out sometimes. Good morning."

Sarah Checkley watched the Jaguar proceed smoothly down her drive and out of view, before gently closing the front door. In her white, Dior, size five sandals, she walked slowly past the spot where her husband had died and headed towards the kitchen, wondering just how much Superintendent Ellery really knew. Anyway, she smiled to herself, the police wouldn't be in touch again, unless it was to send her a medal.

Glossary

Antecedents
Biographical and social history available to police. Includes records of previous criminal convictions.
Arraignment
The formal putting of the indictment to the Defendant at Plea and Directions and the recording of his pleas of Guilty or Not Guilty.
Bar Council
Body that governs, inter alia, the professional conduct of Barristers. The Disciplinary Committee has the power to disqualify a barrister from practice.
Barrister
Counsel. Self-employed but operating from a set of chambers with other barristers. Sharing administration expenses.
Barrister's Clerk
Employed by a set of Barristers who practise together from a set of chambers. Traditionally received a percentage of the individual Barrister's brief fee. A barrister cannot practise without a clerk.
Brief Fee
The fee charged for all preparatory work and the first day of the trial. For each subsequent day in Court the barrister receives a refresher fee, much lower than the brief fee.
Bung Merchant
Taker of bribes.
Chambers
A set of offices from which barristers operate. Although each barrister is self-employed this is a means of sharing administrative costs. Many chambers are very difficult to get into. The reputation of a set of chambers is of paramount importance.
Circuit Judge
Judge appointed by the Lord Chancellor to sit in the Crown Court and try all but the most serious criminal and civil cases. Wears purple robes.
Collator
Police officer who monitors, analyses and controls all Police Intelligence.

Commercial Bench

Division of the High Court that hears complex, high-value commercial cases.

Counsel

Barrister.

Court of Appeal

Sits at the Royal Courts of Justice in The Strand. Hears appeals against convictions and sentences from the Crown Court. Normally consists of a 3 man Court. One Lord Justice of Appeal and two High Court Judges. More recently, senior Crown Court Judges have become entitled to sit as one of the Judges.

CRO

Criminal records Office. Depository of antecedents of convicted criminals.

Cross-Examination

The evidence given in answer to the Counsel appearing for the other side and therefore involving leading questions

Crown Court

The Court of first instance where all Judge and Jury Trials take place.

Crown Prosecution Service

Public body in charge of bringing prosecutions. They are wholly independent of the police. The CPS solicitors decide which Counsel to brief for the Prosecution.

Defence Solicitor

A private firm of solicitors instructed by a Defendant (almost always on Legal Aid when the case is criminal). This firm does all the preparatory work and prepares a brief which is submitted to Counsel of their choosing. Counsel will conduct the case in the Crown Court although the solicitor will be in attendance.

Defendant's Costs Order

Costs awarded to an acquitted Defendant from Public Funds.

DNA

Deoxyribonucleic Acid. A chemical which carries genetic information enabling scientists to produce a DNA profile. This profile will not be unique but will express probabilities. The precision with which it can be potentially attributed to a specific individual will depend, inter alia, upon the number of sites within the crime sample (eg blood or semen) at which DNA is found and the extent of any degradation. The better the sample the more precise. In reality, a good sample can produce a match which would only have a random frequency occurrence of 1 in many millions or even one in a billion. New techniques are now commonly producing the statistic that a particular DNA profile will be only be found in 1 out of a billion people. Scientists, guarding professional credibility, will not say the match is unique.

DNA Database
Stored data of DNA profiles taken from different ethnic groups (which can affect the frequency ratio)for the purposes of making sound statistical projections of match probability. These databases are maintained by the Forensic Science Services and by the police who thereby keep permanent records of the DNA of certain convicted criminals.

DNA Match Probability
The random occurrence ratio, ie the frequency with which the matching DNA characteristics were likely to be found in the population at large.

Evidence-in-chief
The evidence given in answer to the Counsel who calls the witness. Hence, it cannot be adduced by the use of leading questions.

HMP
Her Majesty's Prison.

High Court Judge
The highest level of First Instance Judge. Knighted on appointment. Tries only the most serious criminal and civil cases. Wears red robes.

Indictment
The formal Crown Court document on which the charges (Counts) that a Defendant faces are set out and put to him on arraignment.

Junior Counsel
Barrister who conducts trials in the Crown Court. Led by Queen's Counsel in serious cases.

Lord Chancellor's Department
The Government Department with the exclusive right to appoint Judges and Queen's Counsel.

Nark
Informer.

Nonce
Sex offender – particularly relating to offences against children – often homosexual.

Pathology Report
Medical report on a deceased by a Pathologist, required where there has been any kind of suspicious death. Will seek to identify precise cause and mechanism of death and any other injuries.

Plea and Directions
The first important pre-trial formal hearing in the Crown Court when

the Defendant is arraigned and when the Judge gives precise directions concerning the tria.l

Pupillage

Period of 12 months "apprenticeship" served by a newly qualified Barrister. He is allocated to a more senior Barrister (who cannot be a QC) to watch and learn. He cannot accept a case and go into Court with a case of his own until he has completed the first 6 months. Hence known as a "first six and a "second six".

Pupil Master

A senior Barrister (not a QC) who takes on a pupil Barrister and allows him to read his briefs and watch him work so as to learn the job. A pupil will be allocated to the Master for 12 months, although after the first six months the pupil is entitled to accept and do work in Court.

Queen's Bench Division

The Division of the High Court which will try the most serious criminal and civil cases.

Queen's Counsel

Senior Counsel appointed by the Lord Chancellor on merit. Handles only the most serious cases. Normally acts with a Junior Counsel.

Re-examination

The evidence given in answer to the Counsel who calls the witness. This takes place after cross-examination and must be confined to questions which arise out of the cross-examination. Again, no leading questions are permitted.

Refresher

The fee received by a barrister for each day beyond the first day of a trial. The first day's fee is the Brief Fee.

Screw

Prison Officer.

Silk

A Queen's Counsel. A Barrister who "takes silk" because he is now entitled to wear a silk gown as opposed to the stuff gown of a Junior Barrister.

Snout

Police Informer.

SOCO

Scenes of Crimes Officers. Not necessarily police officers, sometimes civilians. They have expertise in fingerprints, footprints, bloodstains etc. and are trained in the gathering of all forensic evidence from the crime scene.

Target Criminal

A known active and serious criminal. Will be made subject of covert surveillance when at liberty in anticipation of his next crime.

Verbal

The false attribution of words to a Defendant by a police officer. The wide incidence of "verballing" was one factor behind the introduction of the Police and Evidence Act (PACE) 1984 and the tape recording of interviews of suspects in Police Stations.

Witness Statement

The written statement of a witness given underneath a solemn declaration as to its truth and a recognition that prosecution may follow if it contains untruths. Normally taken down by a police officer. Always signed on every page by the maker and then served on the Defence and the Court as part of the evidence for the Prosecution.